# EFT and Beyond

# EFT and Beyond

## Cutting Edge Techniques for Personal Transformation

EDITED BY PAMELA BRUNER & JOHN BULLOUGH

Energy Publications Ltd

EFT and Beyond
Cutting Edge Techniques for Personal Transformation
Edited by Pamela Bruner & John Bullough

Energy Publications Ltd

Printed in the United States of America and in the United Kingdom.

Published in the United Kingdom by:
Energy Publications Ltd
Cambridge House, 16 High Street
Saffron Walden
CB10 1AX
United Kingdom

If you are unable to order this book from your local bookseller, you may
order directly from the publisher.

ISBN: 978-0-9562911-0-3
First Edition May 2009

# Co-Authors

In alphabetical order

Ann Adams
Maggie Adkins
Sue Beer
Pamela Bruner
John Bullough
Judy Byrne
Patricia Carrington
Sophia Cayer
Jaqui Crooks
Karl Dawson
Nancy Gnecco
Peter Graham
Rue Anne Hass
Lindsay Kenny

Mair Llewellyn
Tam Llewellyn
Carol Look
Paul Lynch
Gwyneth Moss
Tania Prince
Emma Roberts
Ann Ross
Barbara Smith
Loretta Sparks
Helen Walker
Rehana Webster
Linda Wood

# Table of Contents

# Disclaimer

This EFT-oriented book is provided as a good faith effort to expand the use of EFT and EFT-related techniques in the world. It represents the ideas of the authors and does not necessarily represent those of emofree.com or Gary Craig, the founder of EFT. Complete understanding of EFT and the EFT training videos are available at http://www.emofree.com.

This book is for educational purposes only. While impressive results have been reported with tapping and energy technologies, the field is still considered experimental. Given that, nothing in this book should be construed as a promise of benefits or guarantee of any results.

The individual articles represent the views and the opinions of the respective authors. None of the authors or editors is engaged in rendering medical, psychological, legal, or other professional advice. The reader takes complete responsibility for his or her health and well-being.

The information and instructions in this book are not intended as a substitute for medical or psychological care. If you are under medical or psychological supervision, please consult your health care professional before using the procedures described in this book. The authors, editors and publisher disclaim any liability or loss incurred directly or indirectly as a result of the use or application of any of the contents of this book.

# The Healing High-Rise Today
## HOW THIS BOOK CAME TO BE WRITTEN

*PAMELA BRUNER WRITES:*

It all started with a small idea.

I was chatting with my friend John Bullough, an Integrative Counsellor/ Psychotherapist based in England, and commenting on how powerful and creative I found Karl Dawson's 'Matrix Reimprinting' technique, and Gwyneth Moss' 'Imagineering' technique. *"I'd like to create a book of these kinds of techniques,"* I said to John. *"You can look them up on the Internet if you've already heard about them, but if you haven't heard of them, how do you know where to go for the cutting-edge tapping techniques?"*

The only problem, I noted, was that the project would take a great deal of research, and I'd have to get someone to help me with that. John immediately volunteered, saying that he quite enjoyed research. Several weeks later he came back to me, saying that he knew several of the EFT Masters in the UK and USA personally, and why couldn't we ask them to write up their favorite techniques and we'd edit and compile them?

And so this book began.

Although the amount of work was considerably greater than either of us had foreseen, we are thrilled with the result. As pleased as I am to have contributed to assembling these techniques for the benefit of the world, I have to admit that I'm even more pleased with the transformation of my own abilities since beginning to study these articles. My use of energy work and tapping techniques, both for myself personally and with my clients, has become infinitely more creative, fluid, and effective. It is as though I have gone from having a single fine instrument on which to 'play the music of healing' to having an entire orchestra at my command, full of nuance, capable of infinite combinations of powerful possibilities. It is my hope that each person who reads the book enjoys that same expansion of capability within the exciting field of energy work.

*JOHN BULLOUGH WRITES:*

Coincidentally, when Pamela called me to discuss making a printable collection of groundbreaking techniques such as those developed by Gwyneth Moss and Karl Dawson, I had just been approached by those very same two people to consider taking on a lead role in AAMET, the Association for the Advancement of Meridian Energy Techniques. It seemed to me at the time that there could be great synergy in participating in a collection of cutting-edge techniques from the good and the great of the tapping world, while at the same time working with others to establish professional standards for the training, practice and ongoing development of practitioners. Amongst other things, it seemed likely that the contents of such a collection would make an excellent adjunct to any advanced level training (e.g. Level 3) in tapping and tapping therapy.

So of course I said *"Yes!"*

I was also at the time engaged in preparing to take Gary Craig's Official EFTCert-I exam {see *Glossary*} (ironically, I have been so busy with the above two projects that at the time of writing I still haven't had a chance to do this!). It seemed to me, going through Gary's DVDs for the second or third time, that his EFT Manual, Tutorials, DVDs and Study Guides together provide an elegant and exquisite definition of the ground floor of the healing high-rise that he speaks about in his training materials. It is already over 14 years since Gary first started making EFT available to an eagerly waiting world, and in that time it has taken on a life of its own, flourishing and growing in the hands of countless thousands of practitioners worldwide. Strictly speaking their innovations are *EFT-related tapping* (collectively known as 'meridian tapping techniques') rather than EFT per se, since such developments do not necessarily fit comfortably with the principles described in such detail in Gary's training materials. However, in my view, many of the techniques and ideas being put forward have the potential to take tapping and tapping therapy into new and very exciting territory, and it is this sort of material that we have attempted to attract and describe with this book. Hence the title: *EFT and Beyond*.

## CONTRIBUTORS TO THIS BOOK:

Of the 29 EFT Masters originally designated by Gary Craig, 22 have submitted cutting-edge articles (and in some cases more than one) for inclusion in this book, and it is our hope that in future editions we will be able to include material from the other EFT Masters as well. In addition, we are delighted that Ann Adams, EFTCert-Honors, who originally administered the EFT Masters programme, has contributed an article, as have Helen Walker and Linda Wood, certified AAMET Practitioner/Trainers, who were part way through the selection process when the EFT Masters programme was discontinued. Success Coach (and co-editor of this book) Pamela Bruner, EFTCert-I, has contributed an article specifically for practitioners based on her very considerable experience in applying tapping therapy to success issues, particularly in business. Dr Patricia Carrington, EFT Master, has contributed a fascinating and authoritative foreword to the book entitled 'The Coming of Age of Tapping Therapy'. And finally, certified AAMET Practitioner/Trainer (and co-editor of this book) Dr John Bullough has contributed an overview of the book entitled 'Tapping and Psychotherapy'.

## GENERAL NOTES:

While we are both familiar with EFT, this book is not intended in any way to represent EFT or Official EFT as created and taught by Gary Craig {see *Disclaimer*} and should not in any way be construed as such by the reader.

Along with so many others, we wish to express our deepest gratitude to Gary for his genius and generosity in developing EFT and giving it so freely to the world over the last few years. His work has brought and is continuing to bring healing and relief to countless thousands of people. In Gary's own words *"We are on the ground floor of a healing high-rise"*.

It is our intention with this book to make available in one volume an account of some of the most important work that is being carried out around the world to contribute to the building of further floors in that healing high-rise. And it is our hope that this compilation of cutting-edge techniques and ideas will help to push the boundaries of energy healing and psychology, inspiring others to take up the banner and making it possible for us collectively to add undreamed of dimensions to the healing high-rise of the future.

In editing the book, we made several considered choices with regard to language. One was, as much as possible, to leave each article in the distinct 'voice' of the author. We did not attempt to re-write the articles to make them sound as though they came from a common source, since one of the objectives of the book was to get as many different viewpoints as possible. Because of that, we have also preserved spelling differences that naturally occur between American, British, and Australian writers, such as 'color' or 'colour'. We also have inserted editor's notes in the text of a number of articles. These notes serve two functions. One, a note may draw attention to what we feel are particularly important points in the articles, or two, may point out differences between articles in terms of theory, technique or application. Notes in {} refer the reader to similar ideas in other articles. Finally, in a desire for clarity as well as even-handedness, we have alternated the use of 'he' and 'she' when referring to hypothetical clients and situations, rather than using all masculine pronouns, or the awkward and inaccurate 'they'.

In order to get the most from this book, one should be familiar with either EFT/ Official EFT or a close cousin of it. There are a myriad of ways to use this text. One way is to read it in its entirety to get an overview, and then concentrate on any articles that seem of particular interest. Serious students and practitioners of tapping may wish to learn one new technique a month, incorporate it into their personal tapping routine, and then use it with clients when they become comfortable with it. Also, the article entitled 'Tapping and Psychotherapy', by John Bullough, provides an overview of the material presented in the book, identifying common themes on what seems to work best in tapping and tapping therapy, and relating this to research findings from several decades of psychotherapy.

Many of the authors have additional training materials and classes available for their techniques, and we recommend investigating the wonderful learning opportunities that are available.

As we travel up the floors of the healing high-rise, the vision of what is possible becomes more and more breathtaking. We hope this book will inspire you to come in and join us and enjoy the view!

PAMELA BRUNER, USA

JOHN BULLOUGH, UK

# Tapping and Psychotherapy

## IS SAUCE FOR THE GOOSE
## ALSO SAUCE FOR THE GANDER?

### JOHN BULLOUGH, PhD, MBACP, AAMET TRAINER

Reading through the treasure trove of ideas and experience that our authors have contributed to this book, I can't help but notice the common themes that run like a series of connecting threads through all the articles, uniting them on the subject of what seems to work best in tapping and tapping therapy.

In my own field of counselling and psychotherapy (which I'll simply call 'psychotherapy' here as I have never been able to identify any convincing difference between the two), such common themes have been extensively researched and described over the last few decades.

So let's have a look and see what if anything the two sets of findings have in common. Obviously tapping therapy has some major differences from talk therapy in process terms, but the presenting issues are largely the same, and both clearly involve a practitioner/therapist and a client in some form of therapeutic relationship.

In summary, my aim is to explore:

1. What works best in psychotherapy?
2. What works best in tapping therapy? (based on the articles in this book), and
3. What (if any) are the main differences?

## Part 1: Research findings from psychotherapy

## How important is the therapeutic relationship?

If you talk to a psychotherapist and ask what really counts in terms of client outcomes in psychotherapy, she (I'll assume 'she' for the purposes of this article) is quite likely to mention the therapeutic relationship as the key factor. This is supported by research which over the last few decades has consistently demonstrated a strong overall correlation between the quality of the therapeutic relationship and the success of the therapy.

According to findings quoted by Mick Cooper[1], research shows that the relational factors which most affect the success of psychotherapy are as follows:

*DEMONSTRABLY EFFECTIVE*

- goal consensus and collaboration
- the therapeutic alliance, and
- empathy

*PROMISING AND PROBABLY EFFECTIVE*

- management of counter transference (or 'getting yourself out of the way' in tapping therapy parlance)
- feedback
- positive regard
- congruence
- self-disclosure
- relational interpretations, and
- repair of alliance ruptures.

Sheila Haugh and Stephen Paul[2] report similar research findings, concluding that the key factors include:

- positive engagement in therapy by both parties
- the ability of both parties to work together on the therapeutic task
- the rapport or empathic communication between them
- the communication of positive regard by the therapist, and
- the ability of the client and therapist to develop a constructive understanding of each other.

The therapist is not without influence over these specific factors. But when we speak in general terms about the relationship, it's hard to know which is the chicken and which is the egg. Is it the good relationship that leads to the positive outcome for the client, or is it the positive outcome for the client that helps the relationship to be good? After all, a good therapeutic relationship is not something that therapists necessarily provide for clients, but something that emerges as if by osmosis in the client-therapist interaction. I'm not for a moment suggesting that the relationship is not important, but just that it's hard to be sure that this is the true deciding factor and not simply a consequence of something more fundamental.

## How important is the theoretical approach or model?

Another commonly cited success factor is the theoretical approach or model used by the psychotherapist. Many psychotherapists have invested five or more years of intensive study in becoming proficient in a particular model of the human psyche and its application in working with clients, so it is perhaps not surprising that this investment may have generated fierce loyalty and commitment, sometimes to the exclusion of all else. However, although research shows that certain theoretical approaches sometimes appear more effective than others for certain conditions, in general the model or approach appears to account for less than 10% of success in psychotherapy.

So if it is not the model or the therapist's effort to establish a good therapeutic relationship that really counts in psychotherapy, what is it?

## What about the client?

We're getting closer to the answer when we explore the role of the client himself (I'll assume the client is male for the purposes of this article).

EDITOR'S NOTE:
The fact that client factors are such an overwhelmingly large part of therapeutic success lends strong support to tapping as an approach. Because the client can be, and usually is, taught to tap himself between sessions, such homework can be specifically focused on the client's willingness and ability to 'make use of whatever the therapist provides', thus increasing the probability of a successful outcome.

According to Cooper, research shows that 'client factors are probably the most important determinants of therapeutic outcomes, accounting for 70 percent or more of the overall effectiveness of counselling and psychotherapy.'

Or in tapping language, '70% of success is the client's inside job'.

And of course, these client factors directly affect the therapeutic relationship.

Apparently, the key predictor of outcomes is: 'the extent to which the client is willing and able to make use of whatever the therapist provides'. Or spelling this out in more detail, the client in a successful therapeutic encounter is likely to:

1. be more proactive in choosing to enter therapy.
2. be more willing to adopt the client role.
3. have higher (but not unrealistically high) expectations of therapeutic outcomes.
4. believe that psychological treatments will be of help to him.
5. have realistic expectations about what will happen in therapy.

This makes it sound as if it's all a question of luck from a therapist's point of view, and that much of the outcome of therapy depends on the disposition of the client.

However, research also shows that when the client rates the contributions of the therapist in a positive way, there is a higher probability that the outcome of therapy will be positive.

So how can the therapist achieve positive ratings from her client? And what can she do to influence any of the other client factors listed above?

## What about the therapist or practitioner?

Before addressing this, it's interesting to note that 'most of us grow continually in confidence over the course of our careers, despite little or no improvement in our actual rates of success as therapists'. According to Scott Miller, Mark Hubble and Barry Duncan[3], 'the least effective therapists . . . tend to think they are on par with the most effective.'

Perhaps even more telling, one study showed that '90% of therapists put themselves in the top 25% in terms of service delivery', and I've no reason to suppose this is not also true of tapping therapists. There's a good reason for this of course. As therapists become more experienced, they tend to make fewer obvious mistakes, and thus naturally assume that their performance is improving. However there seems to be no evidence at all to support this assumption. 'Add to this the custom in our profession of conflating success with a particular method or technique', say Miller et al, 'and the door to greatness for many therapists is slammed shut early on.' I'll come to this later, but it's worth noting in passing that we tapping therapists set a great deal of store by our technique (or method) and its superiority over other more tried and tested approaches!

But therapist effects are undoubtedly important. Cooper cites a study by Okiishi et al[4] in which the clients of the most effective therapist in a university counselling centre showed a rate of improvement fully 10 times that of the average, while the clients of the least effective therapist showed an average worsening of problems.

## So what is it that these super-therapists do differently?

The most telling (and exciting) account I've come across on this subject so far is in the paper by Miller et al, mentioned above. They assert, drawing on the work of Swedish psychologist K. Anders Ericsson, that 'lack of natural talent is irrelevant to great success' (across virtually the whole range of human endeavour). What was most startling for me, and it may be for you too, is that 'systematic laboratory research . . . provides no evidence for giftedness or innate talent.' 'The key success factor, it seems, is the amount of time specifically devoted to reaching for objectives just beyond one's level of proficiency.'

'The best of the best simply work harder at improving their performance than others do.'

So if reaching for objectives just beyond one's level of proficiency is the key, how does this translate to psychotherapy practice? According to Miller et al, the secret is to:

1. Determine your baseline of effectiveness,
2. Engage in deliberate practice, and
3. Get feedback from all possible sources, especially the client, and work in tandem to create a cycle of excellence.

Those slowest to adopt a valid and reliable procedure for establishing their baseline performance typically have the poorest outcomes of the lot. Several recent studies convincingly demonstrate that monitoring client progress on an ongoing basis improves effectiveness dramatically. And if you share your baseline—good, bad, or average—with clients, the results are even more dramatic. Dropouts are cut in half, and at the same time, outcomes improve yet again, in particular among those at greatest risk for treatment failure. Such therapists are also much more likely to ask for and receive negative feedback.

I'll comment later in this article about establishing a clearer understanding of one's baseline of effectiveness and setting stretching goals for deliberate practice and improvement in the context of tapping. But first I'll have a look at what the tapping therapists have been saying in this book about the keys to success.

## Part 2: What works in tapping therapy?

With 38 articles to choose from, written by 26 of the world's most experienced tapping practitioners (all of whom are holders of either Official EFT Certification (24 authors) or AAMET certification (19 authors) {see *Glossary*} or in some cases both), the reader is faced with a veritable treasure trove of tapping expertise, experience and wisdom in this book. I think perhaps one good way of accessing the consensus of what works best in tapping therapy will be to look first at how the authors view the issues that seem to be important in psychotherapy and then focus on any pointers that this may provide for the future development of tapping therapy (and psychotherapy and tapping therapy combined).

## 1. Issues emphasised in both psychotherapy and tapping therapy

*GETTING YOURSELF OUT OF THE WAY (GYOOTW)*

Psychotherapists don't tend to use this expression (in my experience anyway). But right from the early days of psychotherapy there has been a strong focus on careful management of *counter transference*, which in effect means coping with any issues that may be triggered in the therapist as a result of the interaction with the client. This is 4th on the list of success factors listed by Cooper (above), and clearly represents an important element of GYOOTW, although not the whole story by any means.

From the articles in this book, however, there is a clear consensus that GYOOTW is seen as THE most important success factor in tapping and tapping therapy by some margin. In her article on excellence, Ann Adams states that GYOOTW 'is probably the most important characteristic of excellence, and this is a lot easier if there is less of you to get out of the way!' Helen Walker devotes much of her article to this subject, and Mair Llewellyn reminds us of the importance of clearing our own issues so that we can help our client to create a bridge to resourceful points in his history. Judy Byrne stresses the vital role of personal peace in the tapping practitioner's self development; Lindsay Kenny talks of the importance of clearing our own personal baggage; Sue Beer helps us to see how easily we can become stuck in our own issues and Carol Look and Jaqui Crooks devote considerable attention to the challenges posed by self sabotage. In introducing their sophisticated tapping techniques, Karl Dawson, Tania Prince, Gwyneth Moss and Linda Wood also allude to the importance of GYOOTW, and Maggie Adkins reminds us of how particularly important this can be in working with severe trauma.

Almost all of the authors in the book address the importance of self development at some point in their articles, either directly or indirectly stressing the key role of GYOOTW. Many of them also explain how to go about achieving this, and in this regard I found Carol Look's articles on safety and on conversing with our own body and Nancy Gnecco's article on working with children to be particularly helpful. And although not specifically addressing therapy in her article, Pamela Bruner spells out the huge importance of GYOOTW in the context of releasing one's full potential in a business sense (particularly in marketing our services as practitioners), and explains in some detail how to do this for ourselves using tapping.

## RESPECT FOR THE CLIENT'S ABILITY TO HEAL

Respect for the client's ability to heal is identified by Ann Adams as the second most important characteristic for excellence in tapping therapy. I suppose in psychotherapeutic language, this equates loosely to a combination of *unconditional positive regard* and *client autonomy*. The former was identified by Carl Rogers many decades ago as one of the cornerstones of Client Centred Therapy, and together with *empathy* and *congruence* and certain other factors (collectively known as the *core conditions*) this has become widely accepted as a vitally important ingredient of successful psychotherapy. In particular, Rogers stressed the importance of clearly communicating this *unconditional positive regard* to the client at every appropriate opportunity. Acceptance that the client already knows (albeit unconsciously) how to heal himself is a cornerstone of humanistic psychotherapy.

Respect for the client's ability to heal is strongly reflected in the examples and phrasing that all of the authors use in this book to illustrate good practice in tapping therapy. One example is Patricia Carrington's emphasis on creating Choices and Personal Resource States that are truly meaningful, vivid and attractive for the client, irrespective of what the practitioner may feel about them. Another is Emma Roberts' sensitive and respectful use of the Tsunami Technique to help the client to bring into the session whatever issues he may feel at an unconscious level are important for his healing. Rue Anne Hass gives us examples of faithful and non-judgemental representation of a client's experience via complex setup choices, and Paul Lynch talks about the value of encouraging our clients to find their own 'Aha!' moments. The key word here is *respect*, and to my mind the vital importance of this is self evident in all the material in this book.

## CONGRUENCE

Again identified by Ann Adams as a vital ingredient of excellence, *congruence* (being true to ourselves) is one of Rogers' *core conditions* and is thus widely accepted in psychotherapy as a key success factor. Trawling through the research papers, it would seem that *congruence* is rated as more important by psychotherapists than it is by their clients, and ranks only 7th in Cooper's list (above). However, there is a clear consensus among the authors in this book that practitioner *congruence* is vital for success in tapping therapy. Ann Ross' articles when taken together provide a definitive exploration of the subject and how to achieve it. Among other things, in *Who do you think you are?*, Ann helps us to understand how easy it is to become lost in the identity of 'who we are not', a close parallel with some of the concepts explored by Eckhart Tolle in his groundbreaking spiritual work, A New Earth[5]. Helen Walker devotes a good part of her article to the importance of self-awareness, a key ingredient of *congruence,* and Peter Graham explains how to work with concepts of identity as a route towards greater *congruence*. And Sophia Cayer stresses throughout her article the importance of trusting your own feelings as practitioner when 'transforming the energy'.

*RAPPORT*

In psychotherapists' language, this equates loosely to what Haugh and Paul (above) refer to as the *empathic communication* between therapist and client, again identified by many researchers (as well as Rogers) as a key ingredient of successful psychotherapy. It also in a way implies a strong *therapeutic alliance, the positive engagement in therapy by both parties, the ability of both parties to work together on the therapeutic task*, and *the ability of the client and therapist to develop a mutual co-understanding of each other*, referred to by Haugh and Paul (above) as equally important success factors in psychotherapy.

In this book, many of the authors refer either directly or indirectly to *rapport* as a vital ingredient of the work. In fact Tania Prince goes so far as to describe it as a 'prerequisite for effective therapy', particularly when using direct hypnotic language. And Tam Llewellyn spells out the vital importance of watching one's client like a hawk, tuning into every possible sign that may help the therapist to distinguish between 'the garbage and the gold'. I would comment here that others may find it equally helpful to 'watch' with their ears or with their internal feelings, somehow tuning in intuitively to what may be going on for their client. Carol Look gives an excellent explanation of the vital role of *listening* in all its variations in her teleclass conversation with Patricia Carrington, downloadable free of charge (at the time of going to print) from Patricia Carrington's teleclass website[6].

## NOT ATTACHED TO THE OUTCOME (NATO)

In my early days as a trainee psychotherapist, I was very attached to the idea of *fixing* my clients; perhaps not surprising considering that I had spent the previous decades in the oil industry measuring my success in terms of the value I added to the company's activities, and the quality of the decisions and solutions I was able to provide.

### FIXING A SUICIDAL CLIENT

I well remember an early client of mine who was deeply suicidal. One morning, when she seemed particularly at risk, I persuaded her to see her doctor immediately, and he in turn promptly put her in a taxi and sent her directly to the psychiatric unit of a local hospital for urgent treatment. It took several sessions in supervision for me to accept that I had had little choice in the matter, and had in fact done exactly the right thing. As far as I was concerned at the time, I felt a complete failure because I had not been able to help her directly myself.

Although *client autonomy* is considered vitally important in psychotherapy, I have the sense from the articles in this book that not being attached to the outcome (or NATO as Ann Adams calls it) takes on an altogether more important meaning in tapping therapy. NATO, Ann explains, 'comes from FULLY respecting that the client has within themselves the ability to heal themselves'. As noted above, this is a central tenet of humanistic psychotherapy, but is perhaps less appreciated in some of the more directive modalities of talk therapy.

It is common in tapping and tapping therapy to speak of the healing coming 'through you not by you' as practitioner. Several of the authors in this book refer to this directly or indirectly, and Ann Adams addresses it in some detail. It is as if one's intuition and creativity are in some way suppressed when one's work is influenced by an agenda other than the client's immediate experience, perhaps creating anxiety that stifles the flow. *Intention* is very different from wanting to *fix* a client, however, and one area where this seems to be of particular importance is in surrogate tapping. An approach to this is described by Gwyneth Moss in her article on working with animals, particularly in her discussion of 'first person' work, where she speaks of 'a stream of consciousness' in which the client/practitioner felt that 'the words came from nowhere'. This is a lovely example of NATO and GYOOTW combined, although note Gwyneth's warning to take the time to de-role after work like this.

*MINDFULNESS OR PRESENCE*

I was lucky enough to attend the world congress on cognitive therapy in Gothenburg in 2005 when the guest of honour was his holiness the Dalai Lama, and the main theme of the conference was *mindfulness*. Cognitive therapy has long recognised the importance of *mindfulness* in the relief of human suffering, and the Dalai Lama was of course in a very special position to speak on that subject (by the way, he clarified in his speech that mindfulness predates even Buddhism).

*Mindfulness,* or paying attention on purpose and without judgement to whatever is happening in the present moment, is identified by Ann Adams as another critical success factor. In fact she explains that it 'can be THE critical element in developing intuition; in allowing the work to come through you not by you'.

Ann Ross, Helen Walker, Sue Beer and Judy Byrne all refer directly or indirectly to the healing power of *mindfulness* and its clear relevance to tapping therapy, and all give examples of *mindfulness* related exercises for everyday practice.

## 2. Success factors from psychotherapy that might enhance tapping therapy

*GETTING FEEDBACK FROM THE CLIENT ON PERFORMANCE*

In contrast to the issues listed above, there is relatively little mention in this book of the importance of getting feedback from the client on what seems most (or least!) effective in tapping therapy. Since research shows that this is a major factor in distinguishing the excellent psychotherapist from the merely average, it would seem to make sense to explore what if anything can be done to introduce this into regular sessions of tapping therapy.

## GENERATION OF CLIENT ENTHUSIASM, EXPECTATIONS AND BELIEF IN THERAPY

Whereas, as a psychotherapist, one might feel to some extent at the mercy of client disposition in terms of his enthusiasm for (and expectations from) the process of therapy, all tapping therapists know that there is a great deal one can do right from the outset to enhance such factors using tapping. Since reading about the above research, I have begun to experiment with this in my own practice, and am looking forward to being able to report on it in some detail at a later date.

## TIME DEVOTED TO REACHING FOR OBJECTIVES JUST BEYOND ONE'S LEVEL OF PROFICIENCY

Arguably, this seems the most promising idea of all in the search for yet more effective results in tapping and tapping therapy, and at the same time one would need to be careful not to be too focused on results in the session itself, and thus potentially fall foul of NATO and/or GYOOTW. Perhaps one way to approach this might be to spend a good deal of time before a session working on one's own issues and concerns as a therapist, using SUDS and other measures to chart progress.

And where should one find ideas for improvement? In this book of course! The material presented here represents a distillation of some of the most exciting developments in tapping and tapping therapy at the present time, and where better to start than reading and rereading the material here, and systematically trying out the ideas presented, both in self development and in client practice. A good example would be the scholarly exploration by Loretta Sparks of working with clients with severe addiction. Her article clearly reflects the fruits of a long and careful study and refinement of what seems to work best in this specialist field.

Other sources of information and ideas include the audio-visual products and writings produced by the authors of this book (see the authors' biographies at the end of each article for contact details) and the growing number of tapping related resources available via the internet.

Reflection on one's practice is a key element of integrative psychotherapy, providing a time to engage in assessing results and feedback from clients as objectively as one reasonably can, and at the same time setting new challenging goals. As regards the sessions themselves though, I suspect it's a little like golf. The time for thinking and planning is on the driving range and in the clubhouse, but once on the course, the player's full concentration needs to be on becoming the swing, allowing all thought of success or winning or hitting straight (or in my case slicing) to evaporate with the wind. At least that's the theory!

## GOAL CONSENSUS AND COLLABORATION

Again, although the authors do not make much of an issue of this in the articles in this book, having seen many of them work with clients either singly or in groups over the years, I'm confident that most regard *goal consensus* as a vitally important factor in tapping therapy, in much the same way as it is in talk therapy. What the client wants from therapy is a key issue to establish early on, whatever the modality, and to return to check progress at frequent intervals.

Perhaps less common in tapping therapy is a systematic focus on *collaboration* as a means of achieving it. In my own field of cognitive behavioural therapy, *collaboration* is emphasised almost above all other aspects as a means of gaining client commitment and understanding of the

> EDITOR'S NOTE:
> Many tapping practitioners have an intake form for clients on which the client can designate the presenting issues, and the goals they wish to obtain from the sessions. Frequently confirming and reconfirming these goals in the session(s) may be a way to create goal consensus.

process. Perhaps we tapping practitioners could take heed of the value of this in other modalities, and build it into our work to the point where it becomes second nature.

## RELATIONAL INTERPRETATIONS AND REPAIR OF ALLIANCE RUPTURES

These refer to ongoing consultations with the client on the relationship itself and what if anything can be done to make it easier, better or more comfortable for both parties; not surprising perhaps, when an effective working relationship is known to correlate so closely with successful client outcomes.

I have built this into my practice ever since my training as a psychotherapist, although I now realise I could do much more of it in the early and middle stages of therapy instead of leaving it mostly to the end when it can be too late to do anything productive about it. Again, tapping provides an excellent way of addressing any difficulties or lack of trust or understanding that may have arisen, and I see no reason why such regular consultations with the client would be in any way less important in tapping and tapping therapy than they clearly are in psychotherapy.

## 3. The importance of the model or technique

Turning finally to one of the most interesting issues of all; do the research findings in psychotherapy (i.e. that the model accounts for less than 10% of success) apply equally to tapping therapy?

## What do you mean by the model?

Before we can address this, we need first to attempt a definition of what we mean by the word 'model'. In psychotherapy, as noted above, this is normally used to refer to a combination of a theoretical model of the human psyche and a particular way (or set of ways) of working with clients.

Taking first the theoretical model of the human psyche, tapping therapy often draws on the principles of NLP (among others), which in turn has its roots in a wide variety of models and approaches. So in a psychotherapeutic sense, tapping is something of a hybrid. What perhaps distinguishes it in a theoretical sense from more conventional approaches though, is its central reliance on what is commonly referred to as the body's 'energy system'. As an engineer by back-ground, I'm comfortable with this up to a point, as it seems to work very well as an assumption and has its roots in ancient Eastern philosophy which has stood the test of time for thousands of years. However the left brained scientist in me is somewhat uncomfortable. It's not normal in science to try to explain one mys-tery with another, and the body's 'energy system' does seem to me to qualify as a mystery, elusive as it is to the surgeon's scalpel and the physicist's instruments. Nevertheless, SOMETHING is happening to cause the extraordinary results that will seem commonplace to the average practitioner of tapping therapy (in my own experience, tapping has been proved time and again to be far more power-ful than any other approach I am trained in, including CBT, which is sometimes referred to as the 'gold standard', particularly by CBT therapists!).

## So what is really going on?

When we add to the mix the extraordinary and apparently inexplicable results available via surrogate tapping, as described in the article in this book by Gwyneth Moss; or tapping on stuffed bears with astounding results, as described by Linda Wood; or the principles of the *heart anchor*, as described so eloquently by Sue Beer; or the mysteries and huge power of the Matrix, as described by Karl Dawson; or the power and influence of working with 'past lives', as described in such detail by Tania Prince, it becomes clear that this is a huge field, with unsolved mysteries worthy of Sherlock Holmes at every turn.

Having carefully read all the material submitted for this book, and in parallel having had the privilege of listening to and reading the writings of Dr Robert Scaer[7], a renowned neurologist and traumatologist, I am inclined to wonder whether the tapping itself, important and effective though it is, is something of a sideshow; a means to an end, *and that the real mechanism of change is something altogether deeper*. For example, research findings in EMDR (Eye Movement Desensitization and Reprocessing), a close cousin of tapping therapy in neurological terms, have shown that the eye movements them-selves may too be a side show[8]. However these are early days, and it is hoped that books like this will serve to spread the word on the enormous power of these techniques, and perhaps help to move us nearer over time to a scientific understanding of what is really going on.

In the meantime, I suspect the jury is still out on whether tapping as a model is more powerful than EMDR (for example), or whether Matrix Reimprinting or Deep State Re-patterning or Imagineering or any of the other techniques described in such detail in this book are more powerful than each other or than Official EFT {see *Glossary*}. Or even whether the success factors discussed in this article are more important than the particular tapping model or technique being followed (which I suspect is the case).

What seems most important to me is that we collectively spread the word about the enormous power of these myriad variations, and try them out both singly and in combination, as often and as vigorously as we can. And most of all that we follow the above success factors at every step, choosing the ideas with which we individually feel most congruent, always seeking to find ways of working that will add height, width, quality and understanding to the healing high-rise that is taking shape so fast before our eyes.

# Conclusions

*LESSONS FROM MY OWN PRACTICE*

Originally trained as an Integrative Counsellor/Psychotherapist, I build into my client sessions a good measure of tapping therapy, underpinned by elements of cognitive behavioural therapy (CBT), rational emotive behavioural therapy (REBT), acceptance and commitment therapy (ACT), mindfulness training, hypnotherapy and gestalt, in fact any approach that seems appropriate for the particular issues we are working on in that session or series of sessions.

In this practice, I find that tapping therapy blends in seamlessly with my more conventional practice as a psychotherapist. This is particularly true of CBT, where the elicitation of automatic thoughts, underlying assumptions and core beliefs is significantly enhanced and accelerated using tapping. And in parallel, I have found that tapping greatly facilitates the client in his preparation for and execution of challenging behavioural experiments, much of which the client can do on his own at home, without intervention from the therapist. In fact the similarity is so close that one can often introduce tapping to CBT therapists as: *"like CBT but with somatic enhancements"*. Phil Mollon[9] has observed similar complementary features in the integration of tapping (in his case TFT) with psychodynamic therapy. As he puts it: 'Integration of Thought Field Therapy (TFT) with psychoanalytic work offers a rich potential for healing trauma when words alone are not enough.' In fact it's probably true to say that talk therapy can almost always be enhanced, simply by tapping along on whichever points feel most appropriate, while doing the traditional talk therapy.

Perhaps partly because of the complementary nature of these two currently rather distinct disciplines in therapy, I believe there is much that each can learn from the other, particularly in terms of what seems to work, where psychotherapy has the clear advantage of several decades of well documented research.

Since reading the article by Miller et al, discussed above, I have made a point of discussing and recording in some detail with my clients what they find most helpful and least helpful in each session, and tailoring subsequent sessions to the results. It has only been a few weeks so far, but my clients and I are already noticing a substantial change in the energy that we are bringing to each session. I have long used standard measures such as the Beck Depression Inventory and the Beck Anxiety Inventory to measure progress and outcomes in therapy, and now plan to expand this to develop a more systematic analysis of what clients find more or less helpful, and what seems to make the biggest impact in terms of progression towards clients' goals.

*LESSONS FROM THE ARTICLES IN THIS BOOK*

In conclusion I would like to pay tribute to the authors of the articles in this book who between them have amassed a wealth of knowledge and carefully worded advice on what in their view is likely to take tapping therapy to new and potentially uncharted heights in this new *healing high-rise.*

It seems clear to me from the above analysis that the factors that are being found to be important in tapping and tapping therapy have much in common with their cousins in psychotherapy. I don't claim by any means to have the answer(s) about the direction in which the art should develop from here. But there must surely be unlimited scope to take the best of each, and blend them with other approaches to make possible as yet undreamed of advances, not only in the transcendence of human suffering, but equally importantly, in the enhancement of human potential and human spiritual awakening.

## AUTHOR'S BIOGRAPHY AND CONTACT DETAILS

Following a successful career as a senior executive in the international oil industry, John re-qualified at University as an Integrative Counsellor/ Psychotherapist and now practises at a doctor's surgery and in his own private practice in Essex (UK). He specialises in helping people to recover from trauma (including childhood trauma and abuse), as well as phobias, stress, panic, relationship breakdown and many other issues typically presented in a doctor's surgery. Tapping therapy is his preferred approach, into which he integrates cognitive behavioural therapy (CBT), acceptance and commitment therapy (ACT), hypnotherapy and various other modalities.

John has contributed actively to the running of the Association for the Advancement of Meridian Energy Techniques (AAMET) including acting as the leader of the Training Panel leaders; a group responsible for the development of professional standards and training within AAMET.

For more information, go to: www.intuitive-connections.co.uk

## REFERENCES:

1. Cooper M (2008) The facts are friendly—what research tells us about therapy. Therapy Today Sept 2008 www.therapytoday.net
2. Haugh S & Paul S (2008) Is the relationship the therapy?—common factors that can be linked to positive outcomes in therapy. Therapy Today. Dec 2008 www.therapytoday.net
3. Miller S, Hubble M & Duncan B (2008) Supershrinks—what it takes to be great. Therapy Today Apr 2008 www.therapytoday.net
4. Okiishi J et al (2003) Waiting for supershrink—an empirical analysis of therapist effects. Clinical Psychology & Psychotherapy. 2003; 10(6):361-373. Cited in Cooper M. The facts are friendly—what research tells us about therapy. Therapy Today Sept 2008 www.therapytoday.net
5. Tolle E (2005). A New Earth—Awakening to Your Life's Purpose. Chapter 2. Penguin, USA and UK
6. Teleseminar # 9 (2008) Carol Look on EFT and Pain Relief. Downloadable free of charge (at the time of going to print) from www.patclass.com
7. Scaer R (2005) The Trauma Spectrum. Norton. New York
8. Gunter R, Bodner G (2008). How eye movements affect unpleasant memories: Support for a working-memory account. Behaviour Research and Therapy, 46 (8), 913-931 http://bps-research-digest.blogspot.com/2008/10/what-is-it-about-eye-wiggling-that.html
9. Mollon P (2007) Integrating Energy Therapy—the powerful mix of talk and tapping. Therapy Today Sep 2007 www.therapytoday.net

# The Pursuit of Excellence

Ann Adams, LCSW, EFTCert-Honors

EFT Practitioners generally work diligently to master the nuances of EFT. They read books and articles and newsletters. They go to workshops and meet other like-minded people. Their goal is to improve their skills and develop mastery in EFT and excellence in its delivery.

## What do you mean by 'excellence'?

Excellence is the ongoing development of (and skillful use of) inner wisdom. Or putting it another way, excellence is mastery, and mastery of any skill involves ongoing mastery of oneself. So this article emphasizes the 'pursuit' rather than the 'creation' of excellence in EFT.

While experience is an essential ingredient of excellence, it does not in itself create excellence. It is possible to repeat the same year's experience many times over, to have experience without growth, to practice without learning, to work without wisdom. Excellence is about ONGOING learning and growth; a lifetime goal if you like, because we are never completely 'done'.

In the video on the EFT DVD Specialty Series 1, on Working with Severely Disturbed Children[1], I referred to seven principal characteristics of excellence:

1. GET YOURSELF OUT OF THE WAY: We are facilitators, the client is the healer.
2. BE CONGRUENT: or as the kids say: *"Walk your talk"*. It is the only way to build credibility and thereby a connection and relationship with your client.
3. BE NOT ATTACHED TO OUTCOME: Your client has the needed resources within.
4. BE MINDFUL AND IN THE HERE AND NOW: Be totally present with your client. It is not necessary to drag your client through 'past' painful experience and experience the event as if it were still happening. You've seen Gary tell someone: *"Stay with me."* His goal, as is mine, is to keep the client in the here and now, to separate THEN from NOW.
5. BE CREATIVE AND FLEXIBLE: Stand out from the long line of other 'helpers' and use creativity when needed in the art of delivery.
6. RESPECT YOUR CLIENT'S ABILITY TO HEAL: This means admiring their courage in dealing with their events, and trusting in their own ability to heal.
7. BE PROFESSIONAL WITH A CAPITAL 'P' in all you do.

These characteristics are intrinsically connected and related, but let's take them one at the time, and along the way keep firmly in mind that MASTERY OF ANYTHING INCLUDES MASTERY OF SELF.

## Characteristic 1: Get yourself out of the way

'Getting yourself out of your own way' is probably the most important characteristic of excellence, and this is a lot easier if there is less of you to get out of the way! One of the most critical tasks of excellence is dealing with your own issues; doing your own work. Those of you familiar with the Abraham-Hicks tapes[2] will know that they frequently say: *"We never get it all done."* But to be truly excellent in your practice you first need to have cleared the major traumas and limiting beliefs in your own life. Mastery of anything involves mastery of *you* first.

Getting yourself out of the way is also easier when you are able to live truly in the present moment (see below). The more present (or 'mindful') you are, the more you are out of your own way. Presentness or awareness is an essential aid to intuition. There are many theories about where intuition comes from, but I am convinced that easy access to intuition is the result of 'getting yourself out of the way'.

# Characteristic 2: Be congruent

The concept of congruence closely fits my definition of professionalism. In other words: 'You walk your talk'. What you SAY you 'believe and do' is what you ACTUALLY 'believe and do'. Your beliefs are reflected in how you manage your sessions and conduct your practice. And these fit with how you live your life and how you market yourself and your work. It all fits together into a congruent whole.

Congruence, like getting yourself out of the way, is possible only when you've cleared much of your inner clutter; when you have resolved the majority of your own unfinished business {see *How to Get Yourself Out of the Way*}. And this creates a confidence that shines through in everything you do.

Congruence also creates credibility. When you are truly congruent, you can feel (and show) a deep interest in your client's experiences; you can be positive, understanding and appreciative, and introduce appropriate humor when it feels right. And credibility is a vital component in creating a meaningful connection with your client.

> There is an old Charlie Brown cartoon in which Snoopy is talking to his bird friend, Woodstock, saying: *"We (dogs) are the highest form of life on this earth! The world revolves around us!"* The next panel shows a worried Snoopy questioning: *"Doesn't it?"*
>
> We all, like Snoopy, tend sometimes to see to see the world as revolving about us. And at the same time, like Snoopy, at a deeper level we realize with some anxiety and concern that this may not be the whole story . . .
>
> Some of us may deny this, and say: *"Oh, no, that's not me. I don't think the world is, or should be revolving around me. I am always thinking of others"*.
>
> If this resonates with you, consider this: 'People who are always thinking of the feelings of others can be very destructive because they are hiding so much from themselves.' May Sarton[3]

*EDITOR'S NOTE:*
This surely resonates with almost everyone's experience; part of the 'dialogue of the lost self', as Ann Ross puts it.

As a congruent person, you understand and accept that each of us defines and colors the world through our individual perceptions and experiences {see Judy Byrne's discussion of 'template matching'}. This makes you more aware and accepting of the way others may color their world and leads to a clearer understanding of limits and boundaries. It is easy for you as a congruent, aware practitioner to make statements such as: *"I don't understand. Can you explain what you mean?"* Or *"What else do I need to know about this?"* Or *"I made a mistake. Let's back up and try that again."* Or, in setting appropriate boundaries in relationships: *"I don't feel comfortable with that. Is there common ground that we can find?"* Or *"I am not willing to do that."*

Congruence also leads to a clearer understanding of the importance of self care, self acceptance and self awareness, in the sense that these are all goals we work toward as we clear our own 'stuff.' One essential element in the pursuit of excellence is to recognize and make the commitment that we will always continue the work on ourselves.

Finally, a congruent person will have a high level of inner calm, a low level of defensiveness and a broader perspective on the world and others in it, not least because she has truly come to believe that everyone is always doing the best they can. The congruent person recognizes that there is always work to do, and that there will always be what we consider 'mistakes'. But, take heart, treat yourself gently. As Abraham[4] says: 'We can't get it wrong, because we will never get it ALL done'. We continue to be a work in progress.

## Characteristic 3: Be 'not attached to outcome' (NATO)

NATO ('Not Attached To Outcome') is a great acronym to identify this concept. Being unattached to the outcome—'Join NATO'—comes from FULLY respecting that the client has within themselves the ability to heal themselves. You realize you are merely a tool in their journey. As practitioners we don't heal anyone; we are facilitators, it is the client who is the healer.

Being unattached to the outcome goes hand in hand with getting yourself out of the way and dealing with your own issues. This doesn't mean that we don't care; we care deeply, and we continue to look for ways to get through to each and every client. The difference is that we clearly realize that any part we may play in the client's healing, as Gary Craig often says, comes THROUGH US, not by us. Accepting this concept is the forerunner, maybe even the basic foundation, of allowing our intuition to develop.

Staying unattached to the outcome is very hard for many practitioners to do. A practitioner new to the helping profession often tends to take it all very personally. Most of us are, after all, in this business because we want to help people. One of my mentors once said: *"You should never work harder at therapy than your client does."* If you find yourself NEEDING to get results, it's a clear sign that you are attached to the outcome.

For example, it is not unusual for a concerned adult, after watching the DVD on my work with children, to email and ask me: *"How do I get my child (or niece or grandchild etc) to 'do' EFT?"* They may as well be asking me how to get them to eat Brussels sprouts! Tell me; when you feel that someone is trying to 'get' you to do something, what is YOUR first response? Do you feel they truly have YOUR best interest at heart? Are they unattached to the outcome? Or does it feel as if they have an agenda that they're attempting to impose on you?

My advice is always the same: You first goal is to deal with YOUR feelings about the child's or the client's issues. If you are working to 'get' someone to do anything, it's a sign that you are attached to the outcome. You are pushing your own agenda, sometimes very hard!

The same philosophy applies to another question I am frequently asked: *"How do I get EFT into hospitals, military, schools, etc?"* Maybe you don't—not yet anyway. Nobody wants to be 'gotten' with anything. I had a lot to say about that in the talk I also gave on the Specialty Series 1 when I owned up to being a bureaucrat [5].

Start where your client is—whether your client is an individual, a group, or an agency. And where they currently are may not be anywhere close to where you want them to be! There's an old social work maxim that very much applies here: "ACCEPT YOUR CLIENT WHERE THEY ARE". Our clients deserve that. Agencies demand it!

## Characteristic 4: Be 'mindful' and 'in the here and now'

Being in the present can be a lot harder than it sounds, and can be THE critical element in developing intuition; in allowing the work to come through you not by you. {See *Inner Peace—An Inside Job*, and *How to Get Yourself Out of the Way*.}

There is much buzz in professional circles these days about the concept of 'mindfulness'. I want to address mindfulness as it applies to the relationship between you and your client. Mindfulness in this context means concentrated awareness, carefully attuning to the process that is occurring between the two of you in the room, right now. This is also a key part of 'getting yourself out of the way' and of 'not being attached to the outcome.' Staying in 'the here and now' means paying close attention to, and trusting, the process of what is happening in the room between the two of you RIGHT NOW, RIGHT HERE, IN THIS MOMENT.

One of the attractions of EFT is that it is often so quick and effective, but this can also cause us to overlook the importance of the process of the relationship. What happens in the therapy room between two people in the here and now, at this moment in time, is significant; it is full of meaning that can be important to the process and to the outcome of a session. So before we rush to intervene and start thinking about the best setup phrase or the next detective question, we need to take a deep breath and attend closely to less conscious factors. Healing often takes place in tiny moments and small places in a relationship. ATTEND TO THE PRESENT.

A mantra when I supervise students is: PAY ATTENTION TO WHAT IS HAPPENING IN THE MOMENT. This process can get lost in our need to make therapy as brief and problem focused as possible. It especially can get lost in our effort and need to 'do' something to help. And along the way, the client's need for safety may be sacrificed {see *Is It Safe to Change?*}.

## How can I be intuitive as well as mindful?

At times we can feel a huge pressure to show how skilled, smart, knowledgeable and intuitive we are, and this may cause us to rush in with our help. We want so much to be helpful—but being 'helpful' is not always helpful! All too often, we are tempted to take over and act, rather than allow the flow of the session to dictate our next move. There is meaning everywhere, and it often flows out more freely when we're able to be patient, or when we're able to honor our client's timing and agenda over our own; when we're willing to sit a while longer with our own uncertainty, discomfort and puzzlement.

Often we tend to jump right in; after all, our intuition has already gone to where it needs to go. Or has it? I have watched many a therapist barrel down a road of their supposed intuition.

## How can I tell the difference between true intuition and my own need to intervene?

NATO provides the answer!—No Attachment To Outcome . . .

Intuition may generate excitement at first thought but it quickly turns to a calm neutral feeling. If you are feeling sure that this is what your client 'needs' to do and set about arranging the session so that the client 'sees' it as well—it is probably NOT intuition (even if you are 'right'). If you are all excited about it and you just can't wait to share your brilliant insight—it is probably not intuition. If you are attached to the outcome—it is not intuition. If you are pushing your agenda—it is not intuition. The problem is we cannot always tell the difference between our agenda and our intuition.

### We Are Much Better At Doing Than Being

I was once sitting with Sally, an adolescent, in my office. We were just 'hanging out', as the kids say. She was sketching on a pad. And I started to get a bit antsy that maybe I was wasting our limited time together. I felt we needed to get down to the real issues and get something accomplished. So I gently asked if there were some goals she'd like to work on or any issues she'd like to resolve. Sally gave me this pained look as only adolescents can do. *"Ms. Ann"*, she said, *"Being with you here is the only place I have where I can just be me. Do we need to fix that?"* Gulp . . . *"You're right Sally"*, I said. *"Just being IS the most important thing"*.

As mentioned earlier, being in the moment is critical to intuition. Trust the process. Sometimes it is not about doing therapy or EFT or tapping. It is just about BEING there, fully present. And sometimes this can feel a lot harder than providing a particular intervention . . .

Years ago I taught crisis intervention skills to volunteers manning a hotline. The hardest concept for the volunteers was learning not to rush to intervene or give suggestions. Over and over I had to reinforce that most often the gift of our time, of just being there, just listening, just accepting the person WAS the greatest action we could take. The volunteers often wanted to DO SOMETHING. They had a hard time understanding that just being fully there WAS doing something very important. Wish I'd had EFT as a great tool to add into that crisis training. But the point here is that your desire to 'do something' is *your* agenda.

## How does intuition (and helping the client feel safe) relate to 'being in the here and now'?

Helping the client feel safe and ready is a critical part of EFT. I have heard many practitioners explain the reason that a client dropped out or that EFT 'didn't work' was that the client didn't want to change or wasn't ready to change. Yes, for a client who is really not ready, the best therapy is still life itself; life will give them more experiences, leading them to readiness to change. However, it is our job to help the client, at whatever place in their readiness, to feel safe enough to begin to share their shame, guilt and deepest fears of inadequacy. In a way we are all resistant. After all, all changes are scary, even the good changes.

No, we don't want our clients to talk on and on, and yes, we do want to be in control of our sessions. Of course, you are going to ask questions about 'what something that happens in the session means'. You are going to share your insights and make an occasional suggestion. We do, however, sometimes forget that the session between the two of you is not about developing the exact setup or having them list all their issues and tap through their list—although those are good things to do. It is about the relationship and providing a safe place to 'be who they are,' a safe place to create change. With EFT, progress can be had even faster after they feel you respect they have the inner resources to resolve their issues and that they have a safe place to both discover who they are and to practice being who they are and/or want to be. Our job is to facilitate the process and to create a safe environment to experiment with new ideas and behaviors. To permanently change a behavior they must feel safe to take each new step. They must feel comfortable with who they are now at each new stage. The expression Safety First is more than an expression {see *Is It Safe to Change?*}. Helping our clients 'see' themselves comfortably in the change EFT has helped achieve is important to making that change permanent in their life.

### How does intuition relate to listening?

Intuition is closely tied to the ability to fully listen and attune to your client. Listening is the key to getting through to a client. BEING FULLY AND DEEPLY HEARD IS A BASIC HUMAN NEED. It is the beginning of being understood.

Anyone can run someone else through an EFT sequence. And because of the effectiveness of EFT, that's often all it takes.

I taught EFT to a four-year-old and watched as she ran her doll through a great little EFT sequence. So cute, tapping on her baby doll with: *"Even though you are feeling sad, you are a really good dolly and*

*I love you."* Tap, tap, tap. Delightful! And easy! A four-year-old can learn and apply effective EFT.

Listening—fully listening—to your client is harder. You listen with both ears. You listen with your eyes, your heart, your entire body, all focused on your client. You may have ideas about what is happening, but you have no preset agenda. If you are 'not attached to the outcome', if you have truly 'gotten yourself out of the way' you are able to see and hear your client totally; it just flows.

We develop intuition by having a clear enough inner world that we are able to hear that inner voice, that inner guidance. We have to quiet our own internal chatter to hear it. It is a total focus on the client; a total being in the 'here and now'.

## How can I ask the right questions and still stay in the 'here and now'?

Being with someone who is fully present and accepting where they are right now is a rare experience for many clients. It is often what they need most to feel safe to take the next step.

EFT is an incredible tool. It works amazingly fast on those nice clean, specific situations. However, all too often the client is not at all specific in their presenting problem. Their life may not be going well for them, and it may take some real detective work to find some specifics to tap for. Less experienced practitioners stay general; the seasoned practitioner knows how to guide a general issue into the specifics behind it.

Detective work is simply asking questions; deep thought-provoking questions. There is no quick way to learn the right questions. It takes study and practice. There are many excellent articles on www.emofree.com about good questions to ask to get to specifics and core issues {see *Finding the Root of the Problem*}.

Questions are the key way we discover what is locked up in our psyche. In another Charlie Brown cartoon, Lucy is asking Linus: *"How can holding a blanket make you feel secure?"* The following scenes show his face vividly as he struggles with his internal answer to that question. It shakes up his world. The right question at the right time can be a powerful change agent.

Professional coaches and top-notch managers and supervisors have long understood the power of questions. Amateurs look for the instant results; the professional realizes that unless the answer comes from within it has little or no meaning for the person. Worse, there is no ownership of the solution. A strong bond is formed when you ask careful questions and then listen carefully to the answers. The participant feels you care what he or she thinks and feels. Remember, being heard and understood is a basic human social need.

## Characteristic 5: Be creative and flexible

It is helpful to set yourself apart from the long line of others who have said: *"I'm here to help you"*. Many of our clients are with us almost as a last resort. Many have been in therapy before, sometimes for years. Therefore be wonderfully flexible in how you conduct a session.

Creativity is a true gift. It is helpful to watch skilled, creative and flexible presenters who expose viewers to a variety of creative approaches. There are uncountable ways to using EFT creatively. I'll share just one example:

My role at the May 2006 Atlanta EFT Masters' Retreat was to be available to the participants for any problems or issues that needed additional help outside the assigned groups. My available time was limited and I was very aware that any work I did with the participants would be one-off sessions. A very bright lady approached me on the second day: *"I have been in therapy for years and nothing helped"*, she said. *"I've been to three EFT practitioners and that's not helping either. And now, I can't relate to anyone in my group. I don't think that EFT will work on me. I've wasted my time and money"*. She had a hopeless look on her face and sounded very depressed but, in a way, almost proud. We become very attached to our stuff!

There is much truth to the quote: *"Despair itself, if it goes on long enough, can become a kind of sanctuary in which one settles down and feels at ease."*[6]

So many long-term clients identify with their issues to the degree that they don't see who they would be without them. It is challenging to work through all the related fears and defenses and reversals to changing beliefs and behaviors. The lady at the retreat had been working with highly qualified EFT practitioners. The EFT Master group she was in had been doing very skilled Borrowing Benefits sessions. And, I had limited time to work with her. If I were attached to outcomes, I would have been worried. These were good people she had been working with. I had no idea what I was going to do. And then in one of those flashes of intuition it occurred to me.

*"OK"*, I said, *"You game to do something totally different?"* [A pre-frame] She looked puzzled but agreed. I asked if she always tapped on herself. *"Yes"*, she said. *"Would you have a problem if I tap on you?"* She said she would not. I then asked her that if she were to take all her problems and set them on the ground beside us what would all those problems look like? This kind of question is disconcerting for clients prone to intellectualizing. Their answers are always interesting. She was taken right out of her head; like with Linus, it shook up her world. She had a blank look and said: *"I have never done this before."* *"Right!"*, I said. *"That's the point. Just pretend you can see your problems sitting over there. What do they look like?"*

Her answer was a huge, ugly, green chalkboard. And on it was written in big thick writing in multiple layers and different colors all the negative things in her life. (I inwardly had to wonder what Gary would think about this representation of his 'writing on your walls' metaphor.) I asked what color and how big and how thick the writing was. We talked a few of minutes about what she was 'seeing.'

She used her hands to describe it. I didn't ask for an intensity level of 1 to 10 as she had been used to doing. My test of whether we would be successful was if one of the writings got lighter or disappeared. I asked her to focus on one statement and one layer of the writing at the time. After each tapping round as I tapped on her I would say, *"OK, pretend you have an eraser in your hand and erase that layer of words."*

Sometimes a physical action of movement of hands or body can make a difference. Sometimes actually physically moving to a different place will give a totally different perspective on his or her problem.

After each round and she'd wiped the board clean of that statement, I'd say: *"OK, focus on the next statement or layer."* We tapped for each layer quickly, and erased quickly, and went on to the next until she reported that everything written on her board was wiped clean. It took a while. Even as fast as we were going, she had lots of negative writing on that board.

Then I asked her what she'd like to have written on the board instead. She formulated some respectful positive statements that I asked her to use her hand to write on the board as I tapped on her. *"I am worthy"* was one important statement that she wrote.

My job at the retreat was to help a person feel safe enough to take the next step so they could go back to their group and participate fully. So, after filling the board with the positive things she would like to think about herself she tapped for her fears of EFT not working for her, that she was too messed up for it to work and that she was wasting her time and money and following a pipe dream. And, I sent her back to her group. The rest of the retreat went pretty well for her and she worked on many issues concerning her family and others who had put those negative writings on her walls—or in her case, her chalkboard.

What was a bit different or creative about the session was the separation of the person from her tightly held issues, and using the physical movement of her hand in the exercise of physically erasing and writing on the board. What was very much the same as any session I conduct is that I fully listened to her problems about EFT and therapy in general. I had no agenda. What I heard was that her entire identity was wrapped around her issues. She was operating totally 'in her head,' as we therapists say, and she had a major internal conflict about resolving anything. My intuition said to separate her from her issues, to have her operate 'out of her head'. How did the idea occur to me? I have no clue. It was just there. Did we solve all her long-term problems? Of course not! But we shifted her perspective enough for her to begin shifting her view of herself and her world.

## What if my client expects me to do EFT by the book?

People who come to you for EFT and have learned EFT from the downloaded manual[7] or The Basic Course[8] or have taken an EFT class expect you to do EFT pretty much as the manual and videos teach it. The most common complaint about EFT practitioners is that the EFT practitioner is not following the process in a way it is taught on the videos. The people who have studied the videos are pre-framed to expect a session similar to the sessions they have seen. And in some cases, if you are not doing EFT the way it shows on the videos, they interpret it that you are doing it 'wrong'.

Sometimes too, a practitioner has changed EFT to the degree it is no longer is EFT. Nothing actually wrong with that—Gary himself says that EFT is one way not necessarily THE way. But if you've changed EFT far beyond what Gary teaches—just don't call it EFT.

Remember the social worker maxim: '*Start where the client is*'. When working with people who have learned EFT in some 'standardized' way, it is often better to go back to the basics of EFT and THEN expand out as you establish more rapport and a relationship. At the very minimum, be sure you pre-frame any differences from the videos that you practice. There are lots of creative uses of EFT, but if you get too creative you may have a problem establishing rapport with a client who comes expecting a session 'like Gary does it.'

There are also variations on EFT, or as Gary calls them—cousins. One of my own favorite EFT cousins is Touch and Breathe. Touch and Breathe uses the EFT points but with a gentle touch of the fingers on each point paired with a slow deep breath instead of the usual tapping. This is a great approach when a slower gentler approach would be preferable to actually tapping.

> A woman who bought my EFT4 PowerPoint comprehensive EFT training package[9] had a trip planned to help Tsunami survivors. She emailed me when she returned and said they didn't like the tapping. It had scared these people because it was like the waves coming at them!

At times it is helpful to have a few other tools in your toolbox. There are many creative uses of EFT on the web site. It pays to be familiar with other ideas for those complex situations where you need a bit of creativity to get over a hump.

## Characteristic 6: Respect your client's ability to heal

Along with 'getting yourself out of your way', respect for your clients' ability to resolve their own problems is probably THE most important point for true excellence. Anything less devalues and disempowers. This is a soapbox I speak from frequently; if you are in any training session with me you are sure to hear me pounding this drum!

### What do you mean by 'respect'?

My definition of respect is tied to the belief that we are all born with an innate ability to heal. Or put this another way: EVERYTHING THAT EACH OF US NEEDS IS ALREADY THERE, WITHIN.

As respectful practitioners, we do not solve problems, heal anyone, or fix anything; we simply share our tools. We do not tell clients what they 'should' do. We simply act as a resource to draw on, helping our clients to access their inner strength, creating a safe haven.

As respectful practitioners, we also admire our clients' courage. Some have had such severe traumas that it is amazing that they are even able to get up in the morning. Deeply respect that courage, and help them to build on it.

We do teach skills and alternatives when necessary, and always in the form of an educational suggestion or, even better, as a question.

## Are questions more respectful than advice?

More respectful AND more powerful! Questions can stimulate powerful learning. Our job is to guide our clients through the process, and help them access their inner resources rather than lead them down OUR healing road. Occasionally we may share an alternative, maybe even make a suggestion; but remember the power of questions. For any answer to be meaningful that answer must come from within.

Do you sometimes yield to temptation and give your client advice? Maybe you do. Actually as a therapist/coach, I am not opposed to occasional advice. But if you ever feel tempted, perhaps first remind yourself that the only thing stronger than the urge to give advice is the ability to ignore it!

> "Giving advice is a doubtful remedy but generally
> not dangerous—since it has so little effect"
> —CARL JUNG

## Why is advice so often ignored?

Many of us will have given a suggestion or advice to a client, only to have it fall flat. Or the client may have agreed that it was a good idea but then didn't follow it.

Why does our advice fail? BECAUSE ADVICE IS ALL ABOUT US RATHER THAN ABOUT THE CLIENT!

In my years as a social worker, I have given terrific advice that was right on. My client would even agree it was the perfect solution. Did they then follow up and do it? Rarely. We've all given advice. It seems to be a universal way we attempt to help one another. It is just not very effective. The urge to give advice is very human; but the ability to ignore advice is even more human!

Even when a client goes to someone and pays for their advice, whether it be a physician or a financial planner, do they always follow their advice? Nope. WHY? BECAUSE THEY HAVE NOT DEALT WITH THEIR INTERNAL CONFLICTS ABOUT THE ISSUE {see *Is It Safe to Change?* and *EFT and Being True to Yourself*}. Our job is to create a safe haven and guide them through the conflicts and feelings and limiting beliefs and create a comfort zone around the change.

However, I have watched practitioners give more than educational suggestions. I have watched as the practitioner told the client what they think the client SHOULD be doing. All in the name of their supposed 'intuition'. We do not 'should' on our clients or lead them down OUR road.

A key stumbling block for newbies is what I call 'leading.' This is having your own agenda that you then impose on your client. I am using the word leading like the judge who tells the attorney to stop leading the witness. Leading in the way I am using it is the opposite of being a member of NATO. When leading, you are VERY 'attached to the outcome'. That's the problem. Leading is meeting YOUR need not theirs.

## Should I use self-disclosure?

A student asked a responsible and thoughtful question: *"How can you tell where appropriate therapeutic self disclosure, teaching new skills, or offering useful suggestions ends and leading/directing/influencing begins? "*

Addressing that question is why I so strongly beat the drum for working on your own issues and increasing your ability to get out of your own way! The interaction in a relationship between any two people by its nature influences both people. That is why it is so important to pay close attention to what is happening in the relationship. Comments such as: *"I notice you are doing _____. What do you think it means?"* Or calling attention to a change: *"Do you see you are now doing/saying ____ when before you were doing/saying_____."* Such clarifying comments and questions can be valid, useful and extremely helpful but the fact that you paid attention to 'this' versus 'that' does influence the session.

Self disclosure should always be limited. Ask yourself if you are sharing this to meet YOUR need to connect/identify with the client or if the personal information you want to share will move the client toward her goals. Metaphors, anecdotes and stories serve the same purpose. But, again, that you chose 'this' story versus 'that' influences the session. The goal is to access THEIR inner knowledge and strength.

Even when your client asks for your opinion, look for the deeper meaning and question behind the request. Offering suggestions and resources for new skills comes only *after* the emotional issues around the identified problem have been resolved. Ask the client: *"What new skill might you need to carry out your goal and/or make this change comfortable for you?"* Often, the client identifies what she needs to move forward. Ask if practicing a future behavior or situation in the session would be helpful. Ask. Ask. Ask. Questions empower. Advice, self disclosure, directing the session or leading the client down your road disempowers. We are like the guide dog for the blind. We work to keep the client safe, we don't direct where she goes.

## How can I use reframes to encourage my clients' ability to heal?

Reframing is a marvelous EFT skill, and questions used in the detective work can be powerful. My favorite reframes happen naturally though out the session. These can be as simple as changing the tense of the client's report:—changing an *"I am . . ."* to a *"You have been . . ."*

For example: *"I am depressed"* can shift to: *"You have been feeling depressed"*. *"I can't do . . ."* can shift to: *"It has been hard for you to imagine . . ."* *"I can't get over . . ."* can shift to: *"This has been troubling you for a very long time."* All statements are accurate. You didn't change the issue or judge, you merely shifted the tense. These are very powerful reframes that move the situation into the 'here and now'.

While there are exceptions, for the most part our clients want to please us. Because of this when we use our own agenda and start tapping for how our client should feel, what she should think, or what she should do, then she will usually tend to go along with it. Even when we tell our clients: *"Hey, I want you to interrupt me and change the words and set me straight"*, many times the client still won't. Because of this, it is very important to guard against trying to disguise 'leading' or having our own agenda with a client as a reframe or a question:

## How important is timing in all this?

Remember the client who said: *"I felt I was being taken where I wasn't ready to go."* Timing issues are another key stumbling block for practitioners. There was a book in the 60s called *Don't Push the River (It Flows By Itself)*.[10] You guide a person skillfully, respectfully through an EFT session and their cognitive shifts happen naturally. Trust the process. To me, watching the person shift how they look at the situation is the real magic of this work.

Examples of poor timing:

- Assuming we have immediate credibility instead of taking the time to establish a meaningful connection
- Jumping to a setup statement before clarifying it with the client. (Make sure you clarify setup statements before proceeding)
- Tapping for the positive before dealing with negative specific events. (Make sure you clear the negative before trying to instill the positive)
- Tapping for alternatives before recognizing and working through what IS. (Make sure you clear the issues first)
- Going straight to forgiveness before exhausting emotions about the issue. (Make sure you clear the negative emotions before going to forgiveness)

Introduce 'forgiveness' too soon and watch the resistance you get! A client may not be ready to forgive for several sessions. Pushing forgiveness may create a block and prevent them from feeling safe enough to move on to deeper core issues.

It also helps to find out what forgiveness means to your client. My own definition of forgiveness is that I have no further emotional response to what that person did or said. I have let the emotions go. Isn't that what EFT does naturally? I sometimes question the need to introduce forgiveness at all. As a client removes all negative emotion and the event becomes neutral for him/her, a sense of calm, understanding and acceptance comes up naturally.

*EDITOR'S NOTE:*
This seems like a particularly powerful and resourceful reframe.

## How important is it to establish a good therapeutic relationship?

We are sometimes so eager to help that we forget that therapy and coaching is a process, even when using EFT, and that relationships and rapport are still important factors in resolving life's issues. Yes, we can sometimes help some-one to resolve a long term issue even without rapport; we may not actually like the person. But this tends to be the exception rather than the rule, even with EFT.

When I first learned EFT, in my newbie enthusiasm I tried it on every-one. If you came within five feet of me I had you tapping. My friends teased me that no one was safe around me. I have since learned much more discre-tion. Did I resolve specific issues? Yes. Did I help some people to reduce to reduce their pain or level of anxiety? Sure; and I had no relationship to speak of with these people.

EFT works so well and so often that newbies rush in where experienced people have learned caution. And, the newbies do get results. The results of EFT often hide the inexperience or lack of knowledge of the practitioner. The amazing results of EFT lull the inexperienced, less educated practitioner into a false sense of competence. They begin thinking this is easy. Just tap and you solve everyone's problems. It takes a few times of stubbing your toe on com-plexities and losing a few clients to gain wisdom.

I get emails from newbies: *"I just learned about EFT. It is fantastic! I always have success. How do I become an EFT master?"* I smile and take a deep breath. Developing mastery is not a quick process. The problem with the apparent ease of EFT is that it may make you complacent. *"I don't need to study all the videos. I know how to do this. You can learn it in five minutes. Just tap."* The importance of practice and the process of the relationship and the study of the nuances on the videos can be lost in that apparent ease of it all.

You become an excellent EFT practitioner through study and practice . . . and practice . . . and practice. And when you have stubbed your toes many times, you begin to realize that true excellence is acquired over time, with experience and practice.

## Do I really need all of the things you're saying in this article?

Most often EFT does make a person feel better if they just tap for few min-utes. It is, after all, a terrific calming technique. And, that doesn't depend on the skill of the practitioner. One theory behind how EFT and other energy techniques work is that when we simulate the acupressure points we are releasing feel good chemicals into our brains. So we often feel better just tapping. Well usually . . .

PROBLEMS ARE OFTEN COMPLEX

I'd like to share a story about a woman who was a real teacher for any EFT practitioner. It really proves the 'don't go where you don't belong' concept. 'Julie' had been using EFT only a few months when she was challenged by a leader in the community to work on his wife to lose weight. Julie saw this as an opportunity to get a foot in the door for EFT in her community. The manager said he would pay her only if his wife lost weight.

Julie had never worked with someone with a complex eating problem and she attacked it just like a simple phobia. Unsurprisingly, the woman had many complex reasons for her weight problem, hidden motivations around the relationship with her husband and many safety fears around losing the weight. After six sessions the client reported feeling 'worse' and had gained more weight. Julie bombed badly.

In retrospect and with wisdom, Julie saw she made several key mistakes, all of which tie into what we are talking about here:

- She was very attached to the outcome.
- She had not gotten herself out of her way.
- She was thinking of the opportunities she would have instead of being in the here and now.
- She did not have respect for where the woman was in the process
- She was focusing on the husband's goals not the woman's.

Don't go where you don't belong. Get lots of practice. Swap sessions with other EFT users. Train with someone who has lots of experience with EFT and has developed a successful practice. Getting consultation and mentoring from someone like that is invaluable.

With experience and good rapport, in depth listening, and a terrific sense of timing you can help guide the client to even deeper levels.

## Do all successful practitioners have these characteristics of excellence?

It may help to tell you a little story:

I had a picnic for some friends on my patio and one friend brought a guest who had a fear of spiders. And, along came a little spider to the picnic. Our guest reacted predictably hysterically. My friends challenged me to 'fix' her. So I did. No pre-frame, no preamble, no questions about history, no real attempt at rapport, I didn't even ask her if she wanted to get over her fear of spiders. Everyone is standing there looking at me. In the impulsive spur of the moment that can happen at parties I picked up her hand. I told her that this was a new process to resolve phobias that used the meridian lines in the body and that I would tap on her at the end points of those meridians and that she should just repeat whatever I said. And I tapped away on her. She followed along obediently and it worked beautifully. Mark one more success for EFT!

Was this because I am an expert at EFT and have the ability to subtly establish rapport? Well, I like to think so, but no. It worked because I was lucky; she had an uncomplicated phobia and EFT works more often than not. But in retrospect it was a foolish thing to do. Not the least of which reason is that I could have spent my evening working on a complex phobia instead of enjoying my friends.

There are one minute wonders in EFT. Less experienced practitioners especially get lulled into thinking EFT will work every time with everything no matter how general. With such experiences it is easy to forget that 'therapy' is a process. It can take great care and detective work to reach and resolve core issues. Most folks come to therapy with complex lives and complex issues—often with an attachment to keeping them. We humans can become very, very attached to our problems.

There is a rather silly but classic American cowboy comedy—Blazing Saddles. The hero makes a comment in this movie which, as many famous quotes do, states the obvious: *"Most problems don't amount to a hill of beans. But this is MY hill and these are MY beans!"* Working through those attachments to OUR hill and OUR beans can be challenging.

As Carol Look notes in another article in this book {see *Is It Safe to Change?*} change can be very scary, even when made easy by EFT. As she points out:

- We fear the impact of the change on our life
- We use our problems and conflicts to protect us from something
- We are often ambivalent about change
- We fear upsetting the balance in the relationships in our lives
- We fear being expected to do more if we change
- We are concerned that we may change and still not be happy thereby upsetting our world for nothing.

People's fears and issues are often deep and complex. At times we have a real challenge to get to the core issue. The professional EFT user becomes a detective, skilled at asking good questions and respecting the client's timing.

My action at the picnic was foolish because I didn't know anything about the woman; I had no relationship. While I had tacit agreement to tap on her, she had not come to me for assistance with the spider phobia. For all I knew she could have been a complicated personality disorder or would abreact right in the middle of my picnic. She could have had a great attachment to her fear of spiders and I was messing with the balance of her life. And she hadn't asked me to do that. I was lucky. It could have been much more complicated.

Besides, my action didn't fall under my definition of professional. I was not paying attention to the process of a relationship between two people. I was not getting out of my own way. I was showing off. I was caught up in the game of the situation. I had an agenda. I was attached to the outcome. I was certainly not being congruent with my own beliefs of respect for the person. According to my belief system about therapy and EFT my impulsive 'treatment' was a very disrespectful thing to have done.

She did thank me later for resolving her spider phobia and it all turned out OK. But it was not one of my crowning moments! Just having a successful EFT session does not excellence make! I learned a valuable lesson that day.

## Characteristic 7: Be Professional with a capital 'P'

Being professional encompasses many of the previous areas that we've discussed. Professionals are able to 'get out of their own way' and 'be totally in the present'. They have a deep knowledge of, and respect for, the inner strengths that each client holds within. They know the client has what they need to solve their own problem. This belief makes it easy for them to be 'unattached to the outcome'.

A professional has confidence in his or her abilities because she has done the work it takes to achieve excellence. A professional is comfortable in her own skin; and has clarity on who she really is. She is congruent in actions and words. What she says, what she does and how she feels are congruent.

But there is even more to it than that. Professionalism is shown in how you carry yourself, how you conduct yourself with people. It shows by your depth of knowledge in your response to questions. It particularly shows in how you respond to negative comments or criticism or demands on your time. It shows in how you treat people who have not yet reached your level of professionalism. It shows in your consideration for others while still respecting your own boundaries.

It shows in your detective work and in your ability to get to the specifics in complex problems. It shows in your careful testing of the results. And, it shows in your ability to use humor appropriately and respectfully:

> I conducted an EFT session once with a young woman I had met on vacation, this time with full permission and with full rapport. Actually I rarely tap on people, but in this instance chose to do so. As we were working on her grief around the loss of her relationship, she apologized through her tears that her nose was running. I said, in a deadpan voice, as I continued to tap: *"No problem, I have hand sanitizer in the car."* For the first time in our short relationship, this very depressed young woman laughed. Humor and laughter can be very healing and can be a dynamite combination when used skillfully with EFT.

Making it look easy is the mark of a highly seasoned practitioner. Timing and right on target setup statements CAN move a client very quickly. How do you best learn that timing and right on statements? Well, partly through bad timing and wrong statements!

Excellence is wrapped up with professionalism and professionalism involves:
- doing your own work so you can be congruent in your actions and words.
- getting yourself out of the way so you can be in touch with your inner guidance.
- respecting people's ability to solve their own problems so you can guide rather than lead.
- becoming unattached to the outcome so the client can fully explore their deepest world.
- trusting the 'process' of the relationship in the here and now between the two of you so you can fully understand your client.
- and—continuing study and practice.

The Pursuit of Excellence is an ongoing journey . . .

# AUTHOR'S BIOGRAPHY AND CONTACT DETAILS

Ann Adams is a licensed clinical social worker with over 35 years of experience in clinical and administrative roles. She served as the Director of the Former EFT Masters Program certifying qualified practitioners. She developed the EFT Training standard, www.EFT4PowerPoint.com, utilized by thousands of EFT Practitioners all over the world. She coordinated and videoed quality EFT programs with creative and unique uses of EFT.

Websites: www.EFTDVDoftheMonthClub.com
www.EFTforAddiction.com

## REFERENCES

1. www.emofree.com, Gary Craig's EFT website, has DVD sets for learning EFT
2. www.abraham-hicks.com
3. May Sarton, American poet and novelist in early 20th Century
4. www.abraham-hicks.com
5. Ann Adams, 'On Getting EFT Accepted into Institutions' from 'Specialty Series 1', available from www.emofree.com. The text of that talk is also on www.emofree.com
6. Charles-Augustin Sainte-Beuve, 'The Life of Joseph Delorme' (1829)
7. From www.emofree.com
8. Available on one of Gary Craig's instructional video sets available from www.emofree.com
9. From www.eft4powerpoint.com
10. Barry Stevens, 'Don't Push the River (It Flows by Itself)', (Celestial Arts, 1970)

# An EFT Formula
# for Specific Trauma

MAGGIE ADKINS, EFT MASTER, EFTCERT-HONORS

## What do you mean by 'specific trauma'?

A specific trauma, such as a car accident or being betrayed by a friend or lover, can have impacts that reach deep into our subconscious, sometimes causing behaviors or fears many years later. Those behaviors or fears may at first seem unrelated to the old trauma that is actually driving them. However, when we look for core issues to current behavior, those old traumas can be revealed as huge saboteurs in our lives.

EFT surpasses anything else I know for releasing the negative emotions and resultant behaviors from a specific trauma. In my experience, the biggest obstacle to success in resolving traumas with EFT is people's lack of specificity about the details or aspects of that trauma.

Sometimes, we just don't know the specifics. If that's true, we use EFT by working with what we do know, even if that information is very general. When we start off with general issues, sometimes that wonderful EFT journey will include remembering more specifics and sometimes it will not. We just work with what we have. When we do know specific details, it is best to do EFT on those details.

What follows is a formula for working with a specific trauma or event when you DO know specifics. This article does not cover situations wherein the client is overwhelmed at the beginning {see *EFT and Continuous Tapping* for dealing with client overwhelm}. If my client is overwhelmed, I would start off with very general phrases. The formula I share with you here is for those times when the trauma is still a major thread in our life, but we are not incapacitated by it.

## What if there is more than one specific trauma?

Central in using the technique is remembering to work with ONLY ONE TRAUMA AT A TIME. It is useful to incorporate different aspects of a trauma in a single round of EFT, however be careful not to switch to another trauma. I often use more than one aspect of a trauma in a single round of EFT when using the 'free flowing language method'. (The free flowing language method is found on many of Gary Craig's DVDs and consists of rounds where the phraseology includes more than one aspect.) If there are multiple traumas, the first question may be: *"Which is the most intense trauma?"* or *"Which one happened first—which trauma from the past may be overloading the more recent trauma?"* I also find it helpful to have the client write down a list of the traumas and then choose the one that feels most pivotal in the healing at this time.

## What do you mean by aspects?

Once the particular trauma is chosen, I like to make a list of all the aspects of that trauma, in as much detail as possible. The aspects are what make up the whole, collective trauma. My favorite analogy of how EFT works is Gary Craig's image of a table top being the issue and the legs being the aspects that hold the table top up. Knock out enough of the aspects and the legs collapse, leaving perhaps a memory, but no more trauma. You don't have to knock out all the aspects for the issue to collapse, just as you don't have to get rid of all the legs of a table in order for the table top to collapse.

What follows are two examples of traumas and what might be the various aspects to work on with EFT. The first example relates to betrayal, the second relates to a car accident.

Sample aspects of a Betrayal trauma:

- He lied about me
- I feel like such a fool.
- I trusted him—how can I ever trust anyone again?
- I chose him as my friend/lover/whatever —can't trust myself to choose again.
- I can't believe he actually did _____ .
- I can't believe he actually said _____ .
- When I tried to counter the allegation, he lied again about me.
- When I told mom about it, she just said, "Get a life!" No support there.
- They will think I'm a liar, a cheat.
- This keeps happening to me—there must be something wrong with me.
- I feel so lonely—there's no one to share this with.
- I don't know what to do.
- I'm embarrassed to face the others again.
- I must be unlovable or people wouldn't keep doing this to me.

Sample aspects of a Car Accident trauma:

- Saw that truck coming toward me and knew it was going to hit me.
- Woke up and smelled gasoline and couldn't open my door.
- The car could have burst into flames any minute and I would have died.
- Had to wait a long time smelling gas before anyone got there to help me.
- What would my five-year-old son have done without his mother if I had died?
- I WAS going too fast—it was all my fault.
- The police didn't even test the other driver's breath for alcohol and I'm sure he was drunk.

## How can we make sure we're dealing with the most important trauma?

The above aspects may all be for a trauma that happened recently and you may automatically do EFT on that trauma. However, it is a very good thing to ask the core issue question: *"What does that remind you of?"*

If a similar trauma happened long ago, it may be that the first experience that is not healed is stockpiling into the more current trauma and we may have to heal the first trauma before we can get great results with the more recent one. If there are multiple similar traumas, I get the best results by doing EFT with whichever trauma has the most intensity. Most often, the first incident has more intensity.

I determine intensity by using the Intensity Meter (0—10) with 10 being the worst intensity. Clients rate how they feel before we work on the issue, then again during the work.

## Does it matter what order we use to address the aspects?

Once you have decided what you want to work on and the aspects are written down, I ask a client to run the movie through his or her mind. After they have run the trauma movie through their mind, they may have more aspects to record. You can do EFT on the general movie name. Examples are: *"that betrayal"*, *"the car accident"*. However, faster healing normally occurs when you work with one of the most intense aspects rather than the entire trauma.

If my client is in overwhelm or extremely emotional, I wouldn't go immediately into the most intense aspect. However, if my client is calm, I would work with the most intense aspect first. Do several rounds on that aspect. Check the Intensity Meter to make sure the intensity is going down. If it does not go down, it is probably because there is a much greater core issue that must be addressed first. If this happens, keep asking questions and probing to discover the appropriate core issue.

*EDITOR'S NOTE:*
The idea that aspects can be interconnected is very important. We are often taught to work on each aspect until it reaches zero before moving to another aspect. However, in some cases it may be that multiple aspects have to be addressed, perhaps together, perhaps sequentially, before they all reach zero.

If the Intensity Meter does go down with the first aspect, keep with that aspect as long as you're getting improvement. I like to get issues down to a zero, but often we have to work with more than one aspect before any go down to zero. Because all aspects are interconnected—like pieces of a puzzle—they may not release until more than one aspect is released.

After working with the most intense aspect first and bringing that intensity down, I'd then ask which of the remaining aspects is the most intense and do EFT with that aspect as long as I continued to get improvement.

## What if a new emotion comes up?

After working with one or two aspects, several rounds each, I like to check in with my client and ask if an emotion has come up. I ask this even if my client is not showing any outward signs of an emotion. If an emotion has come up within the context of working with the specific trauma, it is a part of that trauma.

At this point, combining the emotion with the trauma can be even more powerful than doing EFT on one or the other separately. An example could be:

> ⚜ *Even though I have this car accident sadness, I deeply and profoundly accept myself*

In this case, we are combining sadness and the car accident—two aspects of an issue in one round of tapping.

The emotions that present themselves most often are sadness, guilt, grief, anger, rage and shame. I have found that shame is the emotion least likely to be mentioned by my clients—it is important it be acknowledged if it is present.

---

If the client gets overwhelmed at any time, I use the protocol for overwhelm first. This protocol includes continual tapping—no words—starting with the karate chop point, then going through all the other tapping points and beginning again at the karate chop point, continuing through all the points—until the emotion has subsided. The protocol also includes keeping the eyes open until the emotion is gently released or has subsided.

---

After an emotion has come up and been tapped on, I would ask what Intensity level the person is now experiencing on the original issue and see if it has shifted.

## What is the most appropriate aspect to work on next with EFT?

We can either:
- go back to the aspect list and ask which is most intense now, or
- if any new aspects have come up, we can ask if any other emotions have come up, or
- we can ask if any body sensations have arisen.

If a body sensation comes up when we are doing EFT on a specific trauma, I consider it as part of the trauma; another aspect to be released:

- *Even though I have this car accident nausea in my gut, I deeply and profoundly accept myself*

- *Even though I have this betrayal tightness stuck in my throat, I deeply and profoundly accept myself*

Sometimes the body sensation will move, and a choice then arises as to whether to chase it through the body or go back to the aspect list to see which is most intense now. If the body sensation gets down to a 2—3, I have found it most helpful to go back to the aspect list and see if other aspects are higher than the 2—3. If you have tapped on an emotion or body sensation, go back to some of the original aspects you tapped on and check their Intensity Meter. Sometimes aspects will shift after releasing an emotion or sensation.

This formula reminds me of a dance—moving back and forth between aspects already known, emotions, body sensations, and any new aspects that arise, until the trauma is no more than a distant memory.

## Can you summarize the process for me?

In summary:
- determine whether any previous traumas might relate to the current one
- choose the trauma that feels most pivotal in the healing at this time
- identify (and write down) the different aspects of the trauma
- tap on one or more of the most intense aspects—doing several rounds for each
- ask if an emotion or body sensation has arisen
- tap on the emotion or body sensation or, if neither has arisen, keep tapping on the most intense aspect
- continue to go through this list until you have great improvement

When you are satisfied with your results, I suggest a round of positive affirmation tapping such as: *I am deeply grateful for these healings in my body, mind and spirit and I give thanks*. You can, of course, choose your own words.

Be sure to use the Intensity Meter at every stage; this is an important benchmark and helps you to determine what to do next. Deal with any overwhelm by tapping without words until the client can again address the issues directly. And remember to be as specific as possible. If you are working on your own trauma and it is a complicated one, or if you mix up similar traumas and have difficulty getting results, you may want to work with a skilled practitioner for a session or two. Sometimes we can't see our forest for the trees . . .

## Case Study: A car accident

Here we will take an example of a car accident, aiming to be as specific as possible so that all traces of the trauma can be released.

As discussed above, the best way to make sure you're getting all the aspects is to make a written list:

- My husband told me not to go out on such a cold and wet night for the treat I promised our son. I went out anyway.
- I was driving a little too fast for the slippery road.
- A child ran onto the road and when I slammed on my brakes, my car slid into a ditch.
- When I awoke I smelled gasoline and couldn't open the car door to get out.
- I was trapped—the car could have exploded with me in it.
- No one was around to help and I started to scream and beep the horn.
- When a man came to help, he took one look at me and said, "Oh no."
- I could have died—what would my son have done without his mother?
- All for a stupid treat that I forgot.
- My husband is furious that I went out against his wishes.
- I feel foolish and ashamed that I had the accident for such stupid reasons.
- It's just like all the other stupid things I've done—I'm just so dumb and worthless at so many things.

Ask which of the listed aspects is the worst—which is the biggest on the Intensity Meter of 0—10? 10 is the worst, 0 means it isn't there anymore.

For this demonstration, we'll say that: *"I could have died—what would my son have done without his mother?"* is the most intense and it is a solid 10.

Please note: I use the Short Cut version of EFT. Start by doing the Setup on the Karate Chop point. Then continue with the reminder phrase at all the other tapping points: top of the head, eyebrow, side of the eye, under the eye, under the nose, under the lip, collarbone, under the arm.

✦ *Even though I could have died—what would my son have done without his mother? I deeply and profoundly accept myself.*

REMINDER PHRASE: *Could have died—what would my son have done without his mother?*

Do this for several rounds until the intensity comes down to a 4 or less. This is merely a guideline; if you are stuck at 5 or 6, stop and go to the next most intense aspect or an emotion or body sensation. I like to bring the intensity down to a zero. However with so many aspects, we may have to do EFT on several of the aspects before it collapses to a zero.

If no new emotion or body sensation has arisen, go to the next aspect.

If a new emotion or body sensation has arisen, shift to that now. Incorporate that with the aspect you were working on. For instance, if sadness has arisen, you would say something like:

✦ *Even though I am so sad I could have died—what would my son have done without his mother, I deeply and profoundly accept myself.*

When you combine the new emotion and the aspect you were working on when it arose, that combination can often create more release from both the emotion and the original trauma. Do rounds on this until the emotion subsides.

If a body sensation has arisen, incorporate that into the aspect you were working on when it arose. For instance, if shoulder tightness arose, you could use wording similar to:

✦ *Even though I have this 'could have died tightness' in my shoulders— what would my son have done without his mother, I deeply and profoundly accept myself.*

Do rounds on this until the body sensation subsides, then choose the aspect that is now the most intense.

We'll say that *"going a little too fast and the possibility of hitting a child"* is the most intense now. That is also a 10 on the Intensity Meter, but doesn't feel as big as the first aspect we worked on.

> ☆ *Even though I was going too fast and could have hit that child—never would have forgiven myself, I deeply and profoundly accept myself.*

> REMINDER PHRASE: ***Was going too fast—really stupid—could have hit that child.***

Please note I have added *"really stupid"* in the reminder phrase as an example of how you can change the wording a bit and include another aspect. Feeling really stupid is another aspect and it may or may not need specific rounds of its own. Do several rounds on this until the intensity comes down to a 4 or less. This is just a guideline—if it is a 5 or 6 and you feel stuck, go to the next aspect.

If another new emotion or body sensation has arisen, proceed as described above for emotion or body sensation.

Choose the aspect that is now the most intense. Let's say the next most intense aspect is: *"My husband told me not to go out on such a cold and wet night."* Let's say this aspect has an intensity of 7—it may have already gone down because of the work we have done on other aspects that were stronger.

> ☆ *Even though my husband told me not to go out, he's still angry with me, and I'm angry at me too, I deeply and profoundly accept myself.*

> REMINDER PHRASE: ***He told me not to go out—I'm furious at myself that I was so bullheaded and he is too.***

I have again changed the reminder phrase a bit to encompass a bit more and show how flexible EFT is.

Continue to ask yourself if there is a most intense aspect left. Has another new emotion arisen? Has another new body sensation arisen? Work with whichever of the above is present.

When you have worked with three to five aspects/emotions/body sensations (the number will vary from person to person), go back to the first aspect

# EFT, Addictive States and the Heart

SUE BEER, EFT MASTER, EFTCERT-HONORS

## What will you cover in this article?

This article offers an introduction to heart work and its importance to therapy and personal change. After a brief introduction we will look at using the Heart Anchor; describing what it is, its purposes, and when you would use it. We will look particularly at the importance of the heart to EFT, the parts played by conscious and unconscious processes, and identify and use Primary and Secondary Reversals in the undoing of addictive states, moving through stuckness to reconnect to Love via the Heart Anchor.

## How does tapping relate to Quantum Reality?

It is probably best to go straight in with both feet here and say that I believe that working with energy fields, as we do with EFT and other techniques, is leading us into an understanding—even an experience, of quantum reality.

EFT is a physical therapy, if only in the sense that we use the body by tapping on the points which act as a kind of interface through which we set up communication between different levels of consciousness. Most people now quickly understand the interplay between the emotional and the physical;

what is not so clear is the interplay between physical/emotional and metaphysical. Working with the electromagnetic fields within and extending beyond the body is allowing or maybe forcing us to bridge between physical and metaphysical. Many of the Newtonian beliefs by which we have navigated our lives, like the idea that we are fixed and separate bodies dependent on finite time and space, quantum physics tells are not really true, are illusory. As we begin to understand this theoretically and intellectually, we are still a long way from owning it and its implications. Using EFT and, I believe, this work with the heart, is one way in which we are crossing that bridge.

Sometime soon it may be completely natural to think in terms of a metaphysical dimension to which we are literally connected by the physical organ of the heart and the electromagnetic field that it generates. This will change the way we experience ourselves and our world in rather the same way that changing our minds about the earth being flat did. In fact the shift to quantum thinking makes that change seem like child's play!

---

However, I believe that without expanding our thinking to embrace the quantum, the tapping can keep us stuck.

---

If we only use it to solve a problem created by limited, old world thinking, another one will soon pop up to replace it—swapping one variety of the illusion for another—or, to misquote an old AA saying, rearranging deck chairs on the Titanic! It's just missing the point; like understanding theoretically that the world is not flat and continuing to travel by lines drawn on a map as if it were.

## What is heart energy?

Working with the heart's energy is an important part of my work with EFT and a feature of the workshops 'Opening to Love' and 'Healing the Addicted Heart' [1]. The guiding principle is that the heart (quite literally) remembers our true nature and maintains that connection to our deeper wisdom whenever we may wander into pain, addiction or dis-ease. And through this connection, it can teach us a new way to think. Our true nature or Self has infinite patience and simply waits for the time at any point in our lives when we begin to turn inwards and hear and trust our heart-truth. Heart-truth is the subtler, gentler polarity of mind that gets drowned out by the shrieking of ego-intellect or fear mind. When we lose our connection to our truth we suffer—we feel stressed, uncomfortable, desperate—OUR ENERGY SYSTEM IS DISRUPTING. As we learn to challenge our thoughts and clear the energy disruptions that result from them, we release our authentic power and our lives change.

EDITOR'S NOTE:
An interesting explanation of what 'energy system disruption' may really mean in practical terms.

It is important to realise that this work with the heart is not just a metaphor. Fascinating research coming out of The Heartmath Institute[2] and from others in the new field of neuro-cardiology is showing how the heart mediates between our external perception of reality and our inner, physiological, emotional and spiritual experience. The heart, like a radio receiver, selects the frequencies which provide the brain with reality-making materials. Within our body systems it maintains a constant dialogue with the emotional brain and influences every organ and system in the body.

Using the Heart Anchor to set our intention for love no matter what, to re-mind ourselves of our truth, is not just a nice idea; it has actual physiological consequences.

## What is the Heart Anchor?

This work uses the 'Heart Anchor' to develop (or remember) a connection to heart-truth. This is actually our natural state, our birth right, and the opposite of what I call the 'addicted heart'—that state in which you experience yourself as disconnected from the Field or Source—or at least seem to be. In fact this 'disconnection' can never really happen, and the heart continues its communication—whether you are aware of it or not—despite all the interference coming from the thoughts and beliefs of your personal unconscious that make up 'Fear Mind' or the ego state. The subtle messages from the heart that literally travel along the pathway between the heart and brain in constant dialogue are overridden by the intellect. As you continue to undo the blocks to your awareness of Truth or Love, as well as consciously develop your personal heart connection, both the channel of communication between your own heart and the Field or Source as well as the internal communication between your heart and your brain open up and you notice yourself speaking, feeling and acting from Truth. Ultimately true mind is Heart. No matter where you are starting from, your Heart Anchor is one important way that you can develop a conscious or 'felt' sense of your own connection to Love.

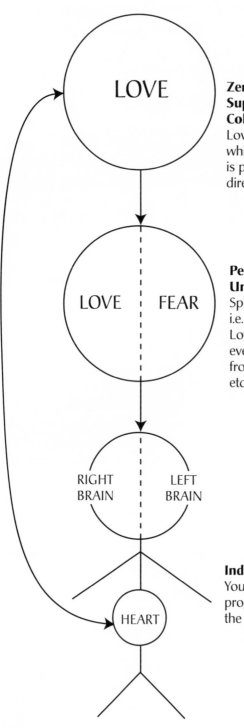

**Zero Point Field,
Superconscious,
Collective Unconscious**
Love is pure potentiality from
which everything takes form,
is possible. The heart retains a
direct link to this.

**Personal/Individual
Unconscious**
Split between Love and Fear
i.e. retains connection to
Love and is vast store of
everything downloaded
from environment, parents
etc. between ages 0-6 years.

**Individuality**
Your unique personal
programme experienced via
the brain and body.

## How can I activate my Heart Anchor?

The first step is to try out the energy points of the Heart Anchor without any particular expectation. Put one hand on the centre of your chest (or heart chakra area) and gently rub. This is the heart point and it is connected to an invisible network of energy channels that spread out and open up the lungs and chest area. Then place your other hand on the Top of the Head Point where you would balance a ball, and rub both points lightly at the same time. There is literally and energetically a pathway that runs from the heart to the emotional brain. Sense that pathway and then sense it going beyond the constraints of your physical body. You may or may not notice tingling, energy moving or some other shift in your physiology as you touch these points. Either way is fine.

Note: an alternative method is to use the heart point and the point a couple of inches behind the ear (either right or left). See which suits you best, or you can alternate.

## What is the metaphysical purpose of the Heart Anchor?

The Heart Anchor actually creates a bridge between the metaphysical and the physical, the abstract and the practical. You are learning to play with your own neurology so that you may come to open your heart, remembering Love. In this way your body is becoming a means for communication rather than separation. It will support you in strengthening your conscious connection between yourself and Love, which is your true power. It only takes a minute or less to do, and when you have done it a few times you will start to feel a positive surge of feeling as soon as you put your hand to your heart, and after a while it will happen just by thinking of it.

The purpose is to re-Mind ourselves of who we really are; Love completely unchanged by anything that was ever said or thought or done, by us . . . or to us.

## How can I develop my Heart Anchor?

1. Close your eyes and go into the Heart Anchor pose

2. Rub both points lightly at the same time.

3. Close your eyes and focus on the physical sensations coming from the

centre, your heart . . . radiating out into those tiny fine channels . . .
opening the heart area . . . connecting heart to mind . . .

4. And, if you like, zoom in to the very heart centre . . . and as you do,
   maybe you can remember the last time you felt really loving . . . or
   were surprisingly successful at something . . . some pleasant memory
   presenting itself to you . . . or maybe just a smile . . .

5. Now open your eyes and come out of the pose. Take a deep breath in and
   out.

6. Close your eyes and go back in—notice how quickly those feelings come
   back. Let any pictures fade now so you are focusing entirely on the
   feeling response as you lightly rub the points.

   • How does it feel?
   • Where is the feeling?
   • How does it move?
   • What is the texture of the feeling?
   • Does it make a sound?
   • What colour is it?
   • What temperature?
   • Where is the warmest part?

7. Open your eyes and come out again. Take another deep breath in and
   out. Go back in for a few seconds.

From now on whenever you feel good for any reason, maybe simply
seeing a lovely flower or the sun breaking through the clouds, notice your
good feelings and touch your heart anchor points—just for a moment. In this
very simple way you are strengthening your connection to Love, and very soon
you will notice a flood of good feelings when you touch the points, whatever
the actual circumstances you are in.

## When should I use my Heart Anchor?

Here are four important uses of the Heart Anchor:

1. When a client accesses a strong positive state (to enhance)

2. At point of choice (processing)

3. After a power question such as: *"Is that really true!?"* . . . (e.g. in response to a statement such as *"I'll never be good enough"*). Following Byron Katie's 'The Work'[3], like a form of meditation, this allows us to reach deeper into our own truth and wisdom

4. Stuckness/addictive states

This area of stuckness/addictive states deserves further exploration here. In the past we have used the term Massive Reversal to describe what is going on when problems seem irresolvable (see *Identifying and Neutralizing Reversals*). This can also be an aspect of what I have called the state of the addicted heart, where we have lost our connection to Source or heart-truth.

One interesting manifestation of the 'addicted heart' is a particular type of stuckness which can come at any time but often emerges when you have already made a lot of progress, perhaps recovered from a major addiction or illness. As you come closer to the light to claim your reality as Love, the ego-mind or fear gets desperate and it is possible to go through a phase where it seems as if you have lost everything you had gained and cannot seem to move forward. My experience is that when we come to recognise this as actually part of the process of change and an indication of healing at a deeper level, the fear lessens, opening the way to move creatively through the deep psychic entanglements that may have built up.

The point is that we never continue to do, think or feel anything for no reason. It is always because we value it.

The problem is really that when we lose our connection to Truth or Love, it is possible, through the split consciousness that results, to value and hate something at the same time.

## What can I do if I simultaneously value and hate something?

Choose a problem you have been working on with EFT—something you have been trying to solve, a change you've been trying to make, a goal you have been trying to achieve that hasn't been working out. Or think of a client. Hold it in your mind as we go through the following ideas and questions.

For now you can put the Heart Anchor on hold and turn your attention to the problem state using questioning skills to disrupt the state of stuckness. Allow previously unconscious information to come through. This is all within the context that you have never really lost your connection although you can think you have. Now is the time to shine light on the illusion, to see it clearly for what it is.

## What if I feel stuck?

All addictive states are a form of stuckness. Most of us find ourselves well and truly stuck at some point in our lives. We just cannot stop doing that particular drug, thing or behaviour, seeing that person, feeling a particular way or perhaps struggling with a physical illness or problem. And it is very easy to convince yourself that everything happens instantly with EFT, that 'one minute wonders' are the rule rather than a possibility, and that if you haven't shifted your own problem (whatever it is) more or less instantly then there must be something wrong ... WITH YOU ... which you knew anyway (so there you go—more proof!). And there you are, stuck in an endless loop. Fear or ego-mind wants you to think there is something wrong with you, its survival depends on it and it does not give up its illusions lightly.

> Ego-mind has a major investment in the belief that we are separate. Heart-truth knows that all our suffering comes from this belief.

## How can I know I'm tapping on the right thing?

What we do know about EFT, for sure, is that when you are authentically tuned in to the problem, the tapping works. However it is quite possible to think you are tuned in to the problem when you are not, and this is where an understanding of both conscious and unconscious thought processes comes in really handy. Research in the fields of linguistics and neurology informs us that roughly (AND ONLY) 7% of any communication is transmitted verbally—that is, through the actual words spoken, while 93% of meaning is taken from non verbal cues such as gesture, tone, facial expression. There is unconscious nonverbal commentary on what is being thought and said. Emma Roberts and I offer a Diploma in Integrated Energy Techniques[4] and one of its

*EDITOR'S NOTE:*
This is particularly true when dissociation is one of your principal unconscious defence strategies.

major teachings is precise observation and questioning skills that get beneath the surface of a client's statements to the 'truth' or unconscious meaning (see below for examples of these).

---

When you do this, you know you are tapping on the right thing.

---

And the interesting thing is that you can learn to do this for yourself. When you are thinking, you are in a very real sense 'talking to yourself' and the same rules of conscious and unconscious processes can apply. In fact, where there is a problem or stuckness, they WILL apply. Powerful, purposeful questioning will move you through the layers of the 'addicted heart' that typically show up in different forms of Psychological Reversal (PR) {see *Identifying and Neutralizing Reversals*}. Wherever there is stuckness there is disconnection. All PR is disconnection from heart-truth. It is just usually hidden from your awareness in the unconscious, still accessible through key questions that take their cue from the non-verbal clues that are always offered, however intractable the problem may seem to be {see *Finding the Root of the Problem*}.

## What if I am addicted to my emotions (positive or negative)?

The fact is that emotions or feeling-states are highly addictive. This might seem obvious when we are thinking about 'positive' states such as peace, joy, happiness. When we have these kinds of experiences we want more, and this urge can lead us to look for the experience in drugs or alcohol, for instance. However what is less likely is that we will consider ourselves addicted to 'negative' emotions or even to the problem itself! If a thought like this ever manages to intrude into our conscious self-talk the chances are we tend to banish it pretty quickly. It is possible to be addicted to any of the following ... and plenty more:

- Anger
- Rage
- Anxiety
- Guilt
- Struggle
- Trying

- Hopelessness
- Worthlessness
- Lack
- Grief
- Depression
- Resentment

## How does this addiction relate to Primary and Secondary Reversals?

And what about stuckness or other addictive states—how might we consciously or more usually, unconsciously, be giving value to these states and how do we go about undoing them?

Let us take a look at how stuck thinking works. The important thing is to find the payoff for keeping the problem. One of the important things we learn in pursuit of EFT mastery is the ability to use language in a refined and elegant fashion to dig beneath the surface and find the ways in which we may have been valuing the problem state—that is, the conflict between conscious and unconscious purposes. For example we can explore the use of Primary Reversals as nuances of language in the set up that can make a difference.

## PRIMARY REVERSALS:

Examples of Primary Reversals would be Safety, Deserving and Desire. These could be used to create set up statements along the lines of:

- *Even though it's not safe for me to get over this problem*
- *Even though it's not safe for others (e.g. mum, husband . . . ) if I get over this problem*
- *Even though I don't deserve to get over this problem*
- *Even though others (e.g. parents, abuser etc) don't deserve for me to get over this problem*
- *Even though I don't want to get over this problem*

I would also suggest Fear, Loss and Self-judgement as Primary Reversals. These areas can be approached through questions while touching the Heart Anchor points.

Take a few moments to ask each of the following questions while sitting in the Heart Anchor position. Tap with any thoughts, feelings or physical sensations that emerge. Connecting to heart-truth while meditating on these questions will often allow previously hidden unconscious material to come into awareness.

*FEAR:*

- Have I been afraid of letting go of the past?
- Have I been scared to move forward in my life?
- Have I been fearing the unknown?

*LOSS:*

- Have I been worried that I'll lose something if I solve this?

*SELF-JUDGEMENT:*

- Have I been concerned that something bad will happen if I get this?
- Am I concerned it will mean something bad about me if I achieve this?

> Self-judgement can often be one of the trickier ways we keep ourselves stuck. For instance I had a client who came to realise that she had been unable to let go of the paralysing grief she still felt over the death of her grandmother two years on, because it would mean she *"hadn't loved her"*. Another client who had been struggling with her weight for years realised that the last time she had been at her goal weight coincided with her son dying suddenly in an accident.

## SECONDARY REVERSALS:

What can be even trickier to deal with are those thought/feeling constructs that I call Secondary Reversals. These are the ones that have become so 'normalised' and so much a part of the everyday fabric of our lives, so innocuous or so apparently positive in their own right, that they snuck right past us! Examples are: Familiarity, Significance, Drama and Excitement, and Love and Attention.

As you go through the following examples, questions and suggestions, stop as soon as anything spikes and sit for a few moments in the Heart Anchor posture, noticing what emerges. Then continue tapping if you need to . . .

*FAMILIARITY:*

Often familiarity equals 'safe'. It's for a good reason that our language has phrases such as 'better the devil you know than the devil you don't!'. Phrases such as this represent deeply held unconscious beliefs.

> ✦ *Even though this is familiar and I'm used to it . . . and maybe I just don't know what to do/who I'd be without it . . .*

*SIGNIFICANCE:*

We may believe that our anger or other feeling gives significance to our suffering, gives it a point. To feel so bad, it must be important.

One client realised that she was living her life from the thought-construct that she had to hold on to the anger she felt towards her parents because it gave validity to the suffering she had experienced in her childhood which in turn gave meaning to her life.

> ✦ *Even though my anger is the only thing that gives meaning to my life . . .*

*DRAMA AND EXCITEMENT:*

This gives importance too; it can make you feel like someone who has interesting things to say. It boosts adrenaline and makes you feel 'alive', if only for a moment in time.

> ✦ *Even though it makes me feel alive . . .*

> ✦ *Even though I don't know what I'd think about without this . . .*

*LOVE AND ATTENTION:*

Feeling bad can get you attention from others, and it may have been the only way you found that seemed to work. Perhaps through the very process of getting involved with therapy or EFT, paradoxically, you might have become hooked on getting attention from others in this way.

> ✦ *Even though it's the only way I can get love . . .*

✢ *Even though I need my problems to get attention . . .*

What other statements come to mind for you?

## What is the practical purpose of the Heart Anchor?

Although so far we have looked primarily at the Heart Anchor as a way to re-mind ourselves of heart-truth, to reconnect to our metaphysical reality as Love, this piece would not be complete without a discussion of its power on a more practical level.

On one level, that is the level of physical brain function, the Heart Anchor is very practical. You begin simply by touching the points and noticing any pleasant feelings that generates, however vaguely. The next step is to deliberately anchor on to the good feelings from any positive memory, while continuing to hold the points. It is absolutely essential to do this since the brain is literally divided into two hemispheres (mirroring Love and Fear) and the left frontal cortex processes positive feelings and experiences which we move towards; and the right frontal cortex processes negative experiences and that which we wish to move away from.

*EDITOR'S NOTE:*
The ramifications of this are considerable. This identification of the different parts of the brain to process desires vs. aversions hints at a possible scientific basis for what is popularly called 'The Law of Attraction'.

This means that positive choices, evaluation of what we want, establishing what we value is processed in an entirely different place from what we do not want. When you are stuck in the state of the addicted heart you are almost entirely focused on what you do not want, which will only bring you more of the same.

Conversely, developing your Heart Anchor will increase the capacity of the left frontal lobe and reawaken choice. It is also fun to do, with practice you will find you can access deep states of happiness, even ecstasy! In the state of the addicted heart this brain function is all but shut down. You can easily continue to value the valueless, it simply seems as if that is all there is.

Keep in mind that this brain training must be valued in its own right, not just as something to compete with the old problem state. For now, think of this as a completely separate area of the brain that needs to be attended to and developed, and which quickly responds by feeling good. How cool is that! Usually when we want to change, we are resisting the problem. We may even hate it, trying to solve it with right cortex functioning. Everything that you have done in the past to avoid your problems has only ever given you more of the problem (even if that means living with continual resistance or avoidance). To paraphrase Einstein, 'you cannot solve a problem with the same consciousness that created it.' And no one ever changed through disliking some thing or behaviour (by using their right frontal cortex).

---

Change happens when you come to value something else more; a whole new way of thinking.

---

Disliking or devaluing the old behaviour or way is the RESULT of the change of mind, not its source. Above all, put yourself wholeheartedly into discovering your Heart Anchor—and enjoy it!

## AUTHOR'S BIOGRAPHY AND CONTACT DETAILS

Sue Beer has a private practice in London, UK specialising in working with addictions and personal transformation. She is also a dedicated student of 'A Course in Miracles', co-founder of The EFT Centre in London, creator of the 'Healing the Addicted Heart: 5 Stages of Transformation' workshops and author of the soon to be published book with the same title.

For more information see: http://theeftcentre.com

### REFERENCES

1. www.theeftcentre.com describes workshops on 'Opening to love' and 'Healing the addicted heart'
2. The Heartmath Institute—www.heartmath.org
3. Byron Katie—The Work—www.thework.com
4. www.theeftcentre.com gives details of the Diploma in Integrated Energy Techniques

# Tapping and Business

PAMELA BRUNER, SUCCESS COACH,
CERTIFIED EFT PRACTITIONER (EFTCERT-I)

Tapping is a perfect technique for removing fears, limiting beliefs, and blocks to positive, necessary action. Running a business, particularly for the entrepreneur or independent service professional, is an activity that brings up fears, doubts, and a host of other negative and disempowering emotions. Overcoming these is often the difference between success and failure.

In this article we'll look at using tapping to overcome negative emotions and limiting beliefs with regard to business, particularly business for the tapping practitioner. These ideas are also useful for practitioners who wish to focus on using tapping for business clients.

## Why is tapping so essential for business?

Triggers for our negative emotions exist in many areas of life—we have triggers in relationships, around our bodies and health, and certainly around money. Business activities can be enormous triggers. Here are just a few examples:

- Sales and marketing may trigger fear, inadequacy, rejection, unworthiness, shame
- Handling technology may trigger inadequacy, feelings of stupidity, frustration

- Planning may trigger fear of failure and fear of success
- Organization may trigger overwhelm, control issues
- Professional relationships may trigger self-doubt, anger, trust issues
- Handling/Making money may trigger fear, shame, unworthiness
- Public speaking may trigger panic, shame, anxiety

All of the above may also trigger bodily sensations such as a pounding heart, sweaty palms, nausea, or difficulty breathing.

It is essential for the tapping practitioner to work on herself to remove the energy disruptions causing fear, distress, or feelings of inadequacy around these activities. If these emotions are not handled and removed, the results can include the following:

- Not enough income/business not viable
- An inability to market services effectively
- Missed opportunities
- Undercharging for services
- Inappropriate spending out of fear

We'll look at some common beliefs that limit business people, and suggest tapping phrases and approaches to reverse those beliefs.

## What's the number one use for tapping in business?

If you have a particular issue, clearing that one will be your number one use! However, the most common business fear for service professionals and entrepreneurs is difficulty around sales and marketing.

Here are some of the most common blocks to sales and marketing, and the suggested tapping phrases.

## 1. Limiting Beliefs About Sales and Selling

### LIMITING BELIEF: 'I don't know what to say in a sales conversation.'

Sales technique is a matter of study and practice. There are many great books on sales techniques and sales conversation.

There was a time when you didn't know anything about tapping, or any other service that you provide. You learned. You can learn to handle a sales conversation also.

The actual emotion behind this phrase could be a feeling of inadequacy, or feelings of stupidity, or the belief could be a cover for other beliefs about sales. One option is to tap on the emotion, as in:

> ⚡ *Even though I feel inadequate in a sales conversation, I choose to love and accept myself.*

Getting to the emotion behind the belief will often uncover core issues, and can be very helpful.

Alternately you could simply tap on the belief:

> ⚡ *Even though I don't know what to say in a sales conversation, I choose to know that I can learn.*

Do a Choices Trio round {see *The Choices Method*} with the negative reminder phrase: **'Don't know what to say in sales'** and the positive reminder phrase: **'I choose to know that I can learn'**

This is an interesting tapping sequence, because the expected outcome is not necessarily that the belief 'I don't know what to say in a sales conversation' will go away, or become untrue. Instead, there are many different possible positive outcomes.

For example:

- You may still believe that you don't know, but become excited to learn.
- You may realize that you knew more than you thought you did.
- The belief may completely diminish in importance, to be replaced by another limiting belief such as 'I don't like sales'. If that is the case, proceed to work on the other limiting belief.

## LIMITING BELIEF: 'I feel inauthentic when I'm selling.'

You have to do a bit of detective work in order to figure out the reason for this. Although you could tap on 'Even though I feel inauthentic when I'm selling' it will be more effective if you go beneath that to the deeper issue.

There are at least two possible reasons for this feeling:

REASON 1: You're not comfortable with the services that you provide. Therefore, when you are trying to 'convince' someone to hire you, you feel inauthentic, or like a fraud.

If you're not comfortable with your services because you're a new practitioner, you have two tasks. One is to gain sufficient experience by working with friends and family, and to study the teaching materials that are available in the tapping world, so that you know your work. The other is to tap away your discomfort so that you can best serve your client.

Sample tapping phrases for this discomfort may include:

- *Even though I don't believe I can truly help people . . .*

- *Even though I'm afraid I may make a mistake as a practitioner . . .*

- *Even though I'm afraid tapping may not work in this situation . . .*

Choices are particularly powerful for replacing these types of beliefs. Some possible Choices include:

- *I choose to remember that healing comes through me, not by me . . .*

- *I choose to know that everyone makes mistakes, I can still help people . . .*

- *I choose to remember that it's not up to me to make tapping work, it's a great modality, and I'm here to help . . .*

- *I choose to allow the Universe (God, Spirit) to work through me . . .*

REASON 2: You're uncomfortable because being a salesperson feels inauthentic to you.

The solution for this is to work on your beliefs about selling being something nasty, undesirable, and something that you just don't do. Yes, you are a salesperson—at least you are if you want to succeed. You are always a spokesperson for your services. If you have limiting beliefs about that label, not only will that hinder your business, but it will keep you from being effective with salespeople who come to you for help. And it's a negative judgment, which hinders your energy.

If you're emotionally uncomfortable with sales, then it's understandable that you don't want to be good at it!

You may see it as being as much of an accomplishment as being a good thief, or a good liar.

REFRAME: You're not selling, you're sharing.

What you have makes a difference in the world, so you have a moral obligation to share it. And you have a practical obligation to yourself to do that sharing well.

Here are some possible tapping phrases:

- ☥ *Even though sales people are sleazy (dishonest, etc) . . .*
- ☥ *Even though I feel cheap thinking about selling . . .*
- ☥ *Even though I shouldn't have to sell my services . . .*

And the positive choices include:

- ☥ *I choose to consider that I'm sharing, not selling*
- ☥ *I choose to focus on the possibilities for healing*
- ☥ *I choose to feel great about bringing tapping to the world*

## LIMITING BELIEF: 'I feel pushy and manipulative when I'm in a sales conversation.'

A possible reason for this is that you're focused on the sale, and not the benefits.

You want to make the sale, or close the deal, so much that you're focused on that, and not the benefits that you provide to your customer. When you focus on the sale, you're going to feel pushy and manipulative, because you're focusing on the benefit that YOU will get if they say 'yes'.

---

REFRAME: Focus on the benefits that your customer will receive.

---

You're going to spell them out to your prospective customer, so listen to what you're saying and get behind it emotionally. Focus on what a big difference this will make in their lives, and back it up with reasons, benefits, and stories.

If you're not clear on the benefits that your customer will receive, then you have some work to do first. A common misconception that new tapping practitioners make is that tapping is a benefit—it is not. Tapping is a technique, a process by which your clients achieve their benefits.

Benefits of working with a tapping practitioner may include:
- Removal of fears or phobias
- Weight loss
- Addiction cessation
- Improved sports performance
- And many, many more!

Once you're clear on your benefits, you can create your tapping statements. If your SUDS level is very high (7 or above), do a round with the setup:

> *Even though I feel pushy and manipulative, I deeply and completely love and accept myself.*

REMINDER PHRASE: ***pushy and manipulative***

When your SUDS level is at a 5-6 or below, switch to a Choices Trio round using one of the following:

> *Even though I feel pushy and manipulative when I'm selling my services, I choose to focus on {the benefit that I provide} . . .*

> *Even though I feel pushy and sleazy when I'm selling my services, I choose to know that my clients get great benefits, including _____ . . .*

In your reframe, or Choices statement, there are many options. Some healing practitioners prefer to distance themselves from sales, and so redefine what they do, i.e. 'I'm not selling, I'm sharing,' or 'I'm not in sales, I'm involved in moral marketing.' I find it more powerful to actually remove the charge from the word 'sales' for two reasons. It will assist you in learning sales techniques that can be valuable for your business, since you won't have negative energy around the word 'sales'. It will also free you to work with sales people who may become your clients, without having judgment about them. Just as you may work to free yourself from any judgments about other activities your clients may engage in, free yourself from judgments about sales.

### LIMITING BELIEF: 'I don't know what to say when potential clients have objections. It feels pushy to try to overcome them.'

A common reason for this is that you're not comfortable with the word 'no'— not comfortable with hearing it, and not comfortable with saying it. Most of the discomfort with sales and sales people, if you're a customer, comes from a natural human desire to want to be nice, and to agree.

Sometimes the product or service that they're offering isn't right for you, and it's your job to say 'no'! It's not the sales person's job to not sell—that's what they are supposed to do. So take responsibility for saying 'no' clearly.

Become a better customer, and you'll be a better salesperson!

---

**HINT:** If you give an explanation for your 'no', the sales person may try to overcome your objection. Again, you have a choice as to whether to see that as 'pushy' or to see that as 'trying to help me get this good thing that they are offering'.

---

Here's an example:

Tapping Practitioner: (after a discussion of the service) *'Would you like to take the next step?'*

Potential Client: *'I don't think so, it's too expensive.'*

The client has just given the Practitioner an objection that she can counter. For example:

Tapping Practitioner: *'It's costing you quite a lot to have this problem. How much (time, energy, money) would you be saving if this problem went away?'*

Do you see this as pushy, or helpful? If you were talking to a friend about a book that had changed your life, you'd be enthusiastic, and attempt to overcome any objections that she might have to reading it. Why wouldn't you do the same for a potential client?

If you see it as pushy, do a Choices Trio round using the following setup:

> ☥ *Even though it feels pushy to try to overcome their objections, I choose to focus on being helpful.*

Whether or not you go on to successfully overcome their objections, you will be focused on being helpful, and being of service. Doing this will completely shift the energy of the sales conversation, and potential clients will usually be grateful for your approach, regardless of whether or not they hire you.

## LIMITING BELIEF: 'People won't like me if I try to sell them my product/service.'

People will either like you or they won't. Some of this doesn't depend on you—if you remind them of their evil 3rd grade teacher, you could be a saint and they probably won't like you. That being said, how likeable you are is up to you, whether you're a service professional or you have a product. People buy based on service; they buy from and hire friendly people. In many ways, YOU are the product. It's important to be likeable.

So do the likeable things:
- Smile
- Indicate that you're interested in the other person
- Make eye contact
- Listen actively
- Be positive and enthusiastic

Since you need to do all of these things to be an effective tapping practitioner, they should be part of your toolkit anyway. And doing these doesn't mean that you can't sell!

If you focus on the benefits, rather than the sale, and are a likeable person, chances are that they'll like you whether or not they hire you. If they don't, it's not your problem.

✢ *Even though I'm afraid that people won't like me if I try to sell my services . . .*

Positive phrases:

✢ *I choose to know that I'm likeable*

✢ *I choose to know that whether or not a person likes me is all about them, not about me*

✢ *I choose to create that I can be likeable and sell easily*

## 2. Limiting Beliefs About Work and Money

### LIMITING BELIEF: 'I'll have to work too hard to be successful.'

Many good people believe that it's wrong to receive more money than you 'rightfully earn'. Some beliefs that indicate that you may be one of them include:

- 'Professional athletes/movie stars shouldn't be paid millions of dollars.'
- 'No one needs over $200,000 a year (or whatever figure you choose).'
- 'No one can legitimately deserve over $100/hour.'

Are any of these familiar to you? If so, you have a belief that there is a certain amount of money that it's OK to earn for hard work, and more than that is not justified.

---

It's great to work hard. It's even better to work smart.

---

If you can find a way to give value to people that benefits them, and work less, why not? If you're trading time for money, you may see a limit on what you can earn. For example, if you help a busy executive who travels frequently to remove her fear of flying, what is that worth? Hundreds of dollars? Thousands? What if you offered your services on a 'results' basis, rather than a 'per hour' basis? Even if you're not ready to step into that possibility yet, just opening your mind to the value that you're providing makes it possible to consider receiving more money for what you do.

- ⚜ *Even though I'll have to work too hard to be successful . . .*

- ⚜ *Even though it takes hard work to be successful . . .*

- ⚜ *Even though I won't have time for my family if I'm successful . . .*

- ⚜ *Even though no one in my profession makes more than $?/year . . .*

- ⚜ *Even though I won't be a good person if I'm successful without hard work . . .*

Positive Choices:

- ⚜ *I choose to find ways to work smarter, not harder*

- ⚜ *I choose to believe that I can find time for my work and my family*

- ⚜ *I choose to create that I can make the money that I want doing what I love*

- ⚜ *I choose to be a good person, work smart, and be successful*

- ⚜ *I choose to leave the 'How' up to the Universe (God, Spirit)*

## LIMITING BELIEF: 'Since healing comes through me, I should give my services away.'

This is such a common belief with healers! Yes, healing comes through you, and not by you. However, you still need to study and learn tapping and other skills in order to help people. You need to do the work to clear your own issues to help people. That learning, that work, can and should be rewarded financially. And you can do far more good in the world as a wealthy person rather than a poor one.

This is a tappable issue, and sometimes has its roots in issues of self-worth. If that is the case, you'll need to pursue that, perhaps with the help of another tapping practitioner.

- ⚜ *Even though healing is a gift, so I should be giving my services away . . .*

- ⚜ *Even though I'm not doing the healing, so I shouldn't charge for it (or shouldn't charge much) . . .*

Positive Choices:

  ✦ *I choose to allow myself to receive*

  ✦ *I choose to know the value of what I provide, and focus on that value*

  ✦ *I choose to allow the Universe to give to me in the form of money, as I give to others*

## 3. Limiting Beliefs About Other Business Issues

It is important for business owners and entrepreneurs, including tapping practitioners, to be comfortable in other arenas such as handling technology, organization and planning.

Not everyone is strong in these areas, and you don't have to be strong in them to be comfortable. Creating comfort using tapping can help you acknowledge your weaknesses, be willing to learn more, and be willing to ask for or hire help when needed. Sometimes creating comfort will also uncover a skill or talent that you didn't know you had, because a limiting belief was blocking your awareness of it!

### LIMITING BELIEF: 'I'm not good with technology.'

Although this belief is almost non-existent with younger adults, many people still have it. As the world and business become more technology based, technology will become easier for us to handle, but also more prevalent. Feeling comfortable with technology will be vital to running a successful business in the upcoming decade.

Since tapping works best with specific issues, you'll get much better results if you make this more specific. What is it that you're 'not good' at?

  ✦ *Even though I feel incompetent when I sit at my computer each morning . . .*

  ✦ *Even though I felt stupid when Mike started talking about technology . . .*

✦ *Even though I get nervous when I think about giving that PowerPoint presentation . . .*

Positive choices:

✦ *I choose to allow myself to learn what I need to know*

✦ *I choose to accept and forgive myself for not being a technology wiz*

✦ *I choose to love and accept the way that I am*

✦ *I choose to consider that technology (my computer, etc) is just a tool and learning to use it is a skill that I can master*

## What is the best way to use tapping for business issues?

There is not one 'best' way, but are many ways to use tapping for business issues. Here are a couple of suggestions:

Using your to-do list or business plan, make a list of upcoming activities for the next week or month. Next to each, rate how positively you feel about undertaking that activity, with 0 being 'completely don't want to do that' and 10 being 'totally enthusiastic'.

If any activity is less than a 5, ask yourself what emotion is associated with that activity, what thought you have about the activity, and then tap on that emotion and thought.

You may want to do this every day for a few minutes, or schedule a longer session once a week. As you begin to remove negative emotions and energy disruptions around business tasks, your business will flow more easily, and you'll be more comfortable, and your bottom line will usually reflect this!

EXAMPLE: 'I don't want to go to the networking event.'

NOTE: don't immediately start tapping on this!
Q:  *'Why not?'*
A:  *'Because I don't know what to say there.'*
Q:  *'How do you feel about that?'*
A:  *'Flustered and embarrassed.'*
Q:  *'How flustered and embarrassed are you?'*
A:  '7' (this is your SUDS level)

Now you have the material that you need for an EFT round:

> ⚡ *Even though I'm flustered and embarrassed because I don't know what to say at the networking event, I deeply and completely love and accept myself.*

REMINDER PHRASE: *flustered and embarrassed*

After the intensity has dropped to a 5 or less:
Q:   *'How would you like to feel instead?'*
A:   *'Calm and assured'*

> ⚡ *Even though I still have some of that remaining flustered and embarrassed feeling, I choose to feel calm and assured at the networking event.*

REMINDER PHRASES for a Choices Trio:

NEGATIVE ROUND: *Remaining flustered and embarrassed*
POSITIVE ROUND: *Choose to feel calm and assured*

In business, often a tapping round like this will result in a decision for action, such as 'I'm going to get some help with my introductory speech' or 'I wonder how other people handle networking events. I'm going to research that'. Now there is action where you were stopped before.

Tapping is a wonderful modality to support business success. Since many business issues are actually personal issues that are being triggered by business events, working on these brings great growth and emotional freedom in all areas of your life. As a tapping practitioner, clearing your own issues around business will enable you to help your clients in many, many ways.

## AUTHOR'S BIOGRAPHY AND CONTACT DETAILS

Pamela Bruner is a Success Coach, Certified Firewalk Instructor, Certified EFT Practitioner (EFTCert-I), speaker, author and musician. Following a career as a computer programmer, Pamela built a hugely successful business as a Celtic harpist and singer, recording over twenty albums. She then began doing motivational work in the music community, and became a Certified Life Coach to better work with people in all walks of life.

Pamela now works with small business owners and solo practitioners who want to make a difference in the world with their businesses. She is committed to helping people achieve success in all of their endeavors. For more information, including free tapping video footage, go to www.MakeYourSuccessEasy.com.

# Inner Peace—an Inside Job

## A GUIDE TO BEING YOUR OWN THERAPIST

JUDY BYRNE, EFT MASTER, EFTCERT-HONORS

*'Peace of mind is clearly an internal matter. It must begin with
your own thoughts and then extend outward. It is from your
peace of mind that a peaceful perception of the world arises'*

FROM 'A COURSE IN MIRACLES'

## What do you mean by an 'inside job'?

A peaceful perception of the world is a big ask in the age of international terrorism and financial meltdown. Yet, in my experience as a therapist, the biggest
barriers to inner peace for most of us lie not in what is going on in the world
around us but in the relationship we have with ourselves. When that relationship is accepting and forgiving we are less easily drawn into and agitated by
the turmoil around us.

So where does that relationship with ourselves come from? And how can
we do some relationship counselling on ourselves?

EFT is a wonderful tool for changing not only how we feel in the moment
but also how we view ourselves. And changing how we view ourselves will
automatically change how we feel in the moment. EFT has more scope than

any technique I have encountered in my 15 previous years as a therapist for people to do profound change work for and with themselves.

I am going to outline here some of the ways that you can do that for yourself. I think if you are willing to embark on a programme and put time and energy into it you can do huge amounts of your own therapy for yourself. I also think it is important to make yourself a promise that if you do open up feelings and memories that you cannot deal with on your own you will consult a professional who can help you. Deal? Then read on . . .

One option is just to follow your feelings now and see where they take you. But I am going to give you a route map to help you plan and track the journey. And I suggest you divide it up into: PAST, PRESENT and FUTURE .

## Should I work with my feelings/memories in chronological order?

There is no right or wrong order. You can cycle between them. Or you can systematically start with your earliest negative memories and end with your future dreams. Your way is the right way for you. When you start working on the past there are advantages in going through memories chronologically. If you do you will often find you have pulled the foundations out from under later ones when you get to them. Some of the sting will have gone out of them even before you start tapping on them.

But I am going to sidestep chronological logic here and start with the present. I think we are often past and future oriented in therapy and overlook the present. In a sense, it is all we have. It is when we have our relationship with ourselves—right now. When we get caught up in the past, in what has happened to us, or we focus on our goals or our fears for the future, we can let present time just slip by unnoticed. Remember: life is a journey, not a destination.

## The Now—Learning to be present to the present

### How can I use EFT for inner peace in the 'now'?

To get started, just read to the end of the next paragraph and then close your eyes and try this out. It is just an experiment in staying in the now.

For a few minutes, concentrate on your breathing. Follow your breath in and out—and out beyond you. Let it take your attention to the tension that needs attention. Notice what you notice. When you sense two or three minutes have gone by open your eyes and write down what you experienced. Forget inner peace for the moment. Just notice. And when you open your eyes, record.

Did you find yourself focusing on physical discomfort? Or what you felt you were supposed to be noticing? Or did you have trouble keeping your thoughts from flying off to all the other things you could be doing right now? Or making judgments of yourself?

Then tap on whatever did come up for you. So it might be:

- ✢ *Even though I find it really hard to stay in the now . . .*
- ✢ *Even though I could not keep my eyes closed for more than two minutes . . .*
- ✢ *Even though my mind went back to what X said to me this morning . . .*
- ✢ *Even though my mind was racing on to what I had to do next . . .*
- ✢ *Even though I started noticing a pain in my left knee . . .*
- ✢ *Even though now is where I am least comfortable . . .*

Or it could be something quite different from these. Just notice—and tap. Even better, do it every day for a while until you begin to find it less difficult to be and stay in the now for a little while. And not just with your eyes closed. Let yourself learn to notice the now in a range of situations, to check in with yourself. And notice when you feel you are already experiencing inner peace—often, once in a while, rarely, never?

## How will I recognize *inner peace* when I find it?

Inner peace is a personal matter. Ask yourself these questions. Ask them one at a time. As you ask each one close your eyes for a few moments and reflect on it. Write down the answers that come up for you before you move on to the next.

- What is inner peace for me?
- When do I expect to have it?
- What happens when I try to imagine it?
- What has to happen before I have it?

- What has to change before I have it?
- What do I have to do before I can have it?
- Am I ever allowed to have it?
- Do I deserve it?

Keep those notes.

And then try slow tapping on inner peace and see what else comes up for you. You can use the notes you made in answer to those questions to devise your own set-ups, as well as to identify what you might need to tap on later.

## What do you mean by *Slow Tapping*?

To slow tap, select a setup that resonates with you from the following list, or devise your own, using insights from the exercises above:

⚘ *Even though I do not have inner peace . . .*

⚘ *Even though I do not know what inner peace is . . .*

⚘ *Even though I do not deserve inner peace . . .*

⚘ *Even though I do not deserve inner peace yet . . .*

⚘ *Even though I would no longer be motivated if I had inner peace . . .*

⚘ *Even though I cannot have inner peace until I have achieved . . .*

⚘ *Even though I might become smug if I had inner peace . . .*

⚘ *Even though I cannot have inner peace until I do . . .*

⚘ *Even though I cannot have inner peace until my mother says she is sorry for . . .*

⚘ *Even though I cannot have inner peace . . .*

⚘ *Even though inner peace is for others . . .*

⚘ *Even though I have stuff to deal with before I can have inner peace . . .*

⚘ *Even though Y has to forgive me before I can have inner peace . . .*

⚘ *Even though I would be less sensitive to others if I had inner peace . . .*

⚘ *Even though I have to forgive myself for A before I can have inner peace . . .*

Use one of these setups or one you devised for yourself. Tap on the karate chop point while you say it three times. Finish with: *"I fully and completely accept myself"* or *"I love and accept myself"* or *"I deeply and completely accept myself"*—whatever you like to use.

Then tap slowly and repeatedly on each short form tapping point repeatedly saying *"inner peace"* and staying with each point for some time to see what comes up. ONLY WHEN YOU SEEM TO HAVE RUN OUT OF INSIGHTS OR THOUGHTS OR FEELINGS OR MEMORIES ON EACH POINT DO YOU MOVE ON TO THE NEXT. Write down everything negative or unhelpful or relevant that comes up for you.

## How do I know what to tap on?

All the answers to your questions and the insights from the slow tapping are tappable. Do them in turn until you feel they are no longer coming between you and discovering your own inner peace in the now, until they no longer have any charge on them. Notice also if you feel some generalization effect when you go back to something that initially had a high level of emotion or certainty attached to it and which now seems different, even before you start to tap on it. This often happens with EFT. We find that when we have tapped on a representative sample of memories or emotional issues or beliefs some of the benefit seems to generalize to others.

## What if I really DON'T accept myself?

Many of us are putting the possibility of inner peace out of our reach for now because we are not yet able to accept ourselves. And we put accepting ourselves on hold until we reach some particular goal or solve some issue or have our lives 'sorted' in some way. The trouble is that we never get there. Get over the crest of the hill and what do you see on the horizon? Usually it is the next hill.

Many of us find it difficult to say: *"I accept myself"* with conviction. Clients I work with will do it reluctantly, or automatically, or to please, or with faith that it is a magic mantra and just saying it will make a difference. If we cannot say it with conviction, inner peace will continue to elude us. Conversely when we can say and mean it, it will be the oil on the parts that speeds up the whole process.

*EDITOR'S NOTE:*

There are differing opinions within the tapping community about what to do if one is uncomfortable saying 'I accept myself'. Gary Craig suggests saying it emphatically. Patricia Carrington substitutes the Choices Method. Judy Byrne suggests adding 'without judgment', Helen Walker suggests adding 'just for now' at the end of the affirmation, and there are other possibilities as well. What is important is to know that self-acceptance can be an issue, and to have a technique for dealing with it.

Do this little test for yourself. Close your eyes and say: *"I accept myself"* several times, really concentrating on what you are saying.

Did it seem like a bad idea when you really thought about it? Did you find yourself thinking it would mean you were smug or complacent or unmotivated? Did you feel too sad or bad to really accept yourself? What were your tail-enders—those sneaky little dissenting bits that get in the way of really accepting ourselves. Write down any you noticed.

Now experiment with tapping on whichever of the following resonate for you, or on the tail-enders you discovered for yourself, but add to the self-acceptance statement *"without judgment"* or *"anyway"*. So, for example:

- ☩ *Even though I think I cannot accept myself until X, I accept myself without judgment.*

- ☩ *I accept myself without judgment, even though I am afraid that if I accept myself I will never achieve Y.*

- ☩ *I accept myself without judgment, even though if I really accepted myself I would be smug and complacent.*

- ☩ *I accept myself without judgment, even though I cannot accept myself because one day people will find me out.*

- ☩ *I accept myself without judgment, even though I do not really mean it when I say "I accept myself"*

- ☩ *Even though I cannot forgive myself for Z, I accept myself anyway.*

- ☩ *Even though I cannot forgive A, I accept myself anyway.*

- ☩ *Even though I am not good enough, I accept myself anyway.*

Whatever you start, keep tapping until the emotion is gone.

And finally, try this. Select a couple of times a day when you will remember to do your 'self-acceptance now' practice. Link it to things in your routine that will make it easy for you to remember. For example, you might make one of them your morning shower. Notice what is going on for you. It might be worrying about a difficult meeting at 11 a.m. Or a difficult conversation you have to have or a telephone call you are dreading.

Then tap round the short form points but using as the reminder phrase not the usual part of the set up statement but: *"I accept myself"*. Or *"I accept myself anyway"* Or *"I accept myself without judgment"*. Do what feels right for you. So you might, for example, be tapping on:

 ⚜ **Even though I am dreading the meeting at 11, I accept myself without judgment.**

You may notice more tail-enders as you do. Tap on them, too. Or you may just find that little by little, you are beginning to get it that you really can accept yourself as you are now, as a work in progress.

---

And notice how, as you accept yourself more and more, inner peace just starts to creep up on you.

---

## The Past —The personal peace procedure

As humans we operate by template matching. It is the only way we can. Even when we walk into an empty room there is more information present for us to process than our senses could possibly handle. So our perception has to make choices unconsciously about what we will even notice, let alone what we will pay attention to. Those choices are not random. We use templates to inform our perception about what might be relevant or irrelevant for us. And those templates are formed and reinforced by all the experiences we have had.

EFT can be a great way to erase 'the writing on our walls'—the views we have of who we are and how safe the world is—that come from specific early experiences and the messages we took from them. It can change our operational templates.

### How can 'writing on our walls' affect our inner peace?

Think, for example, of the little girl who comes home from school and tells her mother that she had a test in school today and she got 98 percent and came second. She is bursting with pride. But the bubble of delight is instantly pricked when her mother says: *"What did you get wrong? Why did you not come top?"* So she works harder and harder and comes home a few weeks later and says: *"I got 100 percent."* And her mother says: *"How many others got 100 percent?"*

This could go either of two ways. She might decide that it is never worth trying because nothing she does will ever be good enough. Or she might decide that she has to try harder and harder and harder. It might set her on the path to a tyrannical perfectionism that will dog her life. She may become the one who cannot finish a report because it might not yet be absolutely perfect, the one who sits up until midnight revising and rewriting and revising again because it might not yet be good enough.

*EDITOR'S NOTE:*
This ability to 'zap your core issues without ever having to discover what they were' is one of the incredible values of tapping as a modality. While there are other methods of dealing with core issues, most involve painfully re-triggering and re-living past events in order to clear them. Tapping does not require this.

How many of us are being run by a decision we made at the age of five or seven or nine?

Disempowering the effects that linger from such experiences, especially at an unconscious level, can be a facilitator for making change in the present easier and more effortless. EFT therapists will usually do sophisticated detective work with clients to find out the core issues that underlie their presenting problems. When you are being your own therapist it is more difficult to have the detachment to stand back and do that. But clearing early memories in the way I describe below is a substitute. By the time you have worked through it, you will have zapped your core issues without ever having had to discover what they were.

## What are the challenges in achieving inner peace?

The Personal Peace Procedure provides a way of working through these memories that is open to everyone, whether they have therapy experience or not. The idea is this: You make a list of every negative memory you have and tap on them one at a time until the emotion has been discharged from them.

Here are some of the difficulties that this project might seem, at first, to present:

- I DON'T KNOW WHAT IS A GENUINE MEMORY AND WHAT I HAVE INVENTED: A memory might be a composite of a number of memories or I might just have imagined it from a family story I have heard. Actually, neither matters. What happened historically doesn't matter at all. What does is what you have stored in your mind. We edit memories constantly. And made-up memories can be as powerful as real ones.

*EDITOR'S NOTE:*
Since tapping works on the energy system, and not the actual memories, using made-up memories is a perfectly valid way to heal. All that is necessary is getting in touch with the negative emotion, and that can be done with an imagined scenario. Then the negative emotion can be released using tapping, and there is no need to make sure one has the 'right' memory.

- THERE WERE SO MANY I DON'T KNOW WHERE TO START. IT WOULD TAKE FOREVER: Actually most people find that when they have processed a representative sample there is a generalization effect and some that had a charge no longer do. But even if you came up with a list of 100 you could clear them in three months just by doing one a day.

- I DON'T KNOW HOW TO DEFINE A NEGATIVE MEMORY: A negative memory is anything you remember as a negative memory even if you don't still have feeling about it. If you remember it as negative, and above all, if you remember it vividly when everything for days or weeks either side of it has faded, it belongs on the list.

- I CANNOT ACCESS ANY EMOTION ABOUT A PARTICULAR MEMORY: Tap on it anyway. Either the emotion will show up, or the quality of the memory will change (becoming distant, faded, fuzzy, an outside view instead of an inside one) in ways that will show you that some change happened to the way you store it.

- I DON'T KNOW HOW TO TAP ON A MEMORY: The 'Movie Technique' is ideal for this. All you do is treat the memory as if it is a movie, run it to see how high (1—10) the emotion goes, give it a title and tap on the title. *"Even though I have this Mother-in-the-Kitchen Movie Memory."* [1] When you can run it again and it seems to have no emotion left, try exaggerating everything about it. Turn up the volume. Brighten the picture. And if you still get no emotion tell yourself the story out loud. If you can still detect no emotion, you are done. Movies should be of memories only a few minutes long. If you want to deal with something longer, chop it up into episodes like a television soap with one emotional peak in each.

- MY CHILDHOOD WAS VERY ABUSIVE AND I WOULD BE AFRAID TO GO TO THOSE MEMORIES: You are right to be cautious. If you do work on them yourself, it is even more important that you first promise yourself to get professional help if you find you need it. But a tip that might help—don't run the memory to see how high the emotion goes. Just guess how high it would do. Don't actually run it until your best guess is moderate to low. And start with some smaller memories first.

- I KNOW I HAVE SOME NEGATIVE MEMORIES BUT I HAVE DEALT WITH THEM: If I had a £/$ for every time I have heard that, I would be personally financing the large EFT charity of my dreams. In my experience people who have dealt with memories without using energy therapy have often desensitized to the idea of them or to talking about them but are still carrying them in their bodies. If they come to mind when you ask yourself what your negative memories are, and you have not tapped on them, you have not dealt with them.

## The Future—Just more of the same?

As I said earlier, humans process by template matching. What we see and what we ignore, what we do and do not pay attention to is determined by the templates we have constructed from our past experiences. We have some options. The templates we operate are influenced by how we are feeling. So a person who feels depressed, whose glass is 'half-empty', is much more likely to focus on every negative memory they have and everything that confirms their negative predictions for the future. An optimist will seize on evidence that confirms their 'half-full glass' view of what is to come.

When we have worked on clearing our past negative memories and on clearing the blocks to accepting ourselves in the present, we are more likely to look to the future with confidence and optimism. When we have reduced our residual anxiety, we will approach our future opportunities in a much less anxious way. We will be operating with revised templates.

And there is more involved here than just how our perception is filtered. What we perceive is just one part of the equation.

## How can I use The Law of Attraction for inner peace?

The Law of Attraction says that we get what we focus on. No exceptions. We put thoughts of a particular vibration out into 'the field' and they attract to us what the thoughts represent. Whether we focus on doubling our incomes or finding inner peace, unless our tail-enders are running a different and contradictory programme out of our conscious awareness, that is what we get. If you are convinced that you cannot have inner peace then you are right. You cannot have it. If you are convinced that if you find it, it will not last, then you are correct again. Your self-fulfilling prophecy will ensure that it will not last.

Have you noticed how when you have a certain image of yourself you do just keep getting more of the same? I recall a while ago I started feeling I was just like a hamster on a wheel. I reeled off the litany of what I had to do that day, that week, that month . . . And I wondered why I just kept getting more of the same old, same old. I was not wishing for it. I was just expecting it. But it was what I was picturing. It was what I was focusing on.

What I needed to remind myself to do was to start visualizing myself in a different mode. The hamster had to get off the wheel. When I started to see myself differently, things just started to fall into place for me. I realized I had to resign from one commitment to get off the wheel. Once I did, it somehow gave me permission to have time to look at all the different options that had been stacking up for me. I began to see them as exciting possibilities and not as just endless toil. Now what I get is more exciting possibilities. I am no less busy than I was. But my perception has changed. I no longer feel like a hamster.

## So what I visualise is what I tend to get?

Yes, very much so. And our 'mirror neurons' play a key role in this process. By comparison, many other brain cells are pretty pedestrian. Mirror neurons are brain cells specialized not for recognizing a straight line, or even for more complex tasks like recognizing faces but for much more sophisticated assignments. Mirror neurons fire in such a way that we actually experience for ourselves what we see someone else experiencing. They are our empathy cells.

Their story is an amazing accidental discovery that goes back more than 15 years to Parma, Italy. A neuroscientist noticed that a monkey he was working with and whose brain he had wired up was responding in very specific and unexpected ways to what he was seeing. If the monkey saw someone working in the laboratory eating a banana, the same class of cells in his brain fired as did when the monkey was eating a banana himself. It was the same with ice cream. The discovery was so unexpected that for a time the scientists could not believe what they were seeing.

It turned out we humans are the same. This could explain why techniques such as visualizing success at sport and in other performances work. We knew back in the 1950's that when someone imagined playing tennis there were micro movements in the relevant muscles. We did not know then that the brain cells needed to know how it would feel to serve and return were firing too. If we picture ourselves doing something, we experience it more fully than we know.

And this is true when we imagine ourselves in any future way we want to be—including with inner peace.

If the picture has reservations and get-out clauses, we can recognize them as tail-enders and tap on them. Once it does not, we can enjoy the inner peace we have created—whatever is happening in the world around us and however much we still intend to change our lives into the lives we want for ourselves.

We are works in progress. Inner peace is possible when we know and accept that we are—and accept ourselves as—travellers on a journey. Not perfect, just perfectly human. Perfect is for robots. Peace is for those who know they are okay right now, just as they are. For those who accept themselves.

## AUTHOR'S BIOGRAPHY AND CONTACT DETAILS

Judy Byrne is an EFT therapist and trainer working in London with clients one-to-one and in groups, face-to-face and by telephone/teleconferencing. She also trains others to use EFT in their therapy practices in London and Brighton in the UK and Australia. She does specialist EFT workshops for Alternatives, the largest not-for-profit personal development organisation in the UK. Judy has presented at international conferences in Europe and Australia and was the organiser for the EFT International Masterclass in London in 2008, with presentations from 12 of the other EFT Masters.

Judy brings her energy therapy into a background in psychology, psychotherapy and hypnotherapy. She has a special interest in working with trauma and has produced DVDs of workshops with practitioners which focus particularly on how to help *non-traumatically* with negative memories. They are available from her website which is www.judybyrne.co.uk. She also continues to promote EFT and EFT-related events, details of which are available on www.eftmasterslive.com

REFERENCES:

1. I have made DVDs that give detailed instruction on and demonstrations of working with memories. They are available from my website, www.judybyrne.com.

# The Choices Method

## A POSITIVE OPTION FOR SETUP AND REMINDER PHRASES

### Patricia Carrington, PhD, EFT Master, EFTCert-Honors

## Why was the Choices Method developed?

The Choices Method began with my reaction to the usual affirmations which people recommend. These positive self-statements concerned me for many reasons long before I had ever heard of Energy Psychology. They seemed to hold special promise but I myself had not had much success with them, either for my clients or myself, and this was despite the fact that some other people were apparently using them successfully.

When I investigated the reasons for this, I discovered that a large number of people were reacting negatively to the essentially 'contrary to fact' nature of these traditional affirmations. This was producing what psychologists call cognitive dissonance (an inner contradiction). When they were repeating such affirmations as: "*I have a wonderfully compatible and creative job that I enjoy*", when in actuality they were working at a miserable job that they disliked intensely, a little voice in their head would say: "*Yeah, right!*" or would tell them: "*That's not true and you know it.*"

EDITOR'S NOTE:
The words of the 'little voice' have come to be referred to as 'tail-enders'. The name may have originated with Gary Craig.

In the early 1980s I found an unexpected answer to this dilemma. It was from a self development course known as 'DMA' created by Robert Fritz. The course used a form of affirmation I found to be immediately effective for just about everyone who encountered it. Fritz had inserted the words: *"I choose . . ."* at the beginning of the affirmation, which turned it into a statement of intention rather than a contrary-to-fact declaration, and this made all the difference. Using a 'Choices' affirmation, I felt absolutely no inner contradiction whatsoever.

## Why are Choices so powerful?

One of the positive spinoffs of the Choices affirmation is that it puts the person who makes it into the 'driver's seat' in their own life. When they make a Choice they are exercising their own will, deciding and committing upon a course of action. I soon found that this freely entered into commitment could have a powerful influence on the desired result, making it far more likely to be obtained.

*EDITOR'S NOTE:*
The Choices Method has now become so familiar and widely used as to be an integral part of many practitioners' everyday practice.

Actually, I had not even heard of Energy Psychology or tapping therapy when I first encountered Choices, and was using Choices affirmations for years with my clients before tapping therapy became the primary treatment modality that I use. Then in 1991, when I was already using this modality as a major component in my practice, I thought of combining Choices affirmations with the setup and reminder phrases—and the 'Choices Method' was born.

## Why use the Choices Method?

The reason I felt it so important to introduce this method into my regular practice of tapping therapy was because I had been less than satisfied with the standard affirmation in the last part of the setup phrase—*I deeply and completely accept myself*—because it did not sit well with many clients although obviously it was effective for others. This phrase is often difficult or impossible to use with people whose self-acceptance is extremely low to begin with—they experience it as artificial and it is extremely uncomfortable for them to repeat. It also does not 'fit' the situation for many newcomers. For example, if they have a pain, it seems irrelevant and foolish to them to repeat the phrase *"I deeply and completely accept myself"* relative to the pain and I often found myself having to convince them to suspend their doubts and 'say it anyway!'. While this frequently would work, it did not address an even more fundamental problem which I found with the tapping technique of the standard version of EFT, now designated as 'Official EFT' by its founder, Gary Craig.

## What is so special about saying "I choose ..."?

Official EFT focuses entirely on problems. It starts with statements like: *"Even though I have this headache ..."* or *"Even though I can't meet my present bills ..."* and completes this statement with the phrase: *"I deeply and completely accept myself"*. The treatment then proceeds by simply repeating the 'problem' in the Reminder phrases, saying at each spot such words as: *"This pain"*.

There's no doubt about it—with Official EFT, you can definitely tap a problem out. But I wanted to also tap a solution *in*, and this is what I was able to do when I substituted a 'Choices' phrase for the traditional EFT self-acceptance phrase. I did this by adding the words *"I choose"* to the last portion of the setup phrase, and then using it in some of the reminder phrases, making it possible for the person to define a specific desired outcome by inserting a positive statement of intent after the words *"I choose"* .

Using Official EFT with my own clients in psychotherapy, I soon discovered that I could get even better results if I allowed them to insert their own positive affirmations into the tapping statement in this manner. The setup phrase could now become perfectly suited to the problems they were addressing.

For example, if a person's hand were throbbing, I would suggest an EFT statement such as:

> ✣ **Even though my hand is throbbing, I choose to have my hand be comfortable and pain free.**

This kind of statement immediately makes perfect sense to the injured person; it expresses precisely what they want to bring about—the cessation of pain and the healing of their hand.

It was through experimenting with my own clients that the 'Choices Method' was refined. To use this method, the person applying it identifies the outcome that they would truly like to have for the problem at hand, and then puts this desired outcome into a phrase which they use at the end of the Setup phrase (in place of: "*I deeply and completely accept myself*"). This new phrase commences with the words "*I choose . . .*"

My method of injecting 'Choices' into tapping therapy soon developed into a systematic Choices protocol known as the 'Choices Trio' which I have found to be extremely effective, not only for my own clients and workshop participants, but for many others as well. I then created the formal 'Choices Method' and began training other people in its use. This approach was almost immediately greeted with enthusiasm by the EFT community, and today many people worldwide are using Choices statements. In particular, psychotherapists, counselors, and personal performance coaches make extensive use of it because it so precisely targets their clients' problems.

## What's the best way to create 'Choices'?

While detailed instructions for using the Choices Method can be found in my Choices Manual[1] , here are six rules for composing Choices statements that I find particularly effective:

### THE SIX RULES OF CHOICES

1. Be Specific
2. Create Pulling Choices
3. Go For the Best Possible Outcome
4. State Your Choices in the Positive
5. Make Choices That Apply to You
6. Make Choices That Are Easy to Pronounce

In short, 'Pulling Choices' use words that draw you in and make you feel involved. They are the opposite of dull, abstract statements. For example, suppose a person were trying to explain to another person (by the name of Susan) their point of view but felt unheard, one way to format the Choices phrase in this person's EFT statement might be:

✢  *. . . I choose to express myself in a way that gets my points across to Susan.*

This is a perfectly accurate statement of intent as far as it goes of course. But an even more appealing version might be:

✢  *. . . I choose to find a creative way to get my points across to Susan.*

The word creative gives the statement excitement and suspense. You wonder what would be a creative way to get your points across. Curiosity is a powerful motivator!

Surprise is another word that can draw us in, so another effective Choices statement could be:

✢  *. . . I choose to surprise myself by finding easy and enjoyable ways to get my points across to Susan.*

Easy and enjoyable are pulling words and they help make this a compelling statement.

Or suppose someone felt sharp pain in their knee. Following these recommendations, you could add specific details about the pain, insert some interesting or compelling ideas about it, describe what you'd rather have, replace negative words (no, not, can't, won't etc.) with positive words, and thereby create a personally rewarding Choices Phrase. For example:

✢  *Even though I have this sharp pain in my knee, I choose to enjoy a relaxed, pain-free game of golf tomorrow, or*

✢  *Even though my knee has me crying out in pain, and I can't believe that this tapping idea is going to make any difference, I choose to give it a good try, or*

✢  *. . . I choose to enjoy doing these EFT exercises, or*

✢  *. . . I choose to have my knee feel completely well.*

## What is the Choices Trio?

The 'Choices Trio' includes THREE rounds of tapping, and also calls for having you try alternating between 'problem' and 'solution' reminder phrases:

1. FIRST ROUND: In the first round of tapping, use 'problem' reminder phrases, such as:

TOP OF HEAD: *stabbing pain*

INSIDE EYEBROW: *so frustrating*

OUTSIDE EYE: *terrible pain*

UNDER EYE *can't move without pain* and so on, through all the tapping points.

Or use the same complete 'problem' sentence on all of the acupoints, such as:

TOP OF HEAD: *I'm upset because my knee is so painful.*

INSIDE EYEBROW: *I'm upset because my knee is so painful.*

OUTSIDE EYE: *I'm upset because my knee is so painful* and so on, through all the tapping points.

2. SECOND ROUND: Then in the second round of tapping, use only positive 'solution' phrases, such as:

TOP OF HEAD: *better already*

INNER EYEBROW: *pain-free*

OUTER EYE: *complete range of motion*

UNDER EYE: *everything's easy* and so on, through all the tapping points

Or use the same complete 'solution' sentence on all of the acupoints, such as:

TOP OF HEAD: *I choose to feel completely well in every way.*

INNER EYEBROW: *I choose to feel completely well in every way.*

OUTER EYE: *I choose to feel completely well in every way.* and so on, through all the tapping points.

3. THIRD ROUND: Then in the third and final round of tapping, alternate between 'problem' and 'solution' phrases. Starting with the Inner Eyebrow, say the negative phrase, then at the Outer Eye say the positive (Choices) phrase, then at the Under Eye spot say the negative again, and so on through all the tapping points, being sure to end on a 'solution' phrase. When doing this, it is usually easiest to alternate between the two complete sentences used above:

INNER EYEBROW: *I'm upset because my knee is so painful.*

OUTER EYE: *I choose to feel completely well in every way.*

UNDER EYE: *I'm upset because my knee is so painful.*

UNDER NOSE:   *I choose to feel completely well in every way.*

and so on through all the tapping points. Be sure your final phrase is positive.

YOU SHOULD ALWAYS FINISH ON A POSITIVE NOTE.

## What are the key reasons for using Choices?

Many people find the 'Choices Method' particularly effective because it helps people figure out not only what they *don't want* but what they DO want. It also installs positive intentions in a remarkably rapid and thorough manner and often brings about more profound and lasting results than standard EFT.

I hope you will learn this method and practice it yourself by trying it out with many different issues using many different kinds of Choices. You may want to place it in your collection of truly useful tapping therapy approaches!

## AUTHOR'S BIOGRAPHY AND CONTACT DETAILS

Dr. Patricia Carrington is a clinical psychologist, widely published author, and one of the pioneers in the field of tapping therapy. She has published numerous research papers on the clinical use of this method as well as on the modern clinically oriented forms of meditation. For eleven years she was a member of the Psychology Faculty at Princeton University, and is presently Clinical Professor of Psychiatry at the UMDNJ-Robert Wood Johnson Medical School in New Jersey.

Dr. Carrington is among a handful of EFT Practitioners to have been awarded the title of 'EFT Master' and also carries the title of EFTCert-Honors, the highest level of expertise recognized in Official EFT. She is the originator of the widely used Choices Method, an advanced tapping technique. Her books, tapes, and computer programs are in the forefront of tapping therapy theory and practice.

For more information visit: www.masteringeft.com or www.patclass.com

## References:

1   Dr. Carrington's Choices Manual gives the definitive instruction in the Choices Method and includes many examples and details of the technique not able to be described in this article. It can be ordered in printed or e-Book form by going to: http://www.masteringeft.com.

# Using Personal Resource States

## A REMARKABLE CLINICAL STRATEGY

### Patricia Carrington, PhD,
### EFT Master, EFTCert-Honors

## What are Personal Resource States?

As we all know it isn't easy to change the way we react to certain aspects of our life because our attitudes feel to us as though they were carved in stone, unalterable. However, I have found that we can alter even very fundamental ways of feeling and behaving by using what I call 'Personal Resource States'[1] in Tapping Therapy.

Those of you who have read my 'Choices Manual[2]' may remember that in it I wrote about the power of those positive inner resources that we all have within us to effect important change. In the past year I have been even more deeply impressed with how effective these resources are when we want to bring about basic change in our lives. The use of Personal Resource States in tapping therapy has greatly increased the scope of my Choices Method. I will give you here an idea of what they are and how they work.

> The concept of Resource States comes from NLP (Neuro-Linguistic Programming) and refers to a memory of a successful moment from one's own life or a memory of someone else's successful handling of a difficult situation. Basically, it is a way of accessing a great many powerful coping strategies within ourselves of which we are usually unaware.

No-one, of course, realizes all the personal resource states that they actually possess within them. One reason for this is that we may have experienced a particular resource state only momentarily, perhaps only once during our whole lifetime. Another reason is that we are hardwired to notice and remember the negative, but we often take for granted or even dismiss the positive memories in our lives. The fact is, however, that if we have a memory of even one moment of outstanding competency, of being loved, of feeling safe, or whatever our desired state may be, even if that state occurred in a more or less trivial context, this is extremely valuable. It can help us make fundamental changes in ourselves and shift our energy patterns in an important way.

## What kinds of Personal Resource States can I use?

There are several kinds of Personal Resource States that you can use in this way and here are the main ones:

1. RESOURCE STATES DERIVED FROM YOUR OWN EXPERIENCE: A desired state you have experienced at least once in your life.

2. RESOURCE STATES DERIVED FROM OBSERVING OTHERS: You have watched another person or animal—directly or through the media or through literature etc.—cope effectively with the very situation you are addressing, and this observation is available to you in your memory.

In changing deeply held attitudes, the kind of Resource State that I find particularly effective is the type that is accompanied by strong emotion, whether the memory is derived from your own experience or your observation of others. You will need to do a little detective work, of course, to locate such a resource and to change an attitude that you held for a long time, but it can be well worth the effort.

Imagine that you are someone who can't conceive of coping with financial challenges without alarm. A question designed to elicit a Personal Resource State to use for this condition might be: *"How do I cope with other situations in my life that have nothing to do with finances? Can I think of some situation (of any kind) that I have handled to my satisfaction during the past year?"*

Most people can come up with at least one or two examples of having coped well with some situation that was initially difficult for them. For example, when your toaster oven went on the blink and you were able to fix it easily, or other incidents like that. Few of us are unable to think of at least one small thing that we coped with well in the past year, and one example is all you need.

Now, ask yourself how well you coped. Did the situation turn out all right? Is this ability to handle things satisfactorily something you would like to experience at other times in your life?

## Can you give me an example of how this works?

Suppose you were alarmed by some financial reverse you were experiencing and yet you could remember that you coped well with the flooding in your home when the main water pipe burst. In this case, you might formulate a tapping statement that goes:

> ☩ *Even though I fear facing financial disaster, I choose to be as resourceful as I was when the water pipe burst . . .*

When tapping on this Resource State you would be using your own positive experience of coping well with the broken water pipe as a model for the way in which, ideally, you would like to be able to cope with your financial problems. Doing this would enable you to transfer those behaviors and attitudes that worked well for you in one area of your life, to another area where they are not yet in use.

EDITOR'S NOTE:
Why Resource States are so effective is an interesting question. Could it have to do with the idea of 'mirror neurons', in which viewing or imagining an action causes similar or identical brain activity to performing that action? Or is there a different energetic explanation?

I find this to be a remarkably effective tactic for the people I work with, and for myself. Resource states can be unusually helpful in changing attitudes because they are so real and compelling. They make use of experiences that actually happened to you or someone you have observed. And since such experiences really happened, they cannot be denied. What you are doing here is simply transferring a positive attitude and capability from one area of your life to another where it is presently not in operation. This way you are expanding your coping ability by applying it to an area where before it was absent.

I find that suggestions made to ourselves while tapping are usually far more effective than suggestions made without using the tapping. You are literally reinforcing a positive memory in yourself, and the effect of tapping-in this positive statement can be profound.

## How can I use Personal Resource States to create tapping statements?

Here is how you go about this:

1. Recall a moment of outstanding competence, or feeling of being loved, or feeling of safety or deep satisfaction, one that you have experienced at any time in your life, or which you have witnessed or read about someone else experiencing.

2. Do some inner detective work to identify any negative attitudes that you may have about the issue you are presently facing.

3. Associate your Personal Resource memory to this negative attitude to create a tapping statement such as:

   ⚡ *Even though I fear facing financial disaster, I choose to be as resourceful as I was when that water pipe burst*

4. Use tapping to transfer your desired state to this area of your life where it is not presently operative, following the instructions for the 'Choices Method' {see *The Choices Method*}.

I suggest you try this highly effective strategy whenever you feel that an undesirable feeling, thought or action seems to be 'impossible to change'. You may find, to your surprise, that profound change in these areas of your life is easy and natural if you approach it this way.

## How can I use this to borrow Resources States from others?

There is a very interesting true story about some research that was conducted in England almost 15 years ago and was well known at the time among educators.

An important examination was being administered to secondary school children, and before the exam the researchers divided the class into two groups. One group took the exam the usual way. The other group was instructed, just before the exam began, to place a special lightweight helmet made of plastic on their heads which they would wear for the entire exam and which would have a special effect on them. The children were told that these were the helmets of top students who had received excellent grades in this exam, and that by placing the helmet on their heads during the exam they would be able to, in effect, use the minds of these top students and handle the exam just beautifully.

The results were dramatic. The group taking the exam the ordinary way had much the same grades that one would expect from children of their age, and from seeing their former grades in the classroom.

However, the group that placed the 'magic helmets' on their heads, believing that by doing this they were borrowing the exam-taking power of the top students, did strikingly better as a group. The differences between the two groups was highly significant statistically, and also those students who wore the helmets scored much higher than could be expected compared to the grades they had achieved previously in the classroom that year.

Clearly we are seeing here a strong suggestion effect and of course we can get these kinds of results under hypnosis as well. But what is interesting is that the children were borrowing resources from other children whom they were told were top students, and when they did this, they achieved far better grades than could otherwise be expected. This is a classic example of the power of borrowing a Resource State from another person.

## What if I've borrowed coping strategies from others that I would rather be without?

Borrowing resources from others through imitation is of course an inborn ability, not just in humans but in animals. It is the major way in which skills are transferred from one generation to another. Apprentices for example, work on this principle, but unfortunately we can also borrow some poor coping strategies in the same way. Children imitate the coping strategies of those they see around them, and sometimes these can be very poor coping strategies. In fact, all of us have probably absorbed some strategies from the adults who surrounded us when we were little that we would rather not have. The best way to eliminate poor coping strategies is to replace them with excellent coping strategies and that can be done with tapping therapy.

Let me give you an example of this strategy in action.

Several years ago I was working with a client named 'Jeannie' (not her real name) who lived in a community where there were a number of black bears in the woods surrounding the houses. Black bears are not particularly aggressive, but nonetheless they are wild animals, and Jeannie was terrified by the thought of encountering a bear when walking in her neighborhood. And this was despite the fact that she had lived in this community for 18 years and raised her children there. The entire community knew exactly what to do if one saw a bear on the path or at the roadside and there had not been any incident of anyone being harmed by a bear during the entire time that Jeannie had lived there. However, like all phobias, this one was not based on reason.

Jeannie lived on a property which had a long winding driveway leading to the roadside where their mailbox was, and it was necessary for her to go down this driveway every day in order to collect the incoming mail. Jeannie was so afraid of meeting a bear on that driveway, however, that she could not walk on it, and had to drive her car to the road where she picked up the mail every time she went there. She wanted very much to overcome this incapacitating fear, and so we worked on it in many ways including tapping therapy. We were only making minimal progress however until I suddenly thought of using a Personal Resource State with Jeannie.

I asked Jeannie if she knew anyone in her community who had a wonderful attitude toward black bears that she would ideally like to have too. Without hesitation she replied *"Of course, Mary!"* and she told me that Mary, who had absolutely no fear of the bears, also had a long driveway which she had to walk each day to retrieve her mail, but that Mary did so without any problem whatsoever. Mary had in fact, once or twice as she walked along seen a black bear and had handled this in exactly the way the community suggested, by standing stock still and not frightening the bear and using other well-known tactics. Bears simply were not an issue for Mary.

Jeannie then formulated this Choice:

**Even though I'm terrified of meeting a bear on the driveway, I choose to be just like Mary.**

Selecting Mary as her personal resource and using this tapping phrase made a dramatic difference in Jeannie's attitude. In a few minutes she was able to tap down her fears of bears to a 1 (on a zero to 10 scale of intensity), and this after only a couple of rounds of tapping.

After our session, she occasionally tapped on this same statement when alone and was able to hold this fear down with no problem.

When I talked to her the next week she told me excitedly that only once or twice had she had any fear at all when walking down the driveway (which she was now doing daily) and was thrilled with this result. When I spoke to her at her subsequent appointment a week later, she reported to me that she had been driving along the road and had actually seen a bear come out of the woods and stand by the road, staring straight at her. She said she slowed the car down and looked back at the bear and actually found it extremely interesting to watch it. She didn't even have to tap but simply said to herself *"I choose to be just like Mary!"* and that did the trick.

## What should I consider when choosing a resource person?

1. Choose somebody you have a good feeling about; somebody you know something about. They should be a person who embodies a certain characteristic that you admire. This person can be someone that you know personally, or a fictional character you have seen in a movie or read about in a novel, or they can be an historical figure or someone you've observed on TV. It doesn't matter. The point is that they should embody the very quality that you need in order to cope well with the situation that is causing you difficulty.

2. This person should not be just a vague symbol but someone whom you know something about. You do not want to want to choose a cliché figure like say, Donald Trump, if you are concerned about finances. You want to be able to really feel the way this person does as you identify with them, and to do so you have to know quite a bit about them.

3. You don't have to choose to be like this person in all respects. Jeannie did not choose, for example, to have the same hairdo as her friend Mary, or the same husband and children as Mary does, or have any of Mary's possible problems. She chose to be like Mary in only one respect—the way she felt about black bears. This is why her strategy was so successful. You don't want to take on the entire identity of another person, but rather, like the children who put on the helmets when they took the exam and then took them off afterwards, to be borrowing a single resource from that person and in the manner in which you want to borrow it. The helmets were

simply there to help them experience one specific resource—the ability to do extremely well on the exam.

## How can I put all this into practice using tapping therapy?

Take a pad and pencil and write on the top of your page the heading:

*SOME THINGS THAT I HAVE IN MY LIFE THAT I DON'T LIKE HAVING*

- Underneath that, write THREE specific things that you don't like having in your life—three feelings or attitudes you would rather not have or three situations you do not want.

- Underneath these three unwanted things, write the name of a person who embodies qualities that would enable you to cope superbly with each of these three issues.

- After the name of each person, indicate how possible it seems to you to be able to be like that person in this particular respect by giving a possibility rating on a ten point scale from zero to 10, with zero representing a feeling that it is impossible for you ever to be like this person, and 10 being total confidence that you can be like this person. You will be indicating how possible you feel it is that you could acquire the characteristics of your resource person.

- Then formulate a tapping statement such as the following:

  ✦ **Even though I feel helpless in this situation, I choose to be as calm and resourceful as (insert name of your resource person)**

## What if tail-enders come up?

You may well run into 'tail-enders' (Gary Craig's name for our inner conflicts about a tapping statement) when doing this because it may not feel comfortable when you adopt the identity of this other person with respect to this issue. This immediately alerts you to the fact that you have an inner conflict about being this way, even though you may have thought you would like to change in this fashion. This is a chance to use further tapping to deal with your conflict or hesitation first, and then continue with your borrowing of resources later.

## What if I choose the wrong resource person?

Some people find that when they tap on being like the resource person whom they chose, it doesn't really feel comfortable to them because they really don't want to be that way. If so, you've chosen the wrong person as a resource person and you need to select another. This is much like going shopping for clothes. You may see a dress or suit on the rack that looks as though it were exactly what you want and be ideal for you, until you try it on and see that the color doesn't suit you, or it is too small, or too big, or unsuitable for you in some other fashion. You then need to go back and select another piece of clothing to try on. You should do exactly the same thing when you are selecting a resource person; your first choice may not always be the final one, but with persistence you can find an excellent example of a resource person, one that will work.

## Any final comments?

I now use Personal Resource States as a regular part of my tapping therapy practice and find that they are one of the most effective strategies I have ever known. I would suggest that you experiment with them for yourself and anyone else you might be working with. This is a new technique that can greatly expand the way tapping therapy can help you. Try it!

## AUTHOR'S BIOGRAPHY AND CONTACT DETAILS

Please see 'The Choices Method' for author's biography and contact details.

REFERENCES:

1. To hear Dr. Carrington lead you in her own voice in the use of Personal Resource States you can visit her teleseminar series at http://www.PatClass.com. In Teleseminar 1 she demonstrates the use of Resource States taken from your own life (this teleseminar is downloadable free), and in Teleseminar 2 she describes the use of animals as well as human models for resource states, a method which has proven very powerful.
2. Dr. Carrington's CHOICES MANUAL gives the definitive instruction in the Choices Method and includes many examples and details of the technique unable to be described in this article. It can be ordered in printed or e-Book form by going to: http://www.masteringeft.com.

# Transforming the Energy with EFT

SOPHIA CAYER, EFT MASTER, EFTCERT-HONORS

## What do you mean by Transforming the Energy?

What if, rather than just 'neutralizing' your negative emotions, you 'transformed' them to precisely the empowering energy required to achieve your goals? I began working with this concept a couple of years ago, and have yet to encounter an individual who has utilized it and not experienced a profound difference. It is a great way to let go of hopelessness and helplessness, and the idea that a part of us is defective or burdensome—and in some cases, insurmountable. When the energy of emotions or feelings is transformed, a sense of empowerment rapidly develops. All those negatives become positives that move us forward, allowing us to accomplish.

What if you turned the fear into strength or confidence? How about turning it into trust in yourself and the Universe to deliver exactly what you feel is missing inside you? What if you transformed that energy to one that helped you feel more empowered; one that helped you feel self-assured and confident?

While many speak of body, mind and spirit as if they were all separate fractions or pieces, from my perception they are inseparable, just as we have an inseparable connection with the Universe.

One of my favorite sayings is: *"Each situation is as unique as we are individuals"*. Please keep this in mind as we work through the following examples together. Alter them to suit your particular situation, trusting that you will know exactly what is needed. If you experience difficulty trusting yourself, please consider tapping on that very thing. If you feel you still can't get there, consider contacting someone a little more seasoned in EFT to help you get started.

## How can I incorporate 'Transforming the Energy' into my EFT practice?

Begin by addressing whatever seems to need attention in your life or your client's life in the most appropriate manner for the situation. 'Transforming the Energy' is similar to a re-frame, in that you are putting forward a positive while there is still some negative energy present. Therefore, you won't use it until the SUDS level is low enough to allow a re-frame to 'land'; that is, for the re-frame to be accepted by the client.

As an example, let's say when you start, the SUDS level is a 10. I suggest that you aim to bring it down to no more than a 4 or 5 with conventional EFT before using the Transforming the Energy technique. You may feel, based on the individual situation, that the level of intensity should be less before you transform the energy. Trust your feelings and go with them. This is one of those times you need to trust your intuition, and truly be tuned in with energies and feelings.

*EDITOR'S NOTE:*
I tried this technique once when I reached a SUDS level of 1-2 and the negative energy seemed stuck yet undefined. Rather than continue to attempt to remove the negative energy, I created a setup statement with a positive Choice of 'Transforming the Energy' and was surprised that the energy immediately seemed positive and life-affirming, rather than draining. In that case, it did have more power than a standard positive reframe.

For those of you wondering what the difference is between Transforming the Energy and simply using positively worded reframes, I would ask you to consider this. While positive reframes most definitely benefit us with generating cognitive shifts, Transforming the Energy can help us to feel that we are taking a more active roll in creating our future. It allows us to decide what energy seems to be lacking and generate it for ourselves.

If you are not sure whether it is time to use the technique or not, go with your feelings without reservation. And, if on this occasion the technique doesn't land well, that's ok too. We all stub our toes now and then. Don't give up on it, because what you may learn, as with everything else, is that it isn't for everyone. The concept may seem too foreign for some. Personally, I haven't run into that challenge yet, but you never know! Go with the flow . . .

Perhaps the best way to explain the technique is to offer examples from actual sessions. Please remember though that nothing is cast in stone. Use what you can. Alter phrases to best suit your specific situation, or get creative based on what you learn. I KNOW you can do this!

## Case Study 1: Auto-immune challenge

In working with a client with an autoimmune challenge, there can be a lot of ups and downs where the potential for progress is concerned. So here's a portion of a session where we began working towards Transforming the Energy. We began with the inner conflict related to hope. The loss of hope when we began felt like an absolute truth—or a SUDS level of 10.

> ⚜ *Even though I have this inner conflict, one part of me seems to have lost hope, while the other part is ready to forge forward. I just can't get it together. I love and accept every part of me anyway.*

> ⚜ *Even though a part of me feels as if it has lost hope, why should I try? I love and forgive myself. I love and forgive every part of me.*

REMINDER PHRASES:
*This conflict within, one part is full of hope and optimism, but the other part has lost hope. It continues to chant: "What's the use? Why try? What the heck is worth the effort? It's useless!"*

*No its not, yes it is, no it's not, yes it is. But I feel optimistic. Well I've lost hope. This conflict within, these parts that keep tango-ing . . . This part that's lost hope, this arguing, and resistance to that part of me that feels hopeful and optimistic.*

At this point the SUDS level had dropped to a 4. And my client reported that while the positive statements were beginning to feel closer to believable and perhaps seemed possible, there was still something there. It was now time to transform the energy:

> ⚜ *Even though I still have this remaining inner conflict, that part that's lost hope doesn't want to cooperate and it keeps nagging me, I am ok anyway.*

✢ *Even though that part of me doesn't feel hopeful, and keeps nagging in the back of my mind, and there is always something there, I deeply and completely, love, honor, respect and accept every part of me. I love and adore every part of me.*

✢ *And I am asking this part of me that is stuck in that negative mode, that may somehow think that it's protecting me from some sort of disappointment, to know that it is safe, to be optimistic, right along with the rest of me. I thank this part for knowing that it is safe, and for its cooperation, in joining the other part of me in optimism.*

REMINDER PHRASES:

*Letting go of all these remnants of energy that have lost hope.*

*TRANSFORMING those energies into joy and optimism. Knowing there's lots of hope, and if I am always filled with enthusiasm and optimism, then hope is no longer a question.*

*TRANSFORMING that energy that has lost hope, into pure joy and optimism, feeling it take place in this moment on a cellular level. I am so happy and grateful that this energy of hopelessness has now transformed to hope and optimism.*

*I thank every part of me for cooperating, TRANSFORMING this energy into exactly what I need to constantly maintain those feelings of hope and optimism. I thank this energy for allowing me to feel empowered, body, mind and spirit.*

The results of this session were wonderful, and while there are still issues to work through, this one is well on its way out the door.

## Case Study 2: Serial abuse

This next example deals with someone who endured intense 'serial abuse'. It had been truly debilitating, but now a sense of hope seemed to be surfacing, along with the idea that resuming a normal life was a distinct possibility.

One of the challenges faced was the idea that my client couldn't let go of the fear or let anyone know the truth, because it could be too painful for her. By holding it in, she was somehow protecting those that surrounded her from experiencing the same pain, or worse yet, she could become so enraged by the events that others could suffer serious consequences.

I gently offered the idea that an alternate game plan might be worth considering. What if, by diffusing the intensity and then TRANSFORMING the energy of the fears to something positive, everyone (including herself) could feel safe and secure?

We began by working through the fear of all the possible consequences. And then began to work on transforming the energies to something beneficial.

There was a lot of work to do to get things to the point where it began to feel 'safe' or reasonable to consider the possibility. With some persistence, we were getting closer.

Here's how things then began to transpire.

> ✢ *Even though a part of me still feels this need to protect ____ and _____ , I choose peace within.*

> ✢ *Even though a part of me still feels the need to protect them, I choose peace within.*

> ✢ *Even though a part of me is firmly convinced that it is my job to protect them from all this, I choose to TRANSFORM, in this very moment, all this negative energy which no longer serves anyone into calm, into optimism, into complete peace within.*

REMINDER PHRASES:

*Letting go of the idea, that I need to keep this locked away. Letting go of the idea that somehow it keeps others safe.*

*I could feel so much better if I just TRANSFORMED all this fear and pain into pure love. Loving and forgiving myself, choosing peace within.*

*Choosing to TRANSFORM all this energy to pure love and peace, in this very moment. I am so happy and grateful that I can feel it happening now.*

*I am so happy and grateful that all that fear has TRANSFORMED to pure love and peace.*

## Case study 3: Identity

In this particular situation, we were dealing with someone with a challenge in accepting their true identity, and who frequently experienced involuntary movement of their head shaking *"no"*. As we worked through the issues, we also discovered a resistance.

🕯 *Even though a part of me (yawning) refuses to let this go, refuses to let me stand in my power and enjoy peace, I love and accept every part of me.*

🕯 *Even though there's a part of me that's resistant to this process, it doesn't feel safe to let this go, I deeply and profoundly love, honor, respect and accept every part of me, unconditionally.*

REMINDER PHRASES: *This resistance that holds me back, this resistance to moving forward, this resistance, that somehow thinks it's keeping me safe, I choose to let it go.*

**TRANSFORMING** *this resistant energy into optimism, enthusiasm, and* **complete peace within** *(lots of head- shaking NOs)* **this resistance, this resistance, this resistance, this resistance . . .**

At this point she told me she experienced a great deal of activity in her head, and was still experiencing the *"No"* shake. Then she commented: *"You could say I saw an electrical energy in the top of my head, signals everywhere, trying to do everything it can to keep me where I am. If I saw it in war, it would be like the enemy doing all it can to scatter, to keep from having to retreat. It's not very strong, but a stubborn thing, resistant."*

🕯 *Even though I have this remaining resistant energy, I love and adore myself.*

🕯 *Even though I have this remaining resistant energy, I choose to let it go.*

REMINDER PHRASES:

*I choose to TRANSFORM it into optimism, into confidence, enthusiasm, and pure love.*

*I choose to let go, of all the underlying causes, that make a part of me feel the need to hang on to this resistance.*

*I choose peace, I choose optimism, I choose to feel self-assured, I know I am safe. I know I am safe. I accept feeling safe.*

*I choose to know I have now TRANSFORMED this energy to optimism, confidence, and pure love. I am safe and free to be the real me.*

# Case Study 4: Fear of change

Here's another example about the fear of change:

⚜ *Even though I have this energy, this energy of fear, I am not sure about all this change stuff, I love and accept me anyway.*

REMINDER PHRASES:

*I'm asking this fear to work with me and take on a new job, knowing that it's safe to TRANSFORM this energy from fear to love. So much love, abundant love.*

*TRANSFORMING this energy from fear to love.*

*TRANSFORMING this energy, from fear to abundant love, embracing the love and thanking the fear for doing its job.*

*Embracing the love, TRANSFORMING all that fear into positive energy that helps me feel calm and confidant, self-assured.*

*Loving and accepting myself on every level, in every cell of my being, body, mind and spirit . . .*

*I feel the TRANSFORMATION, in every cell of my being.*

*I am so happy and grateful that this is taking place, in this very second.*

*I am so happy and grateful that I am so full of love, that I feel so confident and self-assured; I love and adore every part of me.*

Granted we had done some work up front, but the initial comment at the end of this round was: *"Wow, I think I just lost a few pounds. There was a lot of weight to shed! Wow!"*

# Case Study 5: Overload of emotion of unknown origin

⚜ *Even though I don't understand what these tears are all about, or what I might have triggered, I choose to feel safe.*

REMINDER PHRASES:

*These tears, and all this emotion, these tears, and this intense emotion, these tears and this intense emotion, these tears, and all this intense emotion, I don't have a clue what its connected to, but in this moment, I choose to neutralize it.*

*EDITOR'S NOTE:*

Using a positive reframe when doing EFT has to be timed carefully to avoid the client rejecting the positive, i.e. the positive cannot be introduced too early. Similar concerns would seem to attach to Transforming the Energy, although it is possible that the positive statements bring up tail-enders that the tapping then eliminates.

*I choose to TRANSFORM that energy into something that feels good. I choose to TRANSFORM this energy, into something that helps me feel safe.*

*I choose to feel safe. I choose to neutralize these painful emotions, and I don't have to know what they are all about. I simply need to choose to know I am safe.*

## Case Study 6: Downhearted

✤ *Even though I am feeling downhearted and discouraged, I love and forgive myself.*

✤ *Even though I don't want to think about why I feel this way, I love and respect myself.*

REMINDER PHRASES:

*I choose to TRANSFORM this energy now into uplifting feelings, which will carry me through this day.*

*I am so happy and grateful that I can feel the energy TRANSFORMING in this moment, helping me feel sure and positive.*

## Case Study 7: When the SUDs 'won't' come down to a 4 or 5

Here's an example where yes, I broke my own 'rule'. I spoke earlier about waiting until the intensity was down to perhaps a 4 or 5. Remember though; always go with what feels right in the moment. Trust yourself and your inner senses.

REMINDER PHRASES:

*This 7 that doesn't want to leave me, this 7, this intense 7, I still don't know what it's all about, but that's ok, I don't have to know, I simply need to choose to TRANSFORM this energy.*

*I choose to TRANSFORM it in this moment, I am doing it now.*

*This intense 7, is magically TRANSFORMING into love and positive energy.*

*I choose peace, I choose to know I am safe. I want to feel safe. I choose to TRANSFORM this remaining intense energy that feels so uncomfortable into something warm and fuzzy, something that feels really good that helps me feel energized and happy. That let's me know its ok to feel relaxed.*

## Some final remarks

To date, in every situation, the results have been profound. After Transforming the Energy, people are left feeling empowered and much more peaceful within. I believe this is something you will find well worth considering.

You may want to try it on yourself before trying it on clients. (This is a good idea with any new technique!) That way, you can experience Transforming the Energy and be more attuned to the shift from negative energy to positive.

Don't race into it. Take your time and know that when the timing is right, you will sense and feel it. Go with the flow . . .

Peace!

## AUTHOR'S BIOGRAPHY AND CONTACT DETAILS

Sophia Cayer (Co-Founder of the Personal Peace Foundation is an internationally renowned EFT Master and author. Sophia is an ordained minister of the Universal Life Church and a Reiki Master. She was one of the 5 experts who joined EFT founder Gary Craig in California for a week long intensive with veterans suffering with PTSD, the results of which are to be used in a documentary. As an EFT pioneer and passionately dedicated coach/teacher, Sophia has delivered EFT successfully for thousands of physical and emotional issues. While she has specialized in trauma and complex cases for years, teaching with the intention and desire to share the powerful efficacy of EFT with as many as possible, is Sophia's greatest passion. Her website is: *http://www.sophiacayer.com.* The Personal Peace Foundation can be found at *http://www.personalpeacefoundation.org*)

# From Self Sabotage to Success

Jaqui Crooks, EFT Master, EFTCert-Honors

*"All problems were once solutions"*
—Milton Erickson

## Why do we self-sabotage?

When you know what you want or need to do to achieve success, but you find yourself procrastinating, self sabotaging and putting things off, and it feels like you're swimming through treacle and you're getting nowhere fast, THERE'S ALWAYS A VERY GOOD REASON.

There may be a part of you that thinks it's not safe for you to have success.

*EDITOR'S NOTE:*
This is a concept very much embraced by modern cognitive behavioural therapy (CBT).

There can be many reasons for those limiting beliefs, and the majority of them will not be beliefs that you recognise with your logical mind as making sense. That's because they were created much earlier in your life. Often beliefs are created in the first two years of life, sometimes in the womb and sometimes before birth into this life.

Whether you see that as being during past life experiences, or things being handed down through the generations, or just your subconscious creating a metaphor for the issue, that's OK.

If the client says that an issue goes back to past lives, I accept what they say and use the information that they give me as a specific event that I can tap on.

> Some of the most powerful healing I have done is with clients who thought the origins of their current issues went back to Atlantis. At one point I had 3 new clients in a month who spontaneously told me that their issues started in Atlantis and interestingly, they all told me the same story from different perspectives. I don't have to consider if I believe that; they believe it, and it gives me new information to work on.

The healing is enormously powerful and has always impacted very strongly on the current situations in their life, so I'm always pleased when past lives crop up, though it's not a frequent occurrence.

For most people, the initial traumas that have created those fear-based limiting beliefs go back to the time in the womb, birth, or the first two years of life. It can be really helpful to take a client back to as early an event as you can.

Bruce Lipton[1] explains that a child's brain predominantly makes Delta waves until the child is 2 years old. This is the brain wave pattern typically produced in deep hypnosis, allowing information to be downloaded directly to the subconscious, where it becomes 'hard wired'. This means that an enormous amount of information can be downloaded quickly, helping to keep the child safe in its new environment.

## How do you find the earliest event?

A simple way to do this is to ask the client to focus on the issue that they find problematic, to focus on the feeling around that issue, to check where they feel it in their body and to get full details of it: colour, texture, moving/still, sounds etc[2].

When they have a clear representation of that feeling, ask them, with their eyes closed, to imagine going back over their life and to let you know an event from an early time when that same feeling came up.

When you've done some detective work about the limiting patterns that are running in someone's life and you've gone as far back as they can remember, you can use the earliest memory they have and tap on that, and then instruct

the subconscious to clear anything earlier that may have contributed to it.
For example:

- ⚜ *Even though my dad shouted at me for not eating my dinner, I'm OK.*

- ⚜ *Even though my dad shouted at me for not eating my dinner and I felt like this, I'm OK.*

- ⚜ *Even though my dad shouted at me for not eating my dinner and he'd probably shouted at me many, many times before that, those times are over, I'm not a little child anymore and it's OK for me to let those feelings go, wherever they come from and I deeply and completely accept myself.*

'WHEREVER THEY COME FROM' is giving the instruction to the subconscious that you don't need to know about those times, just clear them anyway and the subconscious is usually obliging enough to do that for you.

As you may know, with Borrowing Benefits, you set an intention to work on an issue and then you tap along with the person that you're borrowing from and your subconscious mind automatically makes links between their issues and yours. Things change and you don't always know why; in fact you don't need to know, as the subconscious can do the job without your conscious mind. When you don't know what happened to create the problem, you can create a 'possible scenario' and tap on that, while you tell the subconscious: *"This, or something like this"* and it will automatically look for connections and work to clear them.

An example of this was a client who had relationship difficulties. She had recognised that she was running a pattern. Relationships started well, but after 18 months it was as though someone had thrown a switch and all those emotions switched off. We cleared old relationship traumas and some issues around the parents and I asked, as I do more and more often, whether there were any family stories about her birth and early years. You might be surprised how often there are!

It turned out that when my client was 18 months old, her family was living in another country on an isolated farm. Her mother had been seriously ill when she was pregnant with her next baby (my client's younger sibling). The mother was taken to hospital 40 miles away and the child's father was left to run a farm, visit the hospital and look after an 18 month old. Even when mum returned after weeks, she was ill for several months. We decided that it was possible that that child had been left on her own for several hours at a time and that she may have decided the only way to survive was to cut off her emotions. This may have accounted for her 18 month limit on emotions in relationships.

We created a possible scenario and tapped on it:

- *Even though it's possible that when my mum was ill, my dad had to leave me on my own so he could run the farm, I deeply and completely love and accept myself and him.*

- *Even though it's likely that my little child was terrified and thought she was going to die, she survived and I deeply and completely accept myself and everyone involved.*

- *Even though she was so terrified that she's been running that pattern ever since, I'd like that little child inside me to understand that she's safe and I can look after her now and she doesn't need to run that pattern any more.*

It can be useful to build in acceptance of the person who is believed to have caused the problem, but only if and when the client is comfortable with that.

## Can we work with trauma in the womb or during birth?

Yes, it's quite possible to work with either or both. You've probably had clients who say they were born anxious, and that may well be the case. If their mother was anxious while she was carrying them, they will have become used to adrenaline; they will have experienced the traumas that their mother experienced, and after birth their own body will be creating the adrenaline it had become used to. It is also likely that the child will be affected by what was going on for its parents when the egg and sperm were being formed. One option to deal with this is to do a general tap to instruct the subconscious to clear anything that wasn't the child's at that time.

For two recent clients of mine, their mothers had tried to abort them and failed. Can you imagine what state their mothers were in and the trauma to those foetuses?

Both clients had an underlying belief that they weren't supposed to be alive, and one had been a twin whose brother had died, so there were added feelings of rejection, abandonment and survivor guilt. You can imagine how these issues were affecting their day-to-day lives.

After clearing the trauma of their time in the womb and instructing the subconscious to clear the trauma from 'cellular memory', or anywhere else it had been held, I asked them to continue tapping on their karate point, while they imagined their time in the womb differently. They might even want to reassure their mother.

*EDITOR'S NOTE:*
Work like this is also a key element of Matrix Reimprinting and Deep State Re-patterning.

I then asked them to imagine being born, easily and safely, and to create for themselves the loving welcome that they needed. That was an incredibly moving and powerful session for both of them and they experienced great change in their lives.

A recent client came to me explaining that she felt completely stuck in every area of her life.

She didn't seem to be able to move forward or back and she was experiencing real fear when she tried to move. We did some exploring of those feelings using the colour/texture technique mentioned earlier. The client had many experiences of the same feeling and then she mentioned a recurring dream that had the same feeling.

She was in a pink tunnel and her mother was behind her, pushing her forward, but she could go neither forwards nor back. She was feeling panicky and as though she might die. I asked if there were any stories about her birth and she said that she was born with the cord around her neck. This obviously fitted the dream and the feeling of not being able to go forward or back, so we tapped, linking the probable experience of that baby, to the feelings here and now.

✤ *Even though when I was being born I was really stuck with the cord around my neck and I couldn't go forward or back, I'm OK.*

✤ *Even though I was so stuck and I was terrified and my mum probably was too and I've been carrying that terror stored in my cellular memory ever since, I deeply and completely love and accept myself and my mum.*

> ✦ *Even though that terror has been locked in my cellular memory and maybe other places too, I choose to clear it now. Those things happened and they're over, I survived and so did my mum and I no longer need that fear in my life.*

Several rounds on a similar theme released the fear from the memory of the dream, from the thought of the birth and even from her present day situation. Suddenly she was able to see her current life differently and more creatively. At that point it can be useful to tap on the here and now and the new possibilities of the future.

> ✦ *Even though I've been carrying that fear right up to now, I choose to see the world differently.*

> ✦ *Even though I felt so stuck, I choose to enjoy noticing new opportunities and new ways of thinking and being, because that works best for me.*

> ✦ *Even though I felt so stuck I choose to be free, because it's what I deserve. (You can add, "Whether I believe it or not" for those who don't believe it!)*

## It sounds as if there is a lot that the conscious mind is not aware of. Are you suggesting that we talk directly to the subconscious?

Yes. The more I use EFT, the more I recognise that a lot of my work is talking to the subconscious. We give it suggestions, instructions and negotiate with it, to create new ways of being, rather the old stuck limits it has created for itself.

Problems exist because a part of your subconscious is holding on to strategies that no longer work. These parts have a positive intention for us; it's just that the strategy they've chosen to achieve that positive intention is not working.

For example, the subconscious may see us become anxious in a certain situation and then look for times when it thinks being anxious might be useful. Soon it will recognise hundreds and maybe thousands of triggers that remind it to help you to be anxious, without any conscious thought on your part. That may be why you might start with an occasional panic attack and within a short space of time you're having two or three a day. Each time you experience that panic, the subconscious sees more possible triggers, and so there are more times when it expects you to experience the panic. It doesn't reason whether that strategy is working, it just follows the patterns it has set up.

---

The good news is that the subconscious part of you which activates these negative behaviours will be equally happy to do something more useful for you—IF YOU TELL IT WHAT YOU WOULD LIKE IT TO DO!

---

## Can we work with the part that is holding onto dysfunctional behaviour to create more useful, more effective and more creative strategies to achieve the same positive outcome?

Yes. A possible statement could be:

> ✦ *Even though the part that's creating this anxiety is working hard for me, I'd like it to understand that what it does, isn't working. I'd like it to create a safer, healthier and more creative way of fulfilling its positive intention. I thank it for its help and I deeply and completely love and accept all parts of me.*

Although long, this statement gives an instruction to the subconscious to make safe and healthy changes and also accepts it for what it has done, which collapses the resistance to change.

I often add the word 'fun' into statements, as the client is usually so bogged down in the problem that fun has gone out of the window. Humour is also a great way to reframe a situation, because you can be sure that the client hasn't seen much fun around it before.

## What if the client feels torn or in conflict—how can we facilitate a negotiation between conflicting parts?

Often one part will want one thing and another part will want the opposite {see *The Inner Committee*}. They are constantly in conflict, which uses an enormous amount of energy and still keeps the client stuck. It's rather like an equally matched tug of war. One side starts to win and then the other side puts more energy in and begins to win, and so it goes on . . .

It can be really useful to ask the client, while tapping the Karate Chop point, to go inside and find one of the conflicting parts and to take it out and put it on one of their knees. Ask them what it looks like. It may look like a version of them, often it's something completely different, such as a hard, prickly ball, or a fluffy pink heart. Whatever it is, that's OK[3].

When the part is out on their knee, ask them, as they look at it, what strengths that part has.

EDITOR'S NOTE:
This is a similar process to the use of the screen in Deep State Re-patterning.

They may not see any strengths to start with, but just remind the client that although they might not like the way the part uses their stengths, they are still strengths. A part that won't let go of its old habits will be strong, determined, persistant and those strengths can be useful if used in a more creative way.

Ask what that part is trying to get for them and keep asking that question until you get to either 'safe' or 'happy'.

For example:

Q:   What does that part want for you?
A:   *To keep me stuck.*

Q:   What does it think that will get for you?
A:   *I'll stay as I am.*

Q:   What will that get for you?
A:   *I won't have to take any risks.*

Q:   What will that get for you?
A:   *I'll stay safe.*

Then take out the opposing part and do the same. Get a description, strengths, and what its positive intention is.

If/when you've got both intentions to safety or happiness, you can then point out that although both parts are going about this in different ways, they have the same intention.

Ask the client to ask one of the parts, given that their intentions are the same, if it would help it to do its job well if the other part would share some of its strengths. Ask the other part the same question. If they think that would be helpful, ask if they would consider sharing their strengths so that they could both achieve their positive intention in a new way. Ask if they would consider talking to each other and checking out how they could do it differently together, understanding that if for any reason, the new way doesn't work, they can create new alternatives.

Allow the parts to come together in whatever way works for them and place them back in the body wherever they need to be.

Ask the client to take a few moments to let them settle in and to experience how they feel when those parts are no longer fighting. They might want to imagine their current situation and see how it feels when the parts are co-operating rather than fighting. They usually have a very different feeling/picture of their current situation.

This whole process is usually done while tapping on the Karate Chop point. This is less intrusive than conventional tapping, allowing the client to tap and focus simultaneously.

## Does reframing have a role to play in reconciliation of parts?

Sometimes it may be possible to find when and where a part that is sabotaging was created, and then to find its purpose in your life.

Often we are holding on to beliefs or patterns of behaviour that we created very early on in our life. When we become aware of them and their purpose, it is possible to reframe using EFT (although such reframes should normally only be attempted once the SUDs have dropped to around 5 or below):

> ❧ *Even though when I was little, dad shouted at me and I thought he didn't love me, it's possible that with his background, he didn't know how else to show his love.*

> ❧ *Even though part of me thought letting go of my anger meant letting him off the hook, maybe, it really means me not carrying him and that time with me for the rest of my life.*

## I've heard a lot about the 'Inner Child'—can we use a similar process to work with that part?

Yes; the part that is sabotaging and procrastinating may well be our Inner Child. Typically, this is the name that is used to describe the part (or parts) that was/were damaged early on, or that took on board other people's beliefs or fears in order to keep us safe, or that created mistaken beliefs about itself and the world from what it observed.

Working with the Inner Child can make an enormous difference to any situation. You can safely assume that whatever is going on in a client's life currently will have its roots in a trauma that the client experienced as a young child.

Trauma does not necessarily mean something that you as an adult consider traumatic, however. Anything that made a child feel afraid, sad, angry or guilty will have caused a disruption in the energy system. That moment of trauma will be frozen in the child's system. It's often locked into the cellular memory and it still plays out as though that trauma is current.

---

At any time that you experience a similar emotion to that which you experienced as a child, YOU GO BACK TO THAT STATE AND TIME AND MOST IMPORTANTLY YOU ONLY HAVE ACCESS TO THE RESOURCES THAT YOU HAD AT THAT TIME.

---

This is why, when you understand something logically and know that a particular way to deal with a situation would be the best, when you're actually in that situation, you go straight back emotionally to the age and resources that you had as a child and do what you've always done. Then you may beat yourself up because you 'should' have known better!

*EDITOR'S NOTE:*
The fact that you only have access to the resources you had at the time of the original trauma is very important, not only in understanding reactions to triggers, but in helping to heal the original trauma.

## How can we work with the Inner Child?

There are many ways:

- You can introduce the child into your statements as you tap.

For example:

✤ *Even though my little girl thought she'd got it wrong and it was all her fault, I'd like her to understand that she was doing the best she could, and she's a good girl and I love and accept her and myself.*

- You can have a conversation with your child as you tap the karate chop point, explaining things to her, asking what she needs to feel safe, giving her a hug, letting her know that you can keep her safe now, letting her know how grateful you are to her for all she's done for you up till now, and letting her know that she doesn't have to do it that way anymore, she can do some playing instead and bring some fun into your life.

- You can go to your Inner Child and offer to tap on him to deal with whatever emotions he has. You can even offer to teach him to tap himself, and let him know he can use that as a tool when he needs it {see *Matrix Reimprinting*}. It may clear many events and emotions without you having to do them individually.

- You can tap on the situation that created the trauma for the child and instruct the subconscious to clear it from the cellular memory.

For example:

🌢 *Even though little Jaqui was so scared when that happened, it happened and it's over and we both survived, and I instruct my subconscious to clear it from my cellular memory and anywhere else it's been stored, because it no longer serves me.*

Working with the Inner Child is very rewarding and don't be afraid to experiment. See the child as a real child; what do you think might make him/her feel better?

## Can we also use this process to work with the 'rebel' inside us?

The 'rebel' is very often an aspect of your Inner Child. I see it as the part of you that tries to protect the 'real' you. It is the part of you that wants to keep you safe from following other people's beliefs and coping strategies. This may have worked well for a time in early life. However, it's very likely that by time you become an adult, the rebel is keeping you stuck—just as much as complying with other's expectations keeps you stuck.

If you comply, you have no choice, you can only go this way:        ⟶

If you rebel, you have no choice, you can only go this way:        ⟵

The aim is to HAVE THE FREEDOM TO GO IN EITHER DIRECTION, or anything in between.

The good news is that you can talk to or negotiate with your rebel just as you can with the other parts of you.

You can even give it permission to be ok to change and to be ok to stay the same. That way it has nothing to rebel against.

For example:

⁍ *Even though I really want to hold on to this anger, I'm OK.*

⁍ *Even though I really want to hold onto this anger, I could choose to let it go.*

⁍ *Even though I really want to hold onto this anger, I could choose to let it go and whether I let it go or hold on, I'm OK either way and I'm doing the best I can.*

## How do I get my various parts to cooperate?

I view the parts of us like little cartoon characters who are doing the very best they can for us, in the only way that they know how. In the same way as if you were managing people in a factory, your first tactic might be to talk to a person who isn't doing what you want them to do, negotiate, explain why and how you want them to change and maybe give them a job that suits their talents better . . . you can do all of that with the parts of you that are not working in the way that you want.

If your first contact with people, or parts, is to make them redundant, or fire them, you can be sure that you'll have a battle on your hands. Take the easy way out for everyone. Negotiate; you'll be absolutely amazed by how co-operative all parts of you and/or your clients can be.

And if they're not co-operating? There will be very good reasons for it, usually safety. It's back to the drawing board, more aspects to find. Try asking your client:

*"If you had to guess why a part of you thought it wasn't safe for this to change, why do you think that might be? . . . and it won't be a logical reason."*

This gives your client a chance to be creative and intuitive without worrying about whether they're right or wrong, and you may be surprised what they come up with. When they do, it's back to tapping.

## What if the client doesn't seem to understand why they are holding onto the problem?

Parts can also be used very effectively when your intuition suggests there might be a reason for the client to hold on to the problem, but a reason the client may not recognise or accept. This can be particularly useful when dealing with secondary gain.

If the client accepts that there is a reason to hold on to the problem, incorporate that reason in your statement. It will usually be one of the standard reversals and may often be linked to identity issues {see *Identifying and Neutralizing Reversals*}. IF I LET GO OF THIS, OR CHANGE THIS, WHO WILL I BE THEN?

For example:

- ☩ *Even though part of me is scared to let this go, because who will I be then? I deeply and completely accept myself.*

- ☩ *Even though part of me is scared to let this go, because who will I be then? I choose to be curious and excited about discovering who I am and to be comfortable just being me. It's all I can be, so I may as well enjoy it!*

- ☩ *Even though part of me is scared because I don't know who I'll be without this, I'd like that part to understand that who I'll be is just me without this, no more and no less.*

We often believe that when something changes we have to do something different. Not so; WE CAN CHANGE BELIEFS AND STILL DO EVERYTHING THE SAME. HOWEVER, IT WILL BE A CHOICE, NOT A 'HAVE TO' AND THAT MAKES ALL THE DIFFERENCE. And in practice, things are very likely to change without conscious effort, easily, comfortable, safely.

Be creative with your statements. Don't worry about perfection, just do it. If it doesn't work, do something else instead.

---

Remember –THERE'S NO FAILURE, ONLY FEEDBACK.

---

# AUTHOR'S BIOGRAPHY AND CONTACT DETAILS

Jaqui trained in hypnotherapy and NLP before training in EFT in 1999. She is an EFT Master and has worked and shared with many highly skilled EFT users. She loves helping people to become more of who they are and specialises in changing limiting beliefs and old family and ancestral patterns. She is the creator of 'Reconnecting to the Core', a Meridian Energy Therapy that can be used for deep Personal Transformation, which gives Practitioners the skills to help clients to make changes swiftly and easily at an incredibly deep level. You can find more information on all of the above at Jaqui's website: www.beacontraining.co.uk. Jaqui can be contacted at Jaqui@beacontraining.co.uk .

REFERENCES:

1. Bruce Lipton, 'The Biology of Belief', (Hay House, 2005)
2. Further details of this process can be found on: www.beacontraining.co.uk

# Matrix Reimprinting

## A TRANSFORMATIONAL TECHNIQUE

### KARL DAWSON, EFT MASTER, EFTCERT-HONORS

**Did the Matrix Reimprinting technique develop from your work with serious disease?**

Yes, very much so. I first found EFT when I was searching for ways to overcome my own severe health challenges, and after becoming an EFT Master I soon came to specialise in EFT for the treatment and prevention of serious disease. Alongside my standard EFT training courses, I spent many years creating, refining and teaching my specialist training in EFT for Serious Disease. This course has proved immensely popular among EFT practitioners, GPs, health professionals, and also lay people who want to learn the information to aid their own healing. The course was strongly influenced by the work and research of cell biologist Bruce Lipton, and I have long been aware that traumas and life issues, particularly those from the first six years, if not dealt with and released from the body's energy system, can be a major contributing factor to the myriad of diseases and illnesses that are rife in our society today.

**So how did this develop into the Matrix Reimprinting technique?**

Working in this specialist way with EFT, I began to develop my own variations on the original EFT protocol, and one such variation is now producing results that are far beyond the ordinary. This new variation addresses the same type of issues as traditional EFT, ranging from minor or small 't' traumas to severe, life-threatening or big 'T' traumas. Its distinguishing feature is that it combines quantum physics with EFT to create shifts in the relationship to a person's past, and typically these are far greater than any that I have experienced or witnessed with traditional EFT. The power and efficiency of this technique has led to it becoming the main focus of my work, and I have named it: The Matrix Reimprinting technique.

## How does the Matrix Reimprinting technique relate to quantum physics?

In 1944 Max Planck rocked the world by revealing that we are not truly separate beings, but are in fact connected by a unified energy field which he called 'The Matrix.' In recent years there has been a surge in popularity around this understanding, largely due to the wide circulation of films such as 'The Secret' and 'What the Bleep do We Know?' which have made the theories of quantum physics much more accessible to lay people.

These groundbreaking films, together with a number of similarly themed books such as 'The Field' by Lynne McTaggart and 'The Divine Matrix' by Gregg Braden, have become popular with EFT practitioners and are highly compatible with the principles of Energy Psychology. The emphasis on what we hold in our energy fields has become an area of increasing interest as we learn that 'what we focus on is what we attract', whether we want it or not.

As EFT practitioners, we have learned the importance of clearing disruption from our body's energy system, thereby releasing the negative vibrational energy of past traumas. In turn, as we clear this negativity from our energy fields, we have learned that we can replace it with a much more wholesome relationship to our life experience. Traditional EFT already draws on the laws of quantum physics by changing our point of attraction, and the Matrix Reimprinting technique takes releasing our past and changing our point of attraction to a whole new level, working directly with important phenomena such as the 'freeze response'.

## What is the 'freeze response'?

The 'field' or 'matrix' is not only all around us, but it also connects us to our past. This is because we hold our specific traumas and stressful life experiences in the matrix and they influence our every thought pattern, behaviour and action. To understand how this is so, we can draw on the findings of modern psychology in relation to trauma. When we experience danger, a key survival mechanism—the 'fight, flight or freeze' reflex—is activated. Of particular relevance is the point when the body goes into a 'freeze response', which it often does during a trauma. A fraction of a second before the traumatic experience takes place, our consciousness freezes to protect itself from physical and emotional overwhelm, and at the same time our subconscious compresses all the information, preventing us from experiencing it consciously through our five senses.

During this time it is as though part of us splits off or 'disassociates' to protect us from the trauma, and this is why we often don't remember a traumatic event after it has taken place. Whilst we are often left numb on one level, and may even feel as if the traumatic experience had never happened, on another level it is as if the trauma has never ended, and that it is being repeatedly played out, over and over and over again, ad infinitum.

## Where is this traumatised part being repeatedly played out?

Traditionally, it was thought to be somewhere in the psyche, deep in the mind or in the subconscious, but I would like to offer an alternative view based on my experience over the last couple of years with the Matrix Reimprinting technique. I would like to suggest that the disassociated part goes into the field or matrix. What I have learned is that we hold in our 'fields' the stressful life events that have gone before, not just as memories but as specific energy bodies, which I have named Energy Consciousness Holograms or ECHOs. These ECHOs are the younger versions of ourselves who are holding onto our life traumas for us. Most of us have numerous ECHOs from our traumas and life experiences, and some people have literally hundreds. Our ECHOs are not only from our experiences in childhood but can be from any point in our lives when we experienced anything from a minor to a major trauma. These ECHOs hold the memory and the energy of the trauma for us. And, crucially, the Matrix Reimprinting technique helps us to release this held energy.

## What is the effect on holding onto trauma in this way?

Before learning how to resolve this energy with the Matrix Reimprinting technique, let's take a closer look at why we store trauma in this way. On one level it may seem self-destructive or self-punishing to hold on to the trauma, but we actually do this for self-protection and survival. Our subconscious, wanting to avoid similar events, stores these memories as a way of learning from the past. In many instances, this allows us to learn from our life experience in a highly adaptive manner; however the potential side effect is that as long as the trauma is held by the ECHO, similar events are likely to trigger similar responses. Over and over again we find ourselves attracting and repeating our early experiences in a myriad of similar life events and choices.

Another side effect of storing our traumas in this way it that it requires substantial energy, especially for people who have experienced many traumas or who tend to be frequently retriggered. My experience time and again with my 'EFT for Serious Disease' work is that when the emotional threshold is lowered by continuously retriggering, disease often results.

## So how specifically are traumatic memories held in the matrix?

Scientists have revealed that not only is there a unified energy field that connects all matter and living things, but that we also have local fields around our bodies. Animals and plants have these fields, as well as humans. Since the 1920s, biologists have highlighted how our physical organisation depends on these fields, which are variously referred to as 'developmental' fields, 'positional' fields, 'biological' fields or 'morphogenic' fields. This understanding has been furthered by biologist Dr Rupert Sheldrake, who suggests that the morphogenic fields around our bodies are transmitted from past members of the species through a kind of non-local resonance, which Sheldrake calls 'morphic resonance'. These fields are not fixed, but continuously evolve, contributing to the collective consciousness as each individual *"draws upon and contributes to the collective memory of the species."* [1]

Dr Sheldrake's theories support the understanding that not all memory is stored in the brain. His research indicates that memory is also stored in the 'field'. Specifically, he points out that: *"The morphic fields of mental activity are not confined to the insides of our heads. They extend far beyond our brain through intention and attention."* [2]

Dr Sheldrake further reminds us that: *"We are already familiar with the idea of fields extending beyond the material objects in which they are rooted: for example magnetic fields extend beyond the surfaces of magnets; the earth's gravitational field extends far beyond the surface of the earth, keeping the moon*

*in its orbit; and the fields of a cell phone stretch out far beyond the phone itself.*
*Likewise the fields of our minds extend far beyond our brains."* [3]

His work has helped us to understand how our personal and cultural memories and experiences are held in and transmitted through the matrix.

## So how does this all this relate to disease in the body?

Firstly we need to look to our cells. Over the years the term 'cellular memory' has become popular, but according to leading cell biologist Bruce Lipton, our cells don't actually have the consciousness to hold memory. Instead, Dr Lipton reveals that the cell wall has an 'antenna' that tunes into the 'self' in the field.[4] This revelation helped me to understand that THE 'SELF' IS NOT JUST SOMETHING THAT IS WITHIN US, BUT IS ALSO ALL AROUND US.

But what if the cells are tuning into negative signals in our fields? It appears from the work of medical 'intuitives' that disease is held not only in the body but also in the field. One such medical intuitive, Caroline Myss, has over 90 percent success in diagnosing disease just by looking at a person's 'field'. A number of other medical intuitives have also revealed that disease appears in our local fields before we physically manifest it.

## So how is it that disease is in our 'field' before it is in our body?

I propose that this is something to do with the 'pictures' that we hold in our field. Specifically, that our cells and DNA gradually adapt themselves to the misperceptions contained in the unconscious 'pictures' in our local fields, which originate in our life experience. And this in turn contributes to our physical and mental disease states. Because our subconscious does not know the difference between something that happened in the past and something that is happening now, these pictures affect us on a cellular level. Diseased cells will therefore continuously be replaced by diseased cells until the information in the matrix changes. We can change the information in the matrix using the Matrix Reimprinting technique. We can work directly with the ECHOs which hold these negative images for us, and resolve the negative energetic charge around them. When we release the negative energetic charge around these 'pictures', the body's system can let go and feel safe. Once the 'pictures' change, we can transform our relationship to our past and our emotional and physical health in the present.

# The Matrix Reimprinting Technique

## Can you give me a brief summary of the process?

Matrix Reimprinting is based on the 'Movie Technique', which is why I see it as an enhancement of traditional EFT rather than a replacement. In the Movie Technique you take an old memory that still has some negative emotional charge for you and run it in your mind as though it were a movie, stopping at any point where you feel a change in the body or in your emotions, and use the EFT tapping protocol to resolve the disruption. I've always felt that this is one of the core techniques in EFT, and I have seen excellent results with it over the years.

Matrix Reimprinting includes a number of additional features. Perhaps the most important of these is that with Matrix Reimprinting you can stop the movie at any point and interact directly with the ECHO of your younger self. An effective way to do this is to imagine tapping on your ECHO using the EFT protocol (whilst physically tapping on yourself in the present) and enter into a dialogue, perhaps asking your younger self what life messages were learned from the particular situation. The ECHO you are interacting with may have been working to keep you protected from the effects of the trauma for some considerable time, so this also gives you an opportunity to say thank you. At the same time, you can give your ECHO new tools and/or coping resources, designed to allow that ECHO to express itself differently in the situation. After the emotional intensity has resolved you can then imagine taking your ECHO to a safe and comfortable place of its choosing, such as a beach or a sunny field, allowing it to experience new and positive emotions in the situation.

Now here is what's interesting about this: when you then try to remember the original event, not only have you resolved all your emotional intensity around the issue but you often find the new 'picture' that you have created in your memory. These 'pictures' affect your physiology and psychology on every level. By changing the memory in this way, you are interacting with what you hold in your field, which in turn affects your health and well-being in your current reality.

## What are the steps of Matrix Reimprinting?

The following are very basic instructions for using the Matrix Reimprinting technique. The danger in issuing instructions for any technique is that it can oversimplify the process. So please be aware that these instructions represent Matrix Reimprinting IN ITS MOST BASIC FORM and that many additional possibilities and considerations may arise as you work in the matrix in this way. You are therefore advised to attend a Matrix Reimprinting workshop or training before you attempt to use this process with your clients:

- Begin with the Movie Technique and start the movie at a safe place, before there is any emotional intensity.

- At any significant point of emotional intensity, pause the movie.

- Ask your client if it's OK to tap on them and tell your client to close their eyes, then begin tapping on them (or ask your client to tap on themselves if this is your preference).

- Ask your client to visualise the younger version of themselves, and invite them to describe the image that they see. This younger version of themselves is the ECHO. It is important that the client is disassociated from the ECHO—i.e. OUTSIDE the body of the ECHO.

- Ask your client to explain to their ECHO that they have come to help him to let go of the negative emotions he may be experiencing.

- Explain to your client that you want them to imagine tapping on the ECHO as you (the practitioner) tap on your client. Also ask your client to check with the ECHO that they have permission to do so.

- Encourage your client to converse with their ECHO, asking the ECHO what life messages he may have gained from this situation.

- By this point, the ECHO will have in effect become 'the client', so work with the ECHO as you would in a normal EFT session, asking what he feels in his body or emotions, and resolving whatever arises with EFT.

- Encourage your client to ask their ECHO if there is anything he would like to do to resolve this situation. For example, they can:

- bring in new resources

- change what happened

- invite somebody or something else in for help and guidance

- do what they didn't do or they wished they'd done in that situation

This is usually done in silence. Give them time to complete this.

- When this is complete, ask your client and the ECHO if they would like to go to a safe place of their choosing in their imagination. Examples include a sunny field, the park, seaside etc.

- When the ECHO and client are in a good emotional space, get the client to intensify the colours and emotions and feelings associated with this image.

- Now get the client to bring this 'picture' into their mind, washing the colours and emotions through every cell in their body.

- Then send this image out through the heart back into the matrix. Get the client to feel as much emotion as they can.

- Invite your client back to the present and encourage them to open their eyes in their own time. Ask your client to try to replay the original movie—if there is any intensity remaining then tap in the normal way (the original movie is likely to have changed or disappeared on resolution).

Please note: Although the above instructions are for working on a client, you can also use this technique on yourself.

## What are the benefits of Matrix Reimprinting?

The Matrix Reimprinting technique is easy to use. It is also very gentle on your clients. It enables your client to resolve a whole range of traumatic experiences without being re-traumatised.

*REWRITING THE PAST:*

One of the major benefits of Matrix Reimprinting is that it resources the client and enables them to rewrite their past. This is very different from denying that the past happened. Changing the images and memories in the field in this way not only creates resolution, but changes the function of the cells in the present.

## RESOLVING CORE ISSUES

With the Matrix Reimprinting technique you can also quickly find and resolve core issues. In traditional EFT when someone expresses a core belief such as *"I must be perfect to be loved"*, your work as a practitioner is to find the early memories relating to this belief and resolve them with EFT.

---

With the Matrix Reimprinting technique you not only resolve the memories which contributed to the core issues, but you can also instil new supporting beliefs and experiences. This in turn affects and transforms your current belief system in the present moment.

---

## PRECONSCIOUS TRAUMA

The Matrix Reimprinting technique also locates preconscious trauma, even trauma that has occurred before the first six years. Very few therapies or practices have tools for working with preconscious memories, yet the research of cell biologist Bruce Lipton indicates that this is when most of the damage is done to our perception of self. With the Matrix Reimprinting technique your client can interact with themselves as far back as in the womb {see *Deep State Re-patterning*}, and can access and resolve preconscious traumas, again affecting their health and well-being in the present.

## REFRAMES AND COGNITIVE SHIFTS

Another benefit of the Matrix Reimprinting technique is that it commonly produces client-driven reframes and cognitive shifts. One of the great benefits of the technique is that most of the work comes from the client (although if they get stuck at any point, guidance is needed from the practitioner). As the client leads the process, they decide what is best for them in order to resolve the energetic disruption around the trauma. As the power is with the client, they are much more likely to reframe the situation themselves or emphasise their cognitive shifts. As practitioners we are well aware that these shifts indicate that resolution and, therefore, healing has taken place.

*FORGIVENESS*

Similarly, the Matrix Reimprinting often leads clients to a place of forgiveness, particularly to the perpetrator of their traumatic experience. There are a number of schools of thought which believe that the purpose of any therapeutic intervention is to reach the point of forgiveness. This is not something to be forced on or feigned by the client, and there is often a sticking point in traditional therapeutic practices where a client will say they have forgiven their perpetrator consciously, but will not have forgiven their perpetrator on a subconscious level. The Matrix Reimprinting technique leads the client naturally to a place of forgiveness on all levels of consciousness.

*EDITOR'S NOTE:*
One of the great benefits of using Matrix Reimprinting with clients is the ease of understanding and forgiveness for others that comes from working with the ECHO. After the negative emotions of the ECHO have been soothed, feelings towards other participants in the scene are almost universally loving and forgiving, without any suggestion from the Practitioner. Although this isn't a main reason to use MR, it is a marvellous side benefit.

*PSYCHOLOGICAL REVERSAL AND SECONDARY GAINS*

The Matrix Reimprinting technique also elegantly locates psychological reversal and secondary gains. By interacting with the ECHO we can begin to understand exactly why it is holding onto a problem or an issue which is keeping us stuck in an old pattern of thinking or behaving. The ECHO is most often trying to protect us, or filtering its understanding through the perceptions of a child, and we as adults continue to respond to our own worlds through those same childlike perceptions until the energy around the memory is resolved. This creates more self-understanding from the client who can pinpoint their current self-destructive behaviours to early memories, and replace them with more supporting beliefs and behaviours.

*POSITIVE BELIEFS*

On a similar note, the Matrix Reimprinting technique can instil new positive beliefs into any past memory. One of the issues that many of us face with the traditional EFT protocol is that because we always focus on the negative, there is often a void left when an issue is resolved. With the Matrix Reimprinting technique this void can be filled by allowing your ECHO to have experiences which create new and supportive beliefs and behaviours.

## DISASSOCIATED CLIENTS

Another great benefit is that Matrix Reimprinting works on disassociated clients who have no SUDs levels. As EFT practitioners will be aware, this client group is one of the most challenging to work with. The Matrix Reimprinting technique works perfectly with this client group because when the client works with the ECHO, the technique works more effectively when the client is disassociated!

## TRAUMA RESOLUTION

The Matrix Reimprinting technique is very valuable in its ability to send a message to the body that the trauma is over. It ends the trauma cycle where the trauma is constantly being replayed over and over in the matrix, and thus discharges the 'freeze response'. This enables the body and the cells to respond in healthier ways, and begin to heal.

## RESOLVING THE UNRESOLVABLE

With Matrix Reimprinting you can also help your clients to resolve issues which have previously appeared irresolvable. This is particularly beneficial when clients have lost family members or loved ones and have not had a chance to say goodbye or resolve their differences. Using Matrix Reimprinting, the client can release the emotions around unresolved relationships and let go of the ties which hold them in the past.

## THE LAW OF ATTRACTION

A further benefit of the Matrix Reimprinting technique is that it utilises the Law of Attraction. As mentioned earlier, when we have traumatic experiences and hold them in our matrix, we continue to attract similar experiences. With this technique, once we resolve the trauma we change the point of attraction and begin to draw more fulfilling and life-enhancing experiences.

# Postscript

The results I have seen while working with this technique have been astounding beyond all measure, and these results are being replicated by the many practitioners I have trained who have integrated this technique into their practice. I truly believe we are standing on the edge of a new and very exciting healing paradigm by working in the matrix in this way. I am extremely grateful to Gary Craig for creating EFT and for all that he has taught me. I am now only just beginning to realise the true implications of the Matrix Reimprinting technique and the effects that it could have on the transformation of humanity.

## AUTHOR'S BIOGRAPHY AND CONTACT DETAILS

You can attend a specialist Matrix Reimprinting training with Karl. You can also see the Matrix Reimprinting technique in action on Karl's EFT for the Treatment and Prevention of Serious Disease DVD set or EFT with Meta Medicine DVD set. Coming soon—Look out for the full-length book on Matrix Reimprinting that Karl is co-writing with author Sasha Allenby.

Further information on Karl's courses and products are available on his website: www.matrixreimprinting.com

REFERENCES

1. Dr Rupert Sheldrake, 'Morphic Resonance and Morphic Fields, An Introduction', http://www.sheldrake.org/Articles&Papers/papers/morphic/morphic_intro.html
2. Ibid.
3. Ibid.
4. Dr Bruce Lipton, 'As Above So Below—An Introduction to Fractal Evolution', DVD

# Parents as Partners

## USING EFT FOR CHILDREN'S ISSUES

### Nancy Gnecco, MEd, LPC, EFT Master, EFTCert-Honors

## What causes stress in families?

Are you overscheduled, rushed, over-extended, and generally overwhelmed by the demands of raising a family? Do you struggle with anxiety, depression or sleep issues? Do you get angry, frustrated or impatient with your children? And then do you feel guilty, judging yourself, and wondering why you aren't able to be the perfect parent you imagined you would be? Is your child acting out, demonstrating regressive behavior, having trouble at school? Are you a single parent wondering how to meet your child's needs, make ends meet, have a social life, and still take care of yourself? If so, you are not alone.

What if we could relieve our own stress as parents, empowering and enabling us to be lovingly neutral in dealing with our children's problems? While children can be a tremendous source of joy, their care and upbringing are, inevitably, a major source of stress and anxiety. Parents are often exhausted simply by the amount of time and energy required for the day-to-day responsibilities of job and family. The way of life in many western countries now requires that most families have two incomes in order to make ends meet. This means that there is no one at home to care for our children—hence the necessity for day care, 'all day kindergarten', and after school care—creating another stressor for parents and children alike. Add to the mix any sort of change (illness, loss of a pet, change in school or family relocation, ageing parents, even the welcome addition of a new baby) and you have the perfect formula for major family dysfunction. Where is this most likely to show up? It will show up in the children.

Here is an example from my Energy Psychotherapy practice of a normal, two-parent family in crisis with a child's behavior. The rest of this article describes how EFT can be successfully used by families without the intervention of a therapist.

### Mr and Mrs Smith

I open the door to greet Mr. & Mrs. Smith.

*"I can't take it anymore. I'm totally fed up and exhausted. I feel guilty if I take any time for myself—not that there is any time to take. She fights me getting dressed in the morning, refuses to eat breakfast. We're always rushing. Most days I'm late for work. When I drop her off at day care she clings to me and wails. The teachers literally have to peel her off me. They say she calms right down, but I worry all day, and then when I go to pick her up she won't come with me. It's as if she's punishing me for leaving her. She never used to be like that. When we get home there is dinner to make. Bedtime is a nightmare, and she's started wetting the bed at night. She's been potty trained since she was two. It makes me so mad—sheets to wash every morning. I'm worn down."*

Tears stream down the mother's face, and I haven't even had a chance to introduce myself yet. Dad puts his hand on Mom's back and leads her to the couch.

Kate, the 'identified patient', is being brought to therapy for the bedwetting problem. She is 4 years old and has a baby brother who is 5 months old. This is a family with two loving parents, both of whom work at full-time jobs outside the home. Mom had a six-week maternity leave when baby Kevin was born, and took an extra two weeks without pay before returning to work. Kate's bedwetting started about a week after Mom returned to work.

## How does stress affect the family?

Often, parents are so focused on caring for their children that they forget (or don't take time) to take care of themselves, putting themselves at risk of stress-related emotional and physical problems. Research suggests that stress is linked to 60-90% of health issues such as depression, anxiety, headaches, chronic fatigue, hypertension, even colds.[1] It is well known that long-term stress can affect the brain, making people more vulnerable to pressures and rendering them less able to cope with day-to-day tasks.

Stress is cumulative. Daily life in many families has become complicated by pressures for children to be involved in activities such as sports, scouting, and music and dance lessons. At face value, these activities help to round out the childhood experience, keeping youngsters busy and engaged. However, multiple activities require close scheduling and transportation, increasing the stress for parents who must juggle these along with their own schedules for work and other tasks such as the preparation of meals, grocery shopping, and the care and maintenance of their homes. It is well known that extended or repeated activation of the stress response can take a heavy toll on the body as well as the emotions. The more life changes or daily hassles a person has to deal with at a time, the more intense the stress. There is no question that children respond to their parents' psychological distress. One of the areas in which EFT is the most effective is in neutralizing the effects of stress in adults and children. It is important for parents to learn to use it for themselves, addressing their own anxiety, fear and frustration before dealing with the presenting issues of the child, *"cause if Momma ain't happy, ain't nobody happy"*.

Whenever a child presents with a challenging issue, the entire family system is affected. Consequently, in order for any interventions to be successful, it is critical that the entire family be engaged.

## What are the most common sources of stress for parents?

- Career-driven society—both parents working outside the home
- Constant worrying, hurrying, rushing
- Economic and financial worries
- Negative thinking, self-criticism, self-blame
- Family member ill or in crisis
- Ageing parents (e.g. parents of young children caring for ageing parents of their own)
- Unrealistic expectation or beliefs
- Low self-esteem
- Unresolved or unexpressed emotions, especially anger
- Victim consciousness

- Hunger, pain, fatigue
- Job dissatisfaction or insecurity
- Unemployment
- Poverty
- Financial worries
- Racial, age or sexual discrimination
- Office politics, conflicts with co-workers

## How can I use EFT for children's issues?

When dealing with childhood problems within the family, the initial tendency is to focus on the youngster in order to solve or correct the presenting problem. Generally, this approach is unsuccessful. The family will have the best chance of helping the child when the parents can clear their own issues first while improving skills of communication and negotiation.

> Often the child's behavior is acting as a barometer measuring problems within the whole family structure.

There is a protocol for families which has proven to be very effective. To fully understand it, it is important, as stated above, to look at the issue of stress within the whole family, not just in the child.

It is possible for parents to utilize this protocol on their own without the intervention of a therapist or EFT practitioner.

1. GETTING ON THE SAME PAGE (see instructions below)
   - Parents use EFT together to reduce overall tension and improve communication regarding the effect the problem is having on them individually, and as a family.
   - Practice 'active listening', using EFT to clear intensity as it comes up.

2. TAKING RESPONSIBILITY FOR YOUR OWN 'INSIDE JOB'
   - Make a list of the things your child does that upset you or that are of concern. Be as specific as you can: e.g. *"When (child) does (whatever), I feel (whatever you feel)"*.
   - Rate the intensity of each of these triggers on a 0—10 scale with 0 being neutral and 10 being the worst it could be.

- Do some rounds of EFT on each concern on the list whenever you feel upset, and always before talking with the child about the problem

✦ *Even though (child) does (whatever), and it makes me feel (whatever you feel), I deeply and completely love and accept myself.*

REMINDER PHRASE:  *(whatever you feel)*

3. 'MAGIC TAPPING' FOR KIDS

- At a time and place where both you and your child are comfortable and emotionally neutral, introduce EFT according to the child's age and developmental level (see below)

- Teach the child the tapping 'game' and try it on something that is not the major issue for the child—anything that makes him or her feel mad, sad, bad or scared.

a. If appropriate, use a surrogate such as a stuffed bear {see *EFT and Magic Buttons Bear*} or other favorite doll or stuffed animal, play 'Simon Says', have older children use the 'Tell the Story' technique.

b. If the child is old enough have him or her name the emotion (sad, mad, scared, frustrated, hurt feelings)

> *EDITOR'S NOTE:*
> Having children indicate intensity visually, by using their hands, is a great technique. It can even be used with adult clients who are uncomfortable giving a SUDS number.

c. Indicate an intensity if age-appropriate (e.g. hands touching together is no intensity, hands wide apart is high intensity)

d. Tap the setup using age-appropriate wording (see below)

e. Tap the Sequence

f. Reevaluate and repeat as necessary

## How can parents use EFT to 'get on the same page'?

1. Partners sit down together at a time when they won't be interrupted. That, in itself, could present a challenge. Consider getting a babysitter if necessary (it's a lot cheaper than therapy!). Before discussing the situation, each person observes his or her current level of distress about the problem they are facing. Notice and name the feelings in the moment: e.g. stressed out, angry, overwhelmed, sad, guilty, hopeless, responsible, worried, frantic,

anxious, fearful, resentful. Find the words that best describe the feeling in this moment and write them down, giving them, as a group, an intensity level from 0—10 with 0 being neutral, and 10 being the worst they can be.

2. Combine the feelings into one setup statement that includes all of the feelings and symptoms of both partners, and, with each tapping the karate chop point, both partners say the following:

 ✣ *Even though we are having a problem with (child's name), and we feel (list the feelings you have written down), we are doing the best we can, and we are good parents. Do this 3 times together.*

REMINDER PHRASES: (One partner speaks, both partners tap):

TOP OF HEAD: *all these feelings/emotions.*
EYEBROW: *this problem with (child's name)*
SIDE OF EYE: *(name one of the list of feelings from 2 above)*
UNDER EYE: *(name another of the feelings from 2 above)*
UNDER NOSE: *all these feelings.*
COLLARBONE: *this problem with (child's name).*
UNDERARM: *(if you have run out of words from 2 begin again, go back to "all these emotions", or use the 'stream of consciousness' technique which simply means that you say whatever comes to mind).*

Naming the feelings and emotions while tapping should help to decrease the intensity of distress in both parents so that they are better able to discuss the problems with each other

3. Do another round with the other partner doing the talking and both tapping.

4. Reevaluate the intensity of each person. If both are not at one or zero, do another round using the reminder phrase: *"Remaining emotions (name them if you wish)".*

## Can you describe an 'active listening' exercise?

1. Choose which partner will speak first, and which will listen. The speaker (we'll assume the wife) now goes into as much detail as necessary to explain what she thinks is going on with the child and how it is affecting her (the

wife), adding in anything she might want or need from the listener. Both partners tap while each is talking {see *EFT and Continuous Tapping*}. The listener does not interrupt the speaker and does not speak until she has finished talking.

2. If either partner develops an intensity greater than a 4 on the 0 to 10 point scale, conversation is stopped and the trigger is tapped on by both until it's below a 3. For example:

    ⚕ ***Even though I'm feeling overwhelmed and so sad just talking about this, I deeply and completely accept myself.***

    REMINDER PHRASE: ***Overwhelmed and sad just talking about it.***

    Return to general report of the issue when the specific trigger has been resolved.

3. The listener then responds to the speaker telling what he thinks he heard the speaker say. Again, both partners tap, stopping to tap specifically on any issues that create an intensity greater than a 4. The listener asks the speaker if he got it right, and the speaker clears up any discrepancy. The listener then responds to any requests made by the speaker. (For example, Mom has said: *"I need for you to be home at 6:00 every night."* So Dad may say: *"I can't promise to be home at 6:00, but I could throw the sheets into the washer before I leave for work."*) An agreement is made. The speaker feels heard. Intensity has been jointly tapped away as it has come up.

4. If it feels like too much to talk and tap on all the EFT points, positive results can be achieved by just tapping the collar bone points while speaking/ listening.

5. Switch roles and repeat 1 and 2.

6. Partners are encouraged to do this exercise together weekly as long as the problem remains.

## How can parents work independently with EFT to benefit themselves and the family?

Each parent is encouraged to identify his or her own triggers regarding the problem with the child. Treat them preventatively (WHEN THEY ARE NOT AN ISSUE), and in the moment whenever possible.

1. List the child's behaviors, the personal emotional response, and the intensity of that response. For example: *"When Kate fights me about getting dressed in the morning I feel frustrated and angry. On a scale of 0—10 my intensity is an 8."* The other parent/partner might say: *"When I come home from work and my wife is nursing the baby, Kate is demanding attention and there's no dinner ready I feel overwhelmed. It's a 7."*

2. Remember to tap the karate chop point 3 times while stating the setup phrase with each issue. Develop a setup statement for each of the triggers that includes a choice of how to feel instead {see *The Choices Method*}. Tap on each of these triggers at least once a day WHEN THEY ARE NOT AN ISSUE. For example:

   ⁑ ***Even though Kate may wet the bed again tonight and I usually feel angry and guilty, I choose to be patient and respond to her calmly.***

   Use the stream of consciousness technique as you tap through the points, being sure to include your choice response/feeling. It might look like this:

   TOP OF HEAD: ***I'm afraid Kate is going to wet the bed again.***
   EYEBROW: ***I remember how easy mornings were before this started.***
   SIDE OF EYE: ***My usual anger doesn't help the situation.***
   UNDER EYE: ***I choose patience.***
   UNDER NOSE: ***I choose to deal with Kate calmly.***
   UNDER LIP: ***Maybe it's my fault.***
   COLLARBONE: ***I'm doing the best I can—probably Kate is too.***
   UNDER ARM: ***I choose to be calm if Kate wets the bed again.***

3. The next time the behavior happens, the parent treats his or her own emotional state—his or her own 'inside job', before dealing with the child if possible (or as soon after as possible).

   ⁑ ***Even though I'm feeling really angry that Kate wet the bed again, I deeply and completely accept myself.***

   REMINDER PHRASE: ***"this anger"*** or the 'stream of consciousness technique'

A couple of rounds of EFT tapping should help neutralize the emotional distress in the moment, making it easier to deal with the situation from the 'choice' state. (e.g. patience and calm). Both parents/partners are encouraged to treat their own emotional responses to the situation for at least a week before introducing 'Magic Tapping' to the child.

## Emotional freedom for children: Magic Tapping

SOME COMMON SOURCES OF STRESS FOR CHILDREN:

- Arguing, fighting between parents, rushing
- Divorce, separation
- Illness, death of loved one
- Moving, attending new school or day care
- New addition to the household (sibling, grandparent)
- Over-scheduling of activities—not enough time for creative play
- Peer pressure
- Social pressure—poverty, social functions, parents' financial pressure
- Unrealistic expectations by teachers or parents
- Traumatic event or disaster—watching media coverage of same
- Primary care giver not spending enough time with the child
- Parents pushing kids to excel in athletics
- Media—TV shows, news, images of war, natural disaster, terrorism

Since children are more emotional, intuitive, and empathic than adults, they often carry the dysfunctional energy of the family. Our childhood patterns tend to establish the way we will handle stress and challenges throughout our lives. A child who feels unloved, or who is repeatedly told he is stupid will grow up seeing the world through 'unloving' or 'stupid' eyes, and these limiting identities will increase over time, gathering strength and producing evidence that 'proves' how unlovable or stupid they are. This will, of course limit their happiness and effectiveness in the world.

For this reason it is very important for parents and teachers to help children relieve daily distressing emotions so that issues don't pile up and turn into emotional, behavioral or physical problems. EFT provides an excellent resource that engages children at a high level of enthusiasm and participation as long as it is introduced in a way that resonates for them, both developmentally and individually.

## What is 'Magic Tapping'?

As described above, when dealing with a problem that has been of concern for some time, parents should treat themselves for the things their child does that upset them. This should be done every day for at least one week before involving the child so that the parents can approach the introduction of EFT to the child from a place of loving neutrality. Remember that emotions get transferred from parents to children who then become the barometers of the emotional climate in the family.

Choose a time when the child feels safe and comfortable—a time when the parent can work with him or her without getting personally triggered. If one starts the protocol and discovers that there is distress or upset, stop the session, treat the feelings that come up, and try again at another time. The setup statement might be something like:

⚜ *When I start to talk to Kate about her bed wetting (fighting me getting dressed in the morning, separation anxiety at day care), I feel frustrated and angry, but I deeply and profoundly love and accept myself anyway*

REMINDER PHRASE:  *"This frustration"* or whatever comes to mind at each point (the 'stream of consciousness' technique).

Using words appropriate to the child's level of maturity, parents then discuss the problem and suggest that they have something that might help. If the child is old enough suggest a 'game' that will help with the problem, or, for older children, ask if he is interested in trying it.

If the child is engaged, and interested in playing the 'Magic Tapping' Game (or it could be called the 'Simon Says' Game), that is a good time to begin. If not, don't force the issue. Parents continue to tap on their own frustration that the child doesn't want to participate, then surrogately tap for the child's issue, pretending to be the child, or using a favorite doll or stuffed animal {see *Surrogate Tapping for Animals* and *EFT and Magic Buttons Bear*}.

For example, pretending to be Kate:

⚜ *Even though I wet the bed at night, mommy still loves me/I'm still a good girl/I'm doing the best I can.*

Tap a few rounds having the last round be in the positive:

✶  *. . . I choose to sleep through the night, and wake up dry and happy.*

Do this in front of the child unless he rebels or wanders off. Complete it in any case. If he is interested, he can tap on herself, on the parent, or on a favorite doll or stuffed animal.

Another method is for parents to gently tap or caress the points on the child. It all works, not instantly in all cases, but persistence pays off, and soon the family will be happily tapping on other issues as the priority issue fades.

Ideally, this will be done a couple of times a day when the problem has not just been triggered for you or the child.

It is also advisable to do EFT whenever the problem is activated. For example: Kate is at day care having a tantrum. Mom kneels down to Kate's level, gently rubs her chest (sore spots) or taps her karate chop point (side of her hand). Mom then says something like:

✶  *Even though you don't want Mommy to leave, you are still a good girl and Mommy loves you.*

Mom goes through the EFT points starting by gently rubbing the top of Kate's head and either rubs, taps, or just touches the points with phrases like:

TOP OF HEAD:   *I know you don't want Mommy to leave.*
EYEBROW:   *Remember you always have fun at day care.*
SIDE OF EYE:   *It's okay to be angry with Mommy.*
UNDER EYE:   *You don't want Mommy to leave.*
UNDER NOSE:   *Mommy will be back this afternoon after your snack.*
UNDER LIP:   *Sad that Mommy is leaving.*
COLLARBONE:   *Scared that Mommy is leaving.*
UNDER ARM:   *It's okay to have fun at day care.*

Usually, one to three rounds of tapping will calm the child if the right words are being used. Always pay close attention to the specific words the child is saying and incorporate them into the EFT. For example:

✶  *Even though you don't want Mommy to leave, you are still a good girl.*

REMINDER PHRASES:  *"You don't want Mommy to leave."*

## How is tapping with children different from tapping with adults?

With infants and pre-verbal toddlers one doesn't need to get an intensity rating. It will be dramatic when the energy is clear because the behavior will stop, toddlers will get bored and go off to play. Infants often fall asleep.

With a preschooler or school age child it is often helpful to find out how much a problem is bothering them by having the child hold his or her hands wide apart to indicate a huge problem and closer together as the intensity goes down.

Older children can use a pictorial scale or the usual 0—10 rating

Once the child has learned EFT and is comfortable using it, encourage her to do it whenever distressing thoughts, feelings or events effect her day. EFT is often most effective when performed in the actual moment of distress.

Once language is developed to the point where the child can tell a story, utilizing the 'Tell The Story Technique' or the 'Movie Technique' gives a double benefit. In addition to tapping away any intensity, the child has the full attention of a loving adult which, in itself, can be enormously healing.

Daily use of EFT is recommended by Gary Craig, who suggests that parents sit with the child at bedtime and ask about the good and bad parts of the child's day, or the good and bad thoughts of the day, tapping away any distress that may be lingering before the child settles down to sleep. This is especially useful with children who have nightmares and other sleep disturbances.

## A brighter future

By resolving issues on a daily basis, children are less likely to accumulate what we call 'emotional baggage'—the negative beliefs, limiting identities and learned limitations that prevent us from attaining our highest potential as adults. Consistently done, from an early age, EFT has the potential to launch the next generation into adulthood with self-confidence, the courage to take risks, and to stand by their convictions. They will be smarter, more creative, and less violent. They will have learned how to remove blocks to peak performance, identify and neutralize difficult emotions before they get out of hand, and they will be more likely to view the world as a place of unlimited possibility. What a wonderful world that will be.

# AUTHOR'S BIOGRAPHY AND CONTACT DETAILS

Nancy Gnecco, ACEP Diplomat, EFT Master has extensive training in energy psychotherapy modalities. An international speaker and teacher with a Masters' Degree in Education and a Professional Counseling Licensure, Nancy maintains a private, clinical energy psychotherapy practice in Kennebunk, Maine in which she has specialized in using Emotional Freedom Techniques and other energy psychotherapy modalities for twelve years. For more information please visit her website www.nancygnecco.com.

## REFERENCES

1. http://www.helpguide.org/mental/stress_signs.htm

# EFT for Turning Points

PETER GRAHAM, EFT MASTER, EFTCERT-HONORS

## What do you mean by Turning Points?

The following approaches are designed to help with painful experiences that have been 'turning points' for the worse, especially pivotal events that have had lasting negative consequences or repercussions. This could be any emotionally painful event that has had an adverse impact thereafter in a person's life, or a particular event that keeps coming up and has been the source of ongoing or recurring suffering.

## Should I use conventional EFT first?

The Emotional Freedom Techniques include an extremely effective group of techniques for dealing with trauma and other painful memories: i.e. the Tell the Story Technique, the Movie Technique and the Tearless Trauma Technique. These techniques are thorough and amazingly effective when used skillfully and are consistently used by EFT practitioners around the world.

None of the approaches described below is intended as a replacement or alternative for these essential EFT techniques, which should be thoroughly used first. The techniques and processes below can be considered as further ways of finding or uncovering additional related aspects.

There is no specific order in which these methods should be used. Gather information from and listen to the client to determine which approach or approaches would be most appropriate, and trust your intuition.

# 1. Personal Dialogues

After doing the Tell the Story technique or the Movie technique successfully with a particular event, it can sometimes be useful to test this by asking the client to talk directly to the key person or persons about that experience as if they were present right now.

## How can I use this approach to talk directly to the person involved?

Asking the client what she would like to say to a key person involved in the experience may bring up additional aspects that wouldn't otherwise have come up just by telling the story. This would only be used when it is suspected that there may still be some more associated aspects to be found. This may be the case when the person is clearly not cheerful or appears to be somewhat introspective or when your intuition raises this possibility.

EDITOR'S NOTE:
This is very similar to one of the steps of Matrix Reimprinting.

Example question:
- *"If (person involved) were with us here right now, what would you like to say to (him) about this particular experience?"* (limited to this particular experience, not any other events or issues).
Additional questions:
- *"OK, what else would you like to say to (person) about this experience?"* and/or
- *"Is there anything else you'd like to say to (person) about this experience?"*

The best way to do this is to get the client to speak and express herself as if she is actually talking directly to that person (or people) right now. If needed, you can use an empty chair and get the client to imagine the person in that chair right now. Do EFT on anything that comes up that has emotional intensity. Then ask the same or a similar question again to see if there is anything else, and continue in this way until she has said what she wants or needs to say. Gently draw the person out. Make it clear that it's very OK for her to take her time while doing this or to take time out to discuss what to say or how to express it and then do some more.

## How can I use this approach to talk directly to a client's younger self?

Another important dialogue is to ask the client (as she is now) to communicate with herself (as she was at the time of the event) in a nurturing, encouraging and/or useful way. This is particularly valuable when the Self to be communicated with is a younger person or child who was wounded or overwhelmed during the life experience that is being worked on with EFT. Let the younger self know that she is accepted or approved of or loved and that she will get through this. Maybe offer some useful advice, information, validation or encouragement that the younger self can understand and which may assist the younger self to develop beyond that experience or stage in her life. Watch out for any emotional intensities and tap on them as needed.

*EDITOR'S NOTE:*
Matrix Reimprinting and Deep State Re-patterning provide effective and tested protocols for doing this. There is also a discussion in those articles about how this 3rd person approach (treating the child self as client) can help to prevent the client from associating too strongly with the emotion and thus potentially become overloaded.

Example questions:
- *"What would you like to say to yourself (or your younger or child self) as you were then about this particular experience?"*
- *"What else would you like to say to yourself (or you as a younger person or child) about what happened then?"* or similar.

In asking these or similar questions, make it very clear to the client that the questions and answers are only concerned with this one specified experience or, maybe, a group of closely related or similar experiences. A small percentage of clients have a tendency to widen the scope of such conversations to include all sorts of other events or broader issues, or to generalize. If this happens, gently bring her back to the current incident and emphasize that the focus is only on that experience.

EDITOR'S NOTE:
See also Tam Llewellyn's discussion on the importance of closely watching the client when testing the validity of practitioner interventions (the garbage and the gold), and Ann Adams' mention of the value of asking questions or painting a picture for the client.

Some clients may find it hard to know what to say and may need some assistance or even 'guided positive self-talk'. In this case, you can discuss this or educate the client in what may be useful or suggest things to the client or even feed her possible things to say (perhaps even phrase by phrase). What is communicated should be real, encouraging or nurturing, and designed to help the earlier or younger Self or Inner Child to accept what happened and move on. If the younger self is upset, then tap for her. For example:

⚡ *Even though young Sally feels all alone . . .*

Doing this and tapping on any emotional aspects that come up helps the person to become more at peace with herself and any other people involved. Clients tend to experience a more complete closure after openly expressing their own personal truths about the experience, which quite often also include forgiveness.

## 2. Forgiveness and Letting Go

From an emotional clearing point of view, the purpose of forgiveness is to facilitate acceptance, letting go and moving on. Some cultures place more emphasis on forgiveness than others. In fact many people believe that forgiveness is essential to set themselves free, whereas others hold that we can acknowledge the truth of what happened and simply let go and get on with our lives. Either way, the end result is what is important.

It can sometimes be appropriate to mention to a client and discuss that forgiving someone does not mean that one is endorsing or condoning what happened, nor does it mean pushing it aside or downplaying it.

The simple truth is that when we don't or can't forgive or let go, we continue suffering. Forgiveness is a natural way of getting to acceptance and letting go and it can help to set us free.

Without forcing or directly suggesting or requiring forgiveness, one can raise the subject of forgiveness by asking a question such as:

- *"How do you feel about forgiveness in relation to this?"* and/or
- *"Do you feel that forgiveness may be at all relevant here?"*

This reveals where the client stands on this issue. Often, just raising the subject will bring up more aspects or blocks to forgiveness that can then be tapped on. How can someone forgive another person, even when she wants to, when she is still angry or suffering? These feelings, issues or consequences need to be acknowledged and tapped on.

It is often fruitful to ask the following questions:

- *"Do you feel unforgiving towards . . . . ?"* and if appropriate
- *"Tell me about that?"*

You can then safely tap on what comes up (e.g. ***"I feel unforgiving towards Joey"***) without forcing the issue of forgiveness. An option here is to dig deeper by asking the client to complete:

- *"I feel unforgiving towards . . . because . . ."*

which will often bring up things that are in the way of letting go. Get the client to do this several or more times to get all of them.

It can also be very important to ask:

- *"Do you feel unforgiving towards yourself over this?"*

Then, if needed, ask the client to say and complete:

- *"I feel unforgiving towards myself because .. . . ."*

This can bring up residual aspects that can then be tapped on. It often helps to also tap on *"I did the best I could at the time"* when the person has trouble forgiving herself.

Another option is to discuss her ideas about 'letting go' and, if it appears appropriate, ask the following and take it from there:

- *"Is there anything in the way of you letting go?"* or
- *"Is there anything in the way of you forgiving . . . ?"*

It is usually much harder to forgive or let go when the perpetrator has taken little or no responsibility for his actions or inactions that caused harm, or when he continues to deny or justify his actions or inactions. If letting go of something depends on someone else's actions, then we may be waiting a very long time. If appropriate and when the person is ready for it, the client could tap on something like:

⚜ *I choose to forgive . . . for . . . .*

If a client has no intention or desire to forgive someone or sees no need to, but does want to move on, tap on something like:

⚜ *I choose to let go of that*

⚜ *I choose to move on*

⚜ *I choose to accept that it happened and move on*

The wording could be based on clues present in the way the client expressed herself on the issue or on what her preferred position is, even if it's *"Frankly, I don't give a damn."*

## 3. Beliefs and Decisions

It is often the case that a significant change in a person's belief or beliefs occurs following a seriously painful event or a series of less intense but related experiences (see *The Bundling Baggage Technique*). Typically, an earlier positive (i.e. useful) belief has been weakened or invalidated by the experience and replaced by a new belief that is limiting, negative or downright harmful. Such a belief, thought or story can generate, precipitate or predispose experiences thereafter in his or her life. This shift in beliefs can be life-changing, nearly always for the worse. For example, a person may believe *"I am a good person"* and after the event believe (and may be strongly attached to) *"I am a bad person"*.

A person's belief system (or a subset thereof) directly and indirectly influences how a person views, interprets, experiences and responds to the world. Every decision, choice and solution depends on his or her relevant beliefs and viewpoints at that time. Thus, working with a person's negative beliefs can be beneficial in related areas of her life or in life generally.

## How can I work with 'beliefs'?

Clearing traumatic events with the Movie Technique or Tell the Story Technique will often resolve such beliefs and result in positive cognitive shifts. Sometimes, however, a person has become thoroughly attached to a negative belief and it consistently manifests in her thinking, interpreting and responding. Such a belief needs to be specifically identified and its associated negative energy discharged. EFT is an effective tool for working with negative or limiting beliefs and one way is to use:

   ⚡ *Even though I have the belief that . . .*

   REMINDER PHRASE: *the belief that . . .*

The questions below can help to identify or bring to the surface beliefs that were formed during or after a painful event and which adversely affected the person's life. The beliefs themselves should be tapped on as well as any related emotions or feelings that show up. The person's beliefs may have had negative consequences or set up patterns in her life and it can be beneficial to also identify and inspect these consequences and tap on them as well. Often, there has been more than one consequence and it's important to identify all of them.

The following questions have been found useful in identifying core beliefs which can then be tapped on along with related aspects that may show up:

- *"What did you come to believe as a result of this experience?"*
- *"What have been the consequences in your life from having that belief (or thought or story)?"*
- *"Have there been any other consequences from you having that belief (or thought or story)?"*

Get all the consequences.

Some individuals generate numerous thoughts and beliefs and asking for a conviction may help to zero in on a core belief:

- *"What did you become strongly convinced about during or as a result of this experience?"*
- *"What have been the consequences of having that belief (or thought or story) in your life?"*
- *"Have there been any other consequences that have come from you having that belief (or thought or story)?"*

A conclusion is a type of belief and asking for it can help to identify what the person is left with after the experience:

- *"What conclusion was reached during (or as a result of) this experience?"*
- *"What have been the consequences of that conclusion in your life?"*
- *"Any other consequences?"*

There can be more than one conclusion so it's worth asking the first question a number of times but, usually, there is a main or central one that needs to be thoroughly tapped on.

Certain lessons learned from an experience can also cause problems by locking the person into a particular viewpoint in the area concerned. It may be useful, before asking the following questions, to draw the client's attention to the fact that a lesson or learning can be positive, neutral or negative. We are interested in tapping on the unhelpful, negative or destructive lessons that need to be unlearned to make some room for useful new lessons. Ask:

- *"What did you learn from that experience?"*
- *"What have been the consequences of that lesson in your life?"* and
- *"Any other consequences?"*

There can sometimes be a number of 'lessons' (that support and reinforce each other), so it may be worthwhile to also ask the following question several times:

- *"What else did you learn from that experience?"*

## How can I work with 'decisions'?

Decisions and resolutions are closely related to beliefs and should be handled in a similar way. Decisions are preceded by a conclusion, realization or belief.

Decisions made during or after a traumatic event tend to be 'set in concrete' by the emotional pain and can last a lifetime. Their influence can be like post-hypnotic suggestions, for example: *"Don't ever go near a horse"* or *"I'll never trust another person as long as I live."* In such cases, you might ask:

- *"What decisions (or resolutions) were made during or as a result of this experience?"* and
- *"What have been the consequences in your life of that decision or resolution?"*
- *"Any other consequences?"*

There can be multiple decisions, but there is usually a main one that needs to be found and thoroughly discharged with EFT.

## 4. Interpretations

*'Understand that you do not respond to anything directly, but to your interpretation of it. Your interpretation thus becomes the justification for the response'.*

FROM 'A COURSE IN MIRACLES'.

The response cycle consists of:
1. an event or happening which is observed or experienced
2. followed by an interpretation
3. which leads to a response.

The response depends on, and is directly determined by, the interpretation. An interpretation gives a certain meaning to what happened and it usually has its origins in the person's belief system. An interpretation is essentially a belief such as a meaning, conclusion, judgement, assumption, expectation, definition or prediction. When an interpretation changes, the response spontaneously changes.

### How can I work with 'interpretations'?

One option is to ask how the person interpreted the experience as a whole. Another option is to enquire into how she interpreted the worst parts or most intense parts of the event, and tap on these interpretations. An interpretation may be fixed and unchanging to start with and tapping on it may help to release the emotional charge connected with it and loosen up the person's attachment to it. This opens the door to viewing the experience differently. When a new interpretation or insight emerges, a cognitive shift has occurred.

When an incident has already been thoroughly worked over but the client is still distressed about it or a particular part of it, clarify what the client's emotional response was and locate precisely what happened during the event when she started to get that emotion or feeling. Then, find out what the interpretation was, in that moment or sometimes after what occurred, that led directly to that emotional response. Tap on that interpretation until it no longer triggers anything.

For example, if a person is angry about something, find out what actually happened that made the person angry, when the anger began, and then get the related interpretation(s) by using questions such as:

- *"What did that mean to you (when that happened)?"* or
- *"How did you take that?"* or
- *"What was your interpretation of that at the time"* or
- *"What was the first thought or idea that came into your head when that happened?"* or similar.

If a client's attachment to an interpretation does not shift or the person continues to hang onto it, ask:

- *"Where does that belief or idea come from?"* or
- *"Have you had that same idea or thought before?"* or
- *"What did that (what happened) remind you of?"* or similar.

Such an interpretation may have underlying origins which predisposed the person to interpret that way. Once identified, resolve it with EFT and then re-visit the trigger point in the more recent event to test it and see if there's any remaining emotional intensity.

## 5. Identities

Following a heavy traumatic event, it is not uncommon for the person involved to say things like *"I want to be myself again"* or *"I don't like who I've become"* or

*"This isn't the real me."* Comments like these show recognition of a change of personality or similar that occurred as a result of the experience. Sometimes, however, there is no such recognition, especially when the person is stuck firmly in victim mode.

The events that have the greatest impact in our lives are those events that were painful and overwhelming. These were times when the person felt powerless and had no effective answer or response to what was happening at that time. She was overwhelmed or felt annihilated or defeated by it, whether by the pain, force, shock, confusion, shame, unpreparedness, naivety or similar. The person did the best she could at that time based on her assessment of the situation and her viewpoint, understanding, knowledge, skills, experience, maturity, degree of preparedness or similar. The 'me', as she was at that time, was not able to cope or respond effectively.

This 'me' or Self could be a wounded Inner Child who is four years old, or a naïve teenager out of her depth, or a person who was severely traumatized when she was much older. When the relevant event is triggered, the person temporarily becomes (and acts out being) that same 'me' as in the original incident with her associated state of mind. Sometimes, a person gets stuck with being that 'me' or identity and remains in that state of mind, in a trance state, and the world is viewed and interpreted from that viewpoint.

## How can I work with 'identities'?

The following questions, and tapping on what comes up emotionally, can help the person to wake up from that trance state and can open a door to 'stepping out' of the identity. Before asking these questions, it may be appropriate to introduce and discuss the concept of a Self or 'part of me' or 'identity' or 'wounded Inner Child' having its origins in one or more painful events.

- *"Who (or what) did you become as a result of that experience?"* Describe in detail.
  Another approach is to ask:
- *"Who (or what) were you before that experience?"* and
- *"Who (or what) were you after that experience?"* Describe each in detail.

Having identified a particular self or part, get the person to describe that Self or 'me' or identity in as much detail as possible to notice the personality traits, characteristics, qualities, attitudes or beliefs of that particular beingness.

Note them all down and tap on each of the traits or characteristics that are intense and also on any other intense aspects that show up. Ask for all the personality traits of this Self. If a client has trouble doing this, it can be helpful to find some specific occasions when that Self was fully active and operational and notice all the traits, characteristics, attitudes, qualities and beliefs of that identity in that context.

---

This can be powerful stuff and may bring about profound changes as it helps the person to become the CONSCIOUS OBSERVER of the identity instead of UNCONSCIOUSLY BEING that identity.

---

It assists her to cease compulsively identifying with it and to step out of it and wake up from the trance. It can take some doing to keep on track and to deal with the things that show up, so take good notes and be systematic.

Some of the personality traits or characteristics may have heavy emotional charge or specific painful events connected with them and, if so, these may need to be thoroughly tapped on. When completed, come back to the traits of the identity and continue from there unless it's already fully resolved.

## 6. Different Perspectives

The Tell the Story Technique and the Movie Technique are consistently and extremely effective when used skillfully. Both involve telling the story as it happened and tapping on any intense parts of the story as they arise and doing this several times until the story can be told without any emotionally intense moments or parts.

This EFT approach systematically removes the person's reactions (automatic responses) to various parts of the event. It does this by helping the person to get to where she can accept what happened at each point without a compulsive impulse to resist what happened or withdraw from the pain. When all the parts of the event have been accepted, the incident as a whole becomes simply *"something that happened"*.

There are several specialized ways of using the same Tell the Story approach when a particular event has been a serious turning point for the worse, or when progress is slow and heavy-going, or the person isn't coming out of the associated trance, or when she may be disassociated from it and have no feelings. The methods below provide different ways of viewing or experiencing the event and can help to access aspects that may otherwise remain inaccessible.

## How can I work from the perspective of feelings or emotions?

Get the client to recognize or identify and name each of the feelings and emotions that existed at every point along the way (during the original incident) as the story is told and tap on any that have any intensity now. You may need to repeatedly ask questions like:

- *"What did you feel at this point of the incident?"* or
- *"How did you feel when . . . .?"* or
- *"What emotion came up in you when . . . .?"* or
- *"How did you react to . . . .?"* (or variations thereof)

Ask these question as each part or segment of the experience is related, especially when you would reasonably expect an emotional response in that moment. This approach can be especially useful when the 'repression lid' is still firmly in place or the person is strongly avoiding going there. In some instances, it is best to get the person to tell the story in the first person (e.g. *"I am walking in the door and looking at the mess")* as if she is actually there experiencing it.

## How can I work from the perspective of perceptions?

We experience life through various channels of perception. The following method can open up a client's perceptions and reduce resistance to what happened. It also lessens the resources normally allocated to keeping the 'repression lid' on the person's feelings. The approach consists of noticing and naming (where possible) her sights, sounds, motions (self and external), smells, touches, physical sensations, energetic vibrations, and/or tastes at each distinct point during the experience and especially where there is likely to be some intensity or reaction. It is usually best to go through the event (i.e. Tell the Story Technique {see *Glossary*}) a number of times, each time asking for only one (or two) particular perceptions all the way through to the end point, and then go through it again asking for a another perception (or two), etc.

However, some clients can easily do several or all of them as they relate what happened.

In using these approaches, make sure the client goes through each experience from beginning to end and does not get sidetracked by his or her opinions about what happened or related issues or other events. The client needs to understand that what is required is that the story is told as it happened at the time, in sequence, without any added commentary or analysis of what happened.

## 7. Trigger Points

There can be one or more trigger points within a single traumatic experience. In other words, when the event was happening, one or more earlier unresolved experiences or issues were triggered which added to the intensity or overwhelm of the later experience. This phenomenon is quite common. EFT is exceptional in that it will often rapidly reduce the later event's emotional intensities even when there are underlying issues or events. However, this is not always the case, especially when what was triggered was traumatic and overwhelming.

When a specific trigger point in a traumatic experience was distressing or overwhelming and doesn't resolve easily with EFT, ask questions such as:

- *"What did that remind you of?"* (or similar) or
- *"Has something like that happened before?"* (or similar) or
- *"Have you experienced that exact same feeling before?"* or similar.

When asking these questions, one is referencing a specific part of or moment in the experience. This will often uncover an underlying issue or experience that may have predisposed the person to react the way she did and/or magnify the intensity of her reactions to it. These questions can, on occasion, also be asked of the event as a whole when that seems appropriate.

### How can I work with 'trigger points'?

As a person can be reminded of all types of things, such as moments, events, people, places, smells, patterns, sounds, and so on, how you use EFT to resolve what comes up depends on the nature of what it is. When completed, return to the event and re-visit the previously intense moment in it and test it to see if it's still intense. Usually, it won't have any remaining intensity.

Sometimes, just recognizing the existence of an underlying issue or event can be enough to return it to a dormant state or at least lessen its intensity. If needed, tapping on the fact of being reminded of something tends to break or weaken the link between the later event and the triggered earlier event by bringing it into consciousness. If the client is very emotional about the connection with the earlier event and you want to cool things down first, you can tap on: *"This event reminded me of that"* substituting the *"this"* and the *"that"* with an actual happening or thing. For example, you could tap on:

> ⚡ *"The look on Polly's face reminded me of my uncle"* or

> ⚡ *"The thought of ringing Joe reminded me of the time he yelled at me"*.

When things have cooled down and the time feels right, use EFT to work on the earlier event. There may, however, be times when simply returning the earlier event to a dormant state is all that is required or appropriate in the current session.

## 8. What You Resist, Persists

If you have thoroughly worked with a painful event but the person still seems attached to it or stuck in it or remnants of it still remain, the following questions may be useful. They help the client to explore what and how she is resisting or isn't accepting certain things relating to that experience. This is another way of being more specific.

This approach is based on the principle that 'what you resist, persists'. The person is still resisting one or more things now that isn't or aren't happening anymore and this (or these) need to be uncovered and brought into the light, and tapped on so that the person can cease resisting them.

### What if my client is still attached to the painful event?

The following can be about an incident as a whole or may address a specific part of or moment in the incident (such as the worst part or the most distressing moment). Ask:

- *"In relation to this moment (or incident), what are you resisting?"* and tap on what comes up (e.g. **"I am resisting going there"**).

Then, ask the same question again and tap on what now comes up (e.g. **"I am resisting being judged"**). Continue this until there are no more answers or a noticeable shift occurs such as a cognitive shift or a waking up experience. Then, just to be thorough, ask:

- *"Is there anything you are still resisting now about that moment (or incident)?"* and tap on that, for example: **"I am still resisting admitting I got it wrong"**.

Then, ask the same question again till there are no more answers to tap on or a noticeable shift occurs.

The following questions can also be asked if needed (referring in each instance to the same moment or event) as resistance can take on many forms:

- *"What are you not accepting in this moment (or this event)?"*
- *"What are you still not accepting about that moment (or that event)?"*
- *"Is there anything you are avoiding in this moment (or event)?"*
- *"Is there anything you are still avoiding regarding that moment (or event)?"*
- *"Is there a reality you are not accepting in this moment (or event)?"* and
- *"Is there a reality you are still not accepting concerning that moment (or event)?"*

Get all the available answers to each of the above questions (or until a noticeable shift occurs) and tap on each answer that has some intensity. For instance: **"I am not accepting that I lost the game"** or **"After all these years, I am still trying to avoid that horrible smell"**. If the same resistance comes up again, then tap on it again. Usually, the resistance fades away, the intensity lessens and the person becomes more alert and present. Doing this gets the client to acknowledge and bring into consciousness these various forms of sub-conscious resistance.

## Some concluding remarks

These methods of approach have proven to be very useful for unearthing or revealing more aspects that need to be resolved. As mentioned earlier, these approaches can be used selectively or in any order. They all aim to help the client to clear his or her emotional baggage more thoroughly and efficiently.

## AUTHOR'S BIOGRAPHY AND CONTACT DETAILS

Peter Graham, certified EFT master, is a highly experienced counselor, facilitator, trainer and relationship coach. He has been using EFT in his full time emotional clearing practice in Perth, Western Australia, for over eight years. Peter has found EFT to be the most effective, flexible and useful set of tools he has ever applied and uses a number of innovative ways to assist individuals to wake up into the now from their negative emotional states. As well as doing private EFT sessions, Peter runs EFT workshops from beginner to professional levels and holds the view that quality EFT depends on quality training.

Web site: www.tap4peace.com.au
Email:      pgraham@tap4peace.com.au

# Healing the Future with EFT

RUE ANNE HASS, EFT MASTER, EFTCERT-HONORS

No matter what issues we are dealing with, learning to elicit the positive intention in a person or a situation is about the most powerful, heartening spiritual practice I can think of.

You probably have heard about 'psychological reversals', or 'emotional saboteurs'. Maybe you know that the beginning setup statement in EFT is designed to treat these reversals. I think of them as our internal goodness, distorted, that often seems to show up disguised as the problems in our lives.

At some point in our personal history, a particular behavior, symptom, or belief system appeared to be the best, or safest or maybe the only option available to us. It may still be operating in us now. It feels like who we are now, our identity. We don't question it. We soldier on with it. Maybe we got so used to doing/seeing/feeling that way that we didn't even notice when the saboteur began to cause more trouble than it solved.

But deep inside this behavior or thought or pain, there still glows the need and desire and deserving of the safety and fostering that we are still trying to get for ourselves. It is showing up distorted into a problem now, but there is goodness at its center.

## Can problems really be like Dark Angels in our lives?

Yes, that's exactly what I'm saying. When EFT 'doesn't work' it is often because we haven't yet identified the positive intention behind what seems to be the problem. When you are feeling under siege by an apparently negative emotion, behavior, symptom, or belief, ask the following questions—and expect interesting answers! Turn all the information you come up with into tapping setup statements.

- What might be the positive intention of that emotion/behavior/symptom?
- If the part of you that is running that behavior were trying to get something *for* you, what would it be?
- This sure is getting my attention. What could be good about it?
- What is a context in which this would be useful behavior?
- If the part of me running this symptom/behavior could have access to other, more powerful and much more effective strategies to get the safety/protection/love/attention it has been trying to get for me, would it be interested?

Hmmm . . . what else could I do to get what I really want?

SHOULD I KEEP THE PAIN TO MAKE SURE I LEARN THE LESSON?

I did a telephone session with a woman who asked a wonderful question relating to healing chronic pain. She has had fibromyalgia for 20 years. This was our first session, and she was just beginning to explore EFT as a treatment modality. She had done a little on her own, but hadn't worked with anyone else before using EFT in our session.

After I had gathered some information about her concerns, I asked what particular symptom or pain did she want to work with right now? Well, she said, she had a prior question she needed an answer to before we began.

Was there a chance, she asked, that EFT could be used as an 'aversion strategy'? I asked her what she meant.

"I believe that life is meant to be experienced", she said, seriously. "I don't want to take away the pain if that means I am just taking the easy way out. Is there a lesson for me here that I will miss if EFT takes away the pain? I want to evolve! I don't want to foster the laziness in me. I don't want to not be proactive."

I think that this is one of the most important messages that the EFT/Tapping community can give to the self-growth community at large—the idea that transformation and growth do NOT need to be accompanied by huge amounts of pain and suffering.

I found that very touching. Here she had been in pain for 20 years, and was willing to continue to be in pain if there was still something to be learned from it. Only someone really strong and determined could say that! Or—someone who was 'getting something' from enduring the pain.

How many of us believe that we must endure great hardship in order to evolve into our higher spiritual purpose? While I really honored her desire to learn and evolve, I thought her strength and willingness to 'take it in the name of growth' were seriously misguided.

I personally don't believe that we are meant to suffer IN ORDER to learn. I do believe that our suffering is meant to get our attention, and let us know that there is something awry, something skewed in our personal belief system.

But I want to advance the heretical thought that we can learn just as easily, and better in fact, when we are relaxed and comfortable and looking forward to the creative possibilities instead of back toward all that we have not done perfectly. In my opinion, suffering seldom serves a higher purpose. I think that if it hurts, that is not good. I don't believe in *"No pain, no gain!"*

If this woman has been hurting for 20 years she is definitely not taking the easy way out! She is not lazy. But her strength and resolve are being misdirected: positive intentions, bad strategy.

## Can you give me an example of what you mean?

Coming back to that point about getting something from enduring the pain, it reminds me of a story that I heard about the Japanese soldiers in World War II. In their book: 'The Heart of the Mind' [1], Connirae and Steve Andreas tell about the Japanese garrisons of soldiers who remained on thousands of tiny islands in the Pacific Ocean. Most of these garrisons were dismantled after the war, but there had been so many that some were entirely missed.

The soldiers on these islands often took to the caves, struggling to stay alive and true to the mission that they took on to protect and defend their motherland. They maintained their tattered uniforms and rusting weapons as best they could, longing to be reunited with their central command. Even thirty years after the war had ended, these few remaining soldiers were still being encountered by natives, tourists, and/or fishing boats.

Consider the position of such a soldier. As the Andreas' say: 'His government had called him, trained him, and sent him off to a jungle island to defend and protect his people against great external threat. As a loyal and obedient citizen, he had survived many privations and battles throughout the years of war. When the ebb and flow of battle passed him by, he was left alone or with a few other survivors. During all those years, he had carried on the battle in the best way he could, surviving against incredible odds. Despite the heat, the insects, and the jungle rains, he carried on, still loyal to the instructions given to him by his government so long ago.'

They ask: 'How should such a soldier be treated when he is found? It would be easy to ridicule him, or call him stupid to continue to fight a war that had been over for 30 years.'

But the Japanese government, bless them, took a very different tack with these old soldiers.

The Andreas' continue: 'Instead, whenever one of these soldiers was located, the first contact was always made very carefully. Someone who had been a high ranking Japanese officer during the war would take his old uniform and samurai sword out of his closet, and take an old military boat to the area where the lost soldier had been sighted.

The officer would walk through the jungle, calling out for the soldier until he was found. When they met, the officer would thank the soldier, with tears in his eyes, for his loyalty and courage in continuing to defend his country for so many years. Then he would ask him about his experiences, and welcome him back.

Only after some time would the soldier gently be told that the war was over, and that his country was at peace again, so that he would not have to fight any more. When he reached home he would be given a hero's welcome, with parades and medals, and crowds thanking him and celebrating his arduous struggle and his return and reunion with his people.'

## Can parts of us be just like those soldiers?

I told this story once to a class of people learning EFT. As I finished, I noticed that one woman had tears spilling from her eyes. I asked her if she would be willing to talk about what she was experiencing. She said:

> "I was feeling so sorry for those soldiers, and so moved by how they were treated, and then I realized that this is how I need to treat myself. For so long I have ridiculed or criticized or tried to shut away those parts of me that react so automatically in stuck ways that I don't like myself for.
>
> "I could see how those parts of me are just like those soldiers. When I was little, the temper tantrum, or the crying might have worked, sort of, but those ways of dealing with hard times or difficult people don't work anymore. They just make things worse now! And then I just shut down, and grinned and bore it (but I wasn't doing much grinning). That doesn't work either.
>
> "I have been still fighting battles that have long since ended, and then fighting with myself for doing that. But I can't seem to stop! I get so mad at myself! But hearing this story made me realize that there are parts of me that have just been trying to protect me and keep me safe, and they have been doing their best. But they just have those old tattered uniforms and rusty weapons that don't work anymore.
>
> "Some part of me is probably thinking, I have been this way for so long, I think of it as just who I am. And then the scary question comes—who would I be without these behaviors? How do I know who I really am?
>
> "At least now I know that I should, and can, honor those old soldiers in me. They were just doing the best they could. They meant well. They were trying to protect me when I felt I couldn't protect myself. Once I honor them for what they were trying to get for me, maybe I can find other, better ways to get what I really want, deep inside."

## So what are our Dark Angels or Inner Soldiers?

I believe that our 'Dark Angels' are really these 'Inner Soldiers' that have been working over time (and working overtime), trying to protect us from what we are afraid of. They might show up in our lives as pain, or illness, or allergies, or work-a-holism, or addictions, or anger, or overweight, or compulsions, or hyper-sensitivity, or . . .

These old soldiers may be trying to protect us from:

- responsibility
- new situations
- being seen
- failure
- success
- being overwhelmed
- being found out
- losing love
- being over-stimulated
- giving up guaranteed income
- getting a job
- becoming like our parents

When EFT 'doesn't work', look to these examples of Inner Soldiers who are trying to help.

## So how can I discover what my Dark Angels want for me?

Here are some questions you can ask that might help you to discover the answers:

ASK INSIDE:
- *"You, this part of me that is running this (anger, fear, overwhelm, pain, or . . . ), what are you trying to get for me?"*
- *"What are the benefits for me of feeling/acting this way?"*
- *"If I didn't have (this . . . ), what would I lose? What would be the downside?"*

USE THESE QUESTIONS TO GO DEEPER:
- *So if I had (what I am trying to get), what would having that get for me that is even more important?*
- *When I have (what I am trying to get), how will having that benefit me?*
- *What becomes possible now?*

If you keep asking these questions recursively, the answers *will* go deeper. Listen to your answers:

*Maybe what I really want is attention, not healing. In fact, my unconscious mind might be thinking "if I actually healed, would I still get as much attention?"*

*Maybe I am craving the surge of drama in my life that having the problem creates?*

*Maybe I am unconsciously thinking that if EFT works I won't have an excuse to: take care of myself / meditate / read / take self-help classes / take vacations / or see all these practitioners of healing modalities.*

*Maybe the presenting issue is a red herring or smokescreen for the real issue(s). What is it keeping me from thinking about or feeling?*

*Maybe what I want is actually a 'should', adopted to please someone else.*

*Maybe I've been working on anger, but it is really a cover for fear. Or I've been working on fear, but it is a cover for grief. Or I have been working on sadness, but it is a cover for anger. Or . . .*

Be alert to the possibilities!

## How can I build these positive intentions into my EFT setup choices?

I have done a few here, following my own intuition for the words. Try your hand at it. Doing this will help you to get a feel for the true, deeper, intention that is getting distorted and showing up as the limiting behavior:

- ⚜ *Even though I don't want to get over this problem, and I am resisting getting over it with all my strength, I love and accept myself anyway, and I choose to find better ways of keeping myself safe*

- ⚜ *Even though I am too angry to get over this, I love and accept myself, I forgive myself for being angry, and I choose to learn how to stand up for myself in ways that feel better to me*

- ⚜ *Even though I will be too vulnerable if I get over this problem, I love and accept myself anyway, and I choose to be surprised at how easy it is to discover my own inner strengths*

- ⚜ *Even though I might become powerful and successful if I heal this, and that really scares me because people who are powerful and successful are put down for being selfish—at least that's what my family believes, I love and accept myself anyway, and I choose to act powerfully and successfully in a way that includes other people and reflects their strengths. I can be humble and strong at the same time*

## How can anger (or sadness) have a positive intention?

If you have read my book, 'The 8 Master Keys for Healing What Hurts' [2], you have read much of the amazing story of Leila, who has healed herself from fibromyalgia using EFT. Also, if you have seen the 7 minute video about EFT on the www.emofree.com website, she is there, talking about her success.

We worked together to understand the positive intention of her anger. For a long time she hadn't even recognized that she was angry. It took her quite a while to tap the depths of her feelings. Over time Leila began to understand that deep inside her, anger was a message to her about herself. If she could have put her anger into words, it would have been saying something like: *"Leila— you deserve better than this."*

I always suggest to people that the angry part of them is angry because it knows that there has been injustice here. If whatever happened had been the truth about them, there would just be acceptance inside. This deep sadness or anger means that there is a deeper truth about them that is calling to be recognized and expressed and honored.

Here is part of an email that Leila wrote to me after a telephone session in which we were dealing with anger. She is coming to this realization:

". . . more importantly—I have realized how much stronger my anger is towards my mother over awful things she did to others than it is over anything she did to me. You gently pushed me a bit to recall those feelings and I came up with almost nothing but huge rage over her treatment of others.

Today I thought my way through to understanding that from a very young age I knew two things from my DAD! That I was a disappointment and that young 'soldiers' have to toughen up. So two things developed in me at the same time—an acceptance that I deserved to be thought poorly of, and a toughness to carry pain and 'keep my chin up' and not fight back against the commander—mom.

My Dad's war experience cut him off from his own sensitivities, and he saw his children's frailties as weaknesses.

So now I understand better why I have trouble recalling my buried anger directly related to mom's treatment of ME.

I thought I deserved it and that I had to learn to be tough.

It wasn't until I was a teenager that I began to feel anger—but even that was mainly about mom's treatment of others.

So the origins of my low self-esteem (and the fibromyalgia) are buried very, very deep. Whatever anger I may have felt and buried as a very young child was pushed down even further by the certainty that I was a bad girl and deserved (more than the other children) to be treated poorly—and that my ability to accept that treatment meant I was becoming a good little soldier.

No wonder I have trouble recalling anger over how I was treated, but no trouble recalling anger over how the rest of my family was treated.

That was so interesting to me just how blank I was when you asked me to specifically recall my own personal anger over how I was treated.

I'm onto it now though, and will work on getting some tappable phrases figured out. Thank you. Thank you! . . ."

Obviously writing the above email sparked her thinking, because a day later this email came:

". . . However, this fibromyalgia is dug in deep. Talking to you last Wednesday really helped me uncover a whole new aspect, when I realized that the enormous anger I carry towards my mother is mainly related to her mistreatment of OTHERS. The anger I carry about her mistreatment of ME is buried much, much deeper.

So why, why, why is that?? And ah—hah! I have finally uncovered my father's involvement!!

By the way, I do fully understand that they were doing the best they could with what they had (their own wounded selves) and the damage they did was completely unintentional—just like me—and look at the unintentional damage I did!!!!!

Yes, the lights are finally coming on here!!

So, for fibromyalgia, it feels necessary to do the 'hard work in the trenches' even after having these mental breakthroughs. Do you find that to be generally true?

Here are what I found to be tappable phrases about my father's involvement in my ability to stuff my anger way down deep into potential fibromyalgia territory. I haven't tapped on them yet, but when I do I'll let you know how it goes. I am so looking forward to breaking out of all this into the light—I know I'm already well on my way . . ."

Leila designed her own tapping routines based on these insights:

⚡ *Even though—(each of the below)—I deeply and completely love and accept myself and am open to healing the situation now.*

- *my dad treated me like I was a disappointment.*

- *my dad treated me like a young soldier who had to toughen up.*

- *my dad taught me to accept that I deserved to be thought poorly of.*

- *my dad taught me how to be tough.*

- *my dad taught me to keep my chin up and carry the emotional and physical pain.*

- *my dad taught me not to fight back against mom.*

- *my dad saw his children's frailties as weaknesses.*

- *my dad's war experience cut him off from his own sensitivities.*

- *I have trouble recalling my buried anger directly related to mom's treatment of ME.*

- *I thought I deserved it and I had to be tough.*

- *the anger I felt was pushed very far down inside.*

- *the origins of the low self esteem are buried very deep.*

- *the anger was pushed down by the certainty that I was a bad girl.*

- *the anger was pushed down by my certainty that I deserved to be treated badly.*

- *my ability to accept that treatment meant I was becoming a good little soldier, which won dad's silent approval.*

## How can I use this process to Heal the Future?

Most of our EFT training is about what to say at the beginning of the setup phrase, but I find my heart and my imagination are always drawn to the second half of the equation.

In the second half of the setup we are healing the future, supporting and honoring and welcoming our own presence in it. We are holding the 'problem' differently within our energy field, and therefore inviting and allowing ourselves to be held differently in the whole as well.

Here is where we can state our positive intention. Here is where we accept what happened in the past and how we reacted to it as being the best choice we had available to us then. Given what we knew and the situation we found ourselves in, and how important it was to protect ourselves, we were doing the best we could.

In the second half of the EFT equation we can credit ourselves for our good intentions, and heal the future by directing ourselves consciously now toward the healing path that will best serve us and our mission.

One of my clients got a lot of good results from beginning with *"Even though . . ."* stating the problem, and then adding the phrase: *"and that doesn't make me a bad person."*

Let's try it! Care for Your Soul! Use all that freed up power to appreciate yourself, instead of beating yourself up!

## Can you give me some examples of how I could use this?

Use these affirmations—or even better, make up your own:

- ✦ *Even though that happened and I am really angry about it . . . it wasn't fair . . . and I couldn't even say what I felt or be heard . . .*

  - *it is OK and safe to let myself experience that anger and that doesn't make me a bad person.*

  - *I am choosing to resist my usual story about this pain and that doesn't make me a bad person either.*

  - *that doesn't make me a bad person. These are just thoughts and I don't have to believe them*

  - *that doesn't make me a bad person and I can go ahead and feel what I feel anyway.*

  - *I wish things were different and that doesn't make me a bad person.*

  - *I love and accept myself enough that my symptoms can go away now.*

  - *I love and accept myself enough that I can just feel the wrong-ness and be OK with that anyway.*

  - *I am doing the best I can.*

  - *we are all doing the best we can.*

  - *I honor myself for how hard this has been.*

- *I can surrender what I thought I knew and open to a deeper truth about myself!*

- *I am a better person than I thought I was!*

- *soldiering on and toughing it out is not required! Healing is OK!*

A good list of suggestions for affirming phrases comes from Betty Moore-Hafter (www.holistichypnotherapyeft.com)

✣ *Even though [the negative], I deeply and completely accept myself and . . .*

- *I'm willing for this to change.*

- *I'm willing to see it differently.*

- *I'm willing to accept all of my feelings without judgment.*

- *I honor myself for facing this difficult issue.*

- *I want to bring healing to this.*

- *I'm choosing to make my peace with this and let it go.*

- *I'm ready to let go of _____*

- *I choose to know and believe_____*

- *The truth is, _____*

- *I'm open to the possibility that __*

- *I'm ok with _____*

- *I open myself to_____*

- *I'm freeing myself from_____*

- *I honor myself for how hard this has been.*

- *I honor all my feelings . . .*

- *I honor myself for . . .*

- *I honor the child part of me . . .*

- *I honor this part of me that has been trying to protect me . . . help me . . .*

- *That was then and this is now.*

- *I'm willing to forgive myself . . . I was doing the best I could . . .*

- *I'm willing to forgive ___. She (or he) was just coming from her/his human limitations and pain . . .*

❧ *Even though this _____ served me in the past . . . it no longer serves me and . . .*

- *I'm sending a message to my [part of the body] . . .*
- *I'm getting through to [this part of myself] . . .*
- *I'm sending a message to [the child within] . . . I want her/him to know . . .*
- *I surrender what I thought I knew for a deeper truth.*
- *I'm taking back my power . . . I refuse to be a victim anymore.*
- *I'm letting go of my need to control___*
- *I'm willing to let ___ be what it is*
- *I'm willing to consider that something good can come out of this—I can find some learning in this.*
- *I CHOOSE_____*
- *I choose to feel_____*
- *I choose to respond with_____*
- *I choose to be free of_____*
- *I choose not to take ___ personally*
- *I choose to respond with_____*

## SUMMARY

If something is blocking the flow of spirit through a person toward manifesting the best of him or herself in the fullest possible way, I always assume that this block has some positive intention. I think of it as a part of us that has been trying forever to get something for us, usually safety or protection. It is like a horse with blinders, a single-minded one-trick pony.

This part only knows how to do this one strategy, and it is stuck in the ON position. It doesn't realize that it is now causing you problems. It only notices that whatever it is so desperately trying to protect you from is getting worse, so it applies its strategy even more intensively.

I will ask: *"Now, if this part of you could have access to other, more powerful and much more effective strategies to get the safety/protection/love/attention it has been trying to get for you, would it be interested?"* The answer is always yes.

All of these questions make it possible to take the basic, generic recipe of EFT, and design elegant phrasing that touches the hidden parts of our psyche, using the precise words that are the keys to freeing those parts that had been caged.

The 'positive intention' questions and *"Where do you feel that in your body?"* are the two questions I ask most often, especially if some objection seems to be in the way of growth. I use them over and over, in every possible context. They are endlessly useful.

Here is another generative question to ask, when a person has begun to open to the flow of change within, and has a new sense of direction and choice. It is: *"Tell me about times in the past when you felt this positive way, or did this act of goodness, even small times."*

The purpose here is to reveal to the client that he has ALWAYS had this capacity to be smart, creative, loving, assertive, compassionate, even—especially, toward himself. And then I want to affirm to the person that every thought we think and every action we take, no matter how small, is unfolding our future. We can begin healing the future in this moment, each moment, always.

Maybe the whole cage that you have felt trapped in has had a positive intention. It has gotten your attention. It is a revelation to discover that you have been good all along! Continuing to open to the positive intention within us is the most powerful spiritual practice we can do. It changes the world each time. EFT puts the future in our hands, literally. We can be good caretakers!

## AUTHOR'S BIOGRAPHY AND CONTACT DETAILS

Rue Anne Hass is an EFT Master. She fits the temperament profile of Highly Sensitive Person, or Idealist/Healer. She has extensive training in psycho-spiritual philosophy and Energy Psychology therapies, and has been in private practice for 23 years as a counselor and Intuitive Mentor. She works with chronic physical and emotional pain and spiritual life path choices.

Her background includes seven years of university teaching, seven years as a staff member of the Findhorn Foundation in Scotland (an international non-denominational spiritual community and educational foundation), being

a wife and a mother of two young women now in their twenties. Her teaching style is open, welcoming, clear, grounded, intuitive and flexible.
www.intuitivementoring.com

## REFERENCES:

1. Connirae Andreas and Steve Andreas, 'The Heart of the Mind: Engaging Your Inner Power to Change with Neuro-linguistic Programming', (Real People Press, 1989)
2. Rue Anne Hass, M.A., 'The 8 Master Keys for Healing What Hurts' (Out Front Productions, 2006)

# Tapping for the Highly Sensitive Person

## Rue Anne Hass, EFT Master, EFTCert-Honors

Being highly sensitive has its blessings and its drawbacks, sometimes both simultaneously. Much of my work has been about how to use EFT to heal the wounds of the sensitive nature so that we are empowered to use our gifts in the service of ourselves, our families, our communities and the world itself.

Here are some ways to gather information for tapping with a sensitive person (or with yourself if you are that person). A highly sensitive person might want to learn more about their trait, and perhaps even tap for the feelings that being 'so sensitive' has brought up in them. But help them to keep in mind that everything in their experience will be more vivid, more intense, a deeper experience of pain or a richer experience of joy.

I have written this article as if you were working on yourself, but you could equally use it as a guide to helping someone else.

### How can I tell if I am a 'highly sensitive' person?

Does this describe you or anyone you know? (You may wish to tap along as you read)

- You feel emotions deeply, and you can't hide what you feel.
- You are always aware of what people around you are feeling.

- Your feelings are easily hurt by criticism or even a look, and you keep thinking about what happened, and what you might have done wrong, and what you should have done instead.
- You feel deeply for other peoples' suffering. It is difficult to watch the news or to see sad movies.
- Sometimes you can slip easily into feeling anxious or depressed, and once caught in the feeling it is hard for you to move out of it.
- You are not comfortable in large crowds, hectic environments, or around loud music. You get easily overwhelmed when there is a lot going on.
- You are a perfectionist, and you want to be helpful—so much so that you put other peoples' needs ahead of your own.
- You do your best to avoid conflicts.
- You might feel like an alien in your own family. They are practical, industrious, social, while you are quiet, imaginative, thoughtful and creative.
- You have a mission to bring peace to the world. You want to save the world from itself. You can see how good things could be, if only . . .

## What are the positive and negative aspects of being sensitive?

When I have asked groups of sensitive people what they like best and least about their sensitive trait, I have gotten answers that reflect the following qualities (again you may wish to tap along as you read):

*DRAWBACKS TO BEING SO SENSITIVE:*

- I notice more details, and when I comment on them people think I am weird
- I am too attuned to what feels like impending criticism or disapproval
- I feel socially awkward because I am not good at small talk
- I am too empathic—I feel what everyone else is feeling
- Being so sensitive makes me fearful
- I seem to vibrate with the energy around me
- I don't have good boundaries—I seem to become the other person
- I lose myself
- Every nuance of a situation penetrates me
- I get nervous easily
- I try to protect everyone

- I worry about being a victim
- I put other peoples' needs before mine

*BLESSINGS OF BEING SENSITIVE:*

- I am intuitively aware of what another person may be thinking or feeling
- Being sensitive is a great early warning system
- Being so empathic makes me very understanding
- I can 'step into another's shoes'
- I am able to see/sense to the heart of a matter
- I am deeply attuned to beauty
- The 'poetry' of everything comes through
- I have a deep connection with spirit
- I have a richer set of experiences that some others might
- I have a different more finely tuned sense of humor that is deeper, and more readily available
- I can see the beauty in almost anything
- I see wholeness, always, everywhere

## How can I tap on feelings about being sensitive?

- ❧ *Even though . . .*
  - *I worry that I am TOO sensitive*
  - *I feel so deeply*
  - *I am so open to others' emotions*
  - *I am easily hurt and upset*
  - *I don't like conflict*
  - *It's hard to stop feeling sad sometimes*
  - *I can't watch the news or sad or violent movies*
  - *I get depressed easily*
  - *I get overwhelmed*
- ❧ *. . . I deeply and completely love and accept myself*

You might begin later rounds of tapping with *"Especially because . . ."* and follow that with some of the positive phrases in their list. I offer some suggestions for doing this below.

✢ *Even though . . .*

- *I can't stand large crowds*
- *I can't take loud noise*
- *I don't like hectic environments*
- *I wish I were tougher and could let things roll off easier*
- *I think my sensitivity is a weakness*
- *I think something is wrong with me. It is my fault.*
- *I wish things didn't bother me so much*
- *I wish my emotions weren't so obvious to other people*
- *I wish I could let things go and not worry so much*
- *I hide my sensitivity from others*

✢ *. . . I deeply and completely love and accept myself*

## How can I use EFT to break out of the 'Cage of the PASST' (Pain, Anger, Sadness, Stress, Trauma)?

1. What have people said to you about your sensitivity?

   ✢ *Even though people have said _____, I deeply and completely love and accept myself.*

2. How has that made you feel? Where do you feel it in your body?

   ✢ *Even though I have these _____ (feelings, emotions), I deeply and completely love and accept myself.*

3. What did you come to believe about yourself as a result?

   ✢ *Even though I have these _____ (beliefs), I deeply and completely love and accept myself.*

4. Choose a specific disturbing incident from your life connected with being sensitive. Make a movie or inner story of the specific incident. Give it a title. Note the details: clear, fuzzy, movement, still, sound, silent, etc.

   ✢ *Even though I have this _____ (title) story in my body about being sensitive, I deeply and completely love and accept myself.*

Tap while you watch and feel the story unfold. Tap on the worst parts. Tap on all the aspects. Note what has changed after you tap.

## How can I use EFT to turn my problems into preferences, and to enhance, expand, enlarge and deepen my 'gifts'?

Let's start with that tapping list that framed all the problems we experience from our sensitivity, and re-frame them as our gifts. Then we can make them even better!

Now, the following words are mine. You find better ones, ones that fit you and feel good to you! Maybe you like to speak in superlatives—use those. Maybe you have more profound or more spiritual ways of expressing what is truly the best and loveliest and greatest about you—go for it! Use your best words—ones that make you light up inside!

Tap using the normal EFT points, and instead of saying *"Even though . . ."* try saying *"Especially because . . ."*. And in each case, replace the old negative phrase with the positive version, and strengthen it with the words *"I choose . . ."*:

Instead of 'I worry that I am TOO sensitive', say:

 ꙮ *Especially because I LOVE that I am so sensitive, . . . I choose to deepen and expand my sensitivity in powerful and wonderful ways.*

Instead of 'I feel so deeply', say:

 ꙮ *Especially because I have this fabulous capacity to feel deeply, . . . I choose to accept it as an honor, and learn how to share what I know in ways that are helpful.*

Instead of 'I think my sensitivity is a weakness', say:

 ꙮ *Especially because I like that I am sensitive, . . . I choose to love and appreciate and honor this powerful, world changing soul quality that I have been so blessed with. The world needs what I have to offer! I am ready to be more!*

Instead of 'I think something is wrong with me. It is my fault', say:

 ♱ *Especially because I believe that I am a good person, . . . I choose to open to what I know in my deepest heart that I can become! I love and appreciate and honor this precious being that I am!*

Instead of: 'I wish things didn't bother me so much', say:

 ♱ *Especially because I am glad that I am so aware, . . . I choose to trust the Universe to handle the problems and I use my awareness and my energy to make a difference in this world that I care so much about.*

Continue tapping beginning with the phrase *"Especially because . . .":*

 ♱ *Especially because I have this wonderful gift of being able to think and speak in abstract big picture, profound concepts, . . . I choose to deepen and strengthen my ability to be an "Imagineer," and I use my manifestation ability even better so that the goodness I sense has a space to live in, in this world.*

 ♱ *Especially because being cooperative and diplomatic is important to me, . . . I choose to break the rules that aren't working for me and make new ones that feel right, in ways that still honor other peoples' integrity and intentions.*

 ♱ *Especially because I hunger for deep and meaningful relationships, and because I make creating and maintaining a good and satisfying relationship with myself my first priority, and because I value personal growth, authenticity and integrity, . . . I choose to discover my own strengths and excellence, and do everything I can to enlarge them.*

 ♱ *Especially because I am internally deeply caring, . . . I choose to take just as good care of myself as I do of _____.*

 ♱ *Especially because I am deeply committed to the positive and the good, . . . I choose to honor that commitment to myself!*

 ♱ *Especially because I have a mission to bring peace to the world, . . . I choose a mission of bringing peace into my own life.*

 ♱ *Especially because I have a strong personal morality, . . . I choose to stand even taller in my own strong life!*

- *Especially because I often make extraordinary sacrifices for someone/something I believe in, . . . I choose MYSELF!!!!*

- *Especially because I have a good imagination, . . . I choose to find amazing ways of bringing magic into my life where there was only misery before! Evolution itself depends on how good I get at this!*

- *Especially because I think I am unusual and unique, . . . I choose to stand up for myself and express who I am with love and a light heart. No one can resist that . . .*

You may be noticing that you don't have to apply these phases ONLY to the issues of sensitivity! Ask evocative questions, and tap on the responses.

## How can I find the right issues to focus on?

While I am working with someone, I have found it helpful to hold a kind of map in my mind of the experience of being highly sensitive. It helps me to ask the right questions so I know what we might focus on. These are the elements of the map:

*HEART-BREAKING EXPERIENCES:*

Painful experiences are felt more deeply by a sensitive person, especially as a child.

Question:     *"What broke your heart?"*

*EXPERIENCES LEAD TO BELIEFS:*

Those heart-breaking experiences, large and small, can lead to beliefs about who we are and what is possible for us in life.

Question:     *"What did this experience lead you to believe about yourself, or what it is like to be in the world?"*

*WE HAD TO 'STUFF OUR FEELINGS':*

It may not be possible or safe to express the powerful anger, sadness, and fear, and shame that we feel during and after these painful experiences. Those feelings get 'stuffed' or swallowed. Stuffed feelings show up later in our lives as physical and emotional pain and illness. Most people with chronic physical and emotional pain are highly sensitive. The fear of confronting powerful feelings can stop us from beginning a healing journey.

Question:    *"What emotions and feelings does this experience bring up in you?"*

OUR FAMILIES HAD BELIEFS AND FEELINGS ABOUT BEING SO SENSITIVE, TOUGHING IT OUT, NOT STANDING OUT, OR 'MAKING YOU STRONG':

The people in our families who mistreated us did so because this is how they had been treated, and these were the beliefs and feelings they themselves took on from their own family experience. The tendency to replicate these misunderstandings and illnesses gets passed on down through the generations of a family.

Question:    *"What did your family believe about you being 'so sensitive'? Were they trying to 'toughen you up for a tough world'? Did your sensitivity threaten their own carefully covered up or denied sensitivity?"*

OUR PERSONAL HEALING CAN HEAL THE WHOLE FAMILY HISTORY:

Healing our family's history—this is on the way to healing the world! We just thought we had to *start* with healing the whole world, so that it would be a safe place for us. That was pretty exhausting. We left ourselves off our own to-do list!

Question:    *"How can you take care of yourself and your needs without thinking that you are selfish? How could taking care of yourself first be a GOOD thing?*

Hint: I like to think of selfish as spelled 'self-ish', meaning 'care of the Soul', or 'self care'.)

## Can you recommend a way to reframe my sensitivity and tap on any insights that arise?

When a sensitive person chooses a life event to explore with EFT, here is another possible protocol to follow. Of course these questions will be evocative no matter what the issue is, or how sensitive the individual!

The underlying presupposition in the tapping map is this:

✛ *Even though I don't see how I could reframe this event positively, I am open to seeing it differently, and I'm open to seeing purpose and wisdom in the event and in my own and others' response, and I deeply and completely love and accept myself, no matter what.*

1. How did you respond to the event itself? (tap)
   What were your emotions, thoughts and/or your body's response? (tap)
2. How did other people respond to the event? (tap)
   How do you feel/think about your (and others') response? (tap)
3. What regrets, sorrow or other feelings do you have about the event and its effect on you and your life? e.g. *"If only I had known, I wouldn't have suffered, wasted my life, limited myself"* etc (tap)
4. Would things have gone differently if you (and others) had known you are highly sensitive? Now that you understand that you are highly sensitive, what would you (and others) do differently in response to the event? (tap)
5. From the perspective of a wise, sensitive advisor to yourself, what wisdom do you see in your (and others') response? (tap)
6. What does the event and your response mean about you and your capacity to respond to life now?
   What was the *positive intention* of your (and others') response at the time? What were you trying to get for yourself? (tap)

Here are some of the answers that one person, now in her 50's, gave to the above questions, as she considered the effect on her life of having been raped in her senior year of high-school. An EFT tapping setup phrase can be created out of each of these answers.

*HOW DID YOU RESPOND TO THE EVENT? WHAT WERE YOUR EMOTIONS AND THOUGHTS?*

- Trauma, shock, alone, afraid, confused, felt stupid, tricked.
- The dreams of my life were shattered.
- I identified with the upset feelings of my parents more than my own feelings.
- All I wanted to do was protect my father, his reputation.

*OTHERS' RESPONSES:*

- No one knew how to deal with it.
- My mother was in shock and couldn't respond.
- My father wanted to deal with the situation but keep it quiet because of the effect it would have on his career.
- My parents did the best they could.

*IF I HAD KNOWN I WAS SENSITIVE:*

- I come from a family of warriors that has had to hide their identity.
- Pay attention to the real me, not the story about me.
- I could say "stop—I am the one who was hurt here".
- I am not as invincible as I seem.
- My mother would have been able to be there for me.
- I could ask to be held.
- I thought I had to—and could—protect everyone.
- I didn't know that I didn't know how to be safe.
- I would not have been tricked into the situation to begin with.
- I would have found help in healing the trauma at the time, rather than allowing it to shape my whole subsequent life.

*WISE ADVISOR PERSPECTIVE:*

- You were so aware of your father's stresses, and you so wanted to help.
- You were not meant to be here to sacrifice for others.
- Treat yourself as worthy.
- You are worth being protected.
- You can still care for others.
- You can live from that knowing of your own worth.
- Be empathic, continue to feel deeply, but your first priority is to protect yourself.
- This experience taught me to stand up for myself.
- When I speak up for others, I am really wanting to speak up for myself.
- I know how to walk away now.
- That experience blasted me out of the shell that had been holding me in place.
- The blessing is in understanding my sensitivity trait instead of going to blame, shame, or "I have wasted my life."

EFT is the perfect tool for a sensitive person to learn how to 'deeply and completely love and accept' ourselves first! *"I'm not 'introverted', I am reserved, self contained, independent. I am not 'shy', I love and intend to create deep and meaningful interaction."* It is remarkable that when we change our perception of ourselves we automatically change our perception of the world. And then the world changes!

> ♴ **Even though I don't see how I could reframe this event positively, I'm open to seeing it differently, and I'm open to seeing purpose and wisdom in the event and in my own and others' response, and I deeply and completely love and accept myself, no matter what.**

## How is my sensitivity influenced by my Ancestral History?

I once taught a class at an EFT conference in England on the highly sensitive temperament. Let me take you with me to that class, as if it were happening right now:

First I talk about the trait of sensitivity[1]. It is INFP in the Myers-Briggs temperament types[2], and the Idealist-Healer in the Keirsey Temperament Sorter[3]. Here is one list of aspects of this trait (sound like anyone you know?):

- Abstract in thought and speech
- Cooperative
- Introverted
- Appear reserved and shy
- Diplomatic
- Empathic
- Hunger for deep and meaningful relationships
- Value personal growth, authenticity and integrity
- Internally deeply caring
- Deeply committed to the positive and the good
- A mission to bring peace to the world
- Strong personal morality
- Often make extraordinary sacrifices for someone/something they believe in
- Imagination and evolution are the goal.
- Seek unity, feel divided inside
- Often had an unhappy childhood
- May have been raised in a practical, industrious, social family

- Didn't conform to parental expectations
- Often feel isolated, 'like an alien'
- See themselves as ugly ducklings
- Rich fantasy world as a child, may have been discouraged or punished for this by parents
- Wish to please, try to hide their differences
- Believe and are told that their sensitivity is bad
- Drawn toward purity but continuously on the lookout for the wickedness they think lurks in them
- Self-sacrificing to an extreme, in atonement for their failings
- Keep this inner struggle hidden from others

I ask people, as I often do, to share what they most like and most dislike about being so sensitive. The answers range widely and thoughtfully. On the 'like' side, they share about being grateful for their deep sense of empathy and compassion, their appreciation of beauty, a strong sense of justice, their ability to sense what is going on in another person.

On the 'dislike' side, people talk about things like feeling too open to other peoples' feelings, not having good boundaries, getting their feelings hurt so easily, and being criticized all their lives for being too emotional.

People who are sensitive seem to be born into highly critical and maybe emotionally abusive families. Appearances seem to count more than the truth of feelings. Nothing is ever good enough. It is likely that their parents were the same way, and the parents of those people, and the families before them, and on back through the generations of ancestors.

## How is this Emotional Inheritance passed from generation to generation?

Many years ago I found a fascinating, lyrical description of how this emotional inheritance might happen, written by a doctor of Chinese Medicine named William Lieske. He used to have a very informative website on acupuncture (which now appears to have disappeared from cyberspace!). Speaking about the growth of a baby in the mother's womb, he said that the first beat of the brand-new heart is a magical moment that establishes life. And then:

'... The second beat, and the first in what will determine our identity, is the amygdala. The amygdala starts forming immediately after the heart's first beat. It stores all the memories of our life in the womb, with the placenta, the water, the fluids of life and the terror of losing them, and also the joy of being fed, of bouncing, of moving. But the amygdala stores also the life of the mother, her depressions, her fears, her memories. And this accumulation of memories goes on in us till the age of three. Which means that all this time we have lived, our life has been recorded for us in the amygdala.

'After the age of three the hippocampus matures in us. In it, conscious memories are stored and we have access to them. However, in the hippocampus, we have no access to the memories and the life we lived in the amygdala of the previous three years, even if from this point on, amygdala and hippocampus converse with each other.[4]

'What happens to the memories of the amygdala? They become our individual nightmare, the invisible conditioning of all our actions, the blind spot of our lives, the origin of all our terrors, the unknown reason why we do what we do even when we do not know why we do it . . .

'The conditioning of the amygdala can only be removed by the intelligence system previous to it, and this is the heart, with its electromagnetic force and its power of transformation. Otherwise, the amygdala can act on its own, bypassing the intelligence centers of the neo-cortex. [Our limiting beliefs] keep acting, in spite of our good intentions.

I ask the group to think about their own families' beliefs and behaviors and habits. What are some of the good things? Some different examples: *"We are survivors. We get things done. We are always helpful to others. We don't complain. We are achievement oriented—very successful people."*

Then we look at the negative, limiting, rigid expectations and beliefs, the blocked skills, the pain: *"I never felt seen or heard for who I am. Their needs were always more important than mine. My talents and gifts were not appreciated. I wasn't allowed to want anything. I felt dismissed, or actively squashed. I felt so different from everyone else."*

## What if we think this IS our identity?

I ask the participants to think about their own life challenges and their experience of growing up in their families in light these beliefs and behaviors. The environment we grow up in seems to be the truth, as we know it. We think this is our identity.

We consider how these patterns and expectations are replicated in our schools, our religions, our social culture, our national identity (perhaps even, I suggest, the history of the human race itself).

I draw a shape of a vase on the flip chart. I say that it represents the saga of their ancestral family spirit replicating itself through the generations. As a spirit, an information space, a being in itself, the ancestral family spirit is always seeking to grow and expand, across space and time. Just as we do individually, the spirit may feel limited by the rigidly held habitual thinking patterns that have led to pain and dysfunction across space and time, as generation after generation incarnated, and struggled to improve their lot.

I think of each of our family spirits as forming threads in the grand tapestry of history, weaving the future of humanity and the world.

I ask the class participants to imagine that the spirit of their family is rooted in the earth. The earth is a place of instinctual, cyclical, habitual patterns. Everything on earth operates by cycle, habit, unconscious patterning, instinct. There is a vast multiplicity of forms on the earth, always metamorphosing into something new, and still they all follow the patterns set by their inner instinctual blueprint.

And I remind them to be aware of how, even in its most distorted form, their family is also an expression of the best of the human spirit, its sense of freedom and imagination, its creativity.

## How does this relate to the real legend of our ancestral family spirit?

Now I tell them a story. I invite them to imagine that their ancestral family spirit, the group 'being' that represents the thread of their whole family across the generations, wants to evolve towards a release of limitations. It puts out a call to beings that can 'stand at the edge of instinct' and be a catalyst for its inner growth of creativity and possibility.

' . . . Imagine', I say, 'that you are responding to this call. You, with the trait of sensitivity, represent a natural intention toward expansion and opening, freedom, movement, flow—the best of the spirit of Humanity—exactly what is needed to break open old structured habitual patterns of thought and behavior . . . You willingly, maybe even knowingly, come forward into this family.'

(I draw a cloud shape at the top of the vase, with 'YOU: Freedom, Creativity and Imagination' written in it)

'However!' I continue, 'Just as in our relationships with others in our lives—in a marriage, for example—we are often unconsciously invoking way more than we bargained for. As our naturally expansive generative energy contacts the constricted, contracted space of our old family patterns, there is generated apparent discord, disharmony, pain, trauma. This can be represented as a crack in the vase. You are too much for them!'

(I draw a crack down the front of the vase.)

'As the sensitive person caught in the midst of this maelstrom, we fall victim to the experience of the crack: the habitual patterns of belief and behavioral tendencies in the family/cultural identity. Maybe it is over-perfectionism, self-criticism. It might be toughing it out and soldiering on, ignoring our own pain and our own needs. Maybe the crack in our family is about beliefs about our self worth ('There must be something wrong with me! Let me out of here!'). Very likely there are feelings of anger and sadness or fear and shame. "

'What other limitations could the crack in your family spirit represent?'

## GENERATING HEALING–OUR PERSONAL GIFT

'Because we are so close to the crack it feels like our personal identity. We can't see that our intention to heal our own pain is actually generating a healing in this crack as well. And where our ancestors are now' . . . I continue, gesturing out toward space, or maybe in toward inner space (who knows where they are!) . . . 'at least some, maybe many of them, now understand this process that we are immersed in, and they stand in support of it, in support of our healing efforts. They want us to succeed!'

'So, instead of feeling broken and somehow wrong, we could think of ourselves instead as intentionally participating in an expansive evolutionary process, our personal gift to the evolution of consciousness, or the consciousness of evolution.'

'We can think of ourselves as having responded to this call with a personal mission to do what we can to transform the thread of our own family in the tapestry of humanity across space and time . . . In that sense, nothing we have done has been wasted. It is all woven in, changing the picture of everything as we ourselves change.'

And then I bring in the EFT work that we are here to explore more deeply. The essence of it is the phrase: *"I deeply and completely love and accept myself."*

I write that phrase underneath the vase, a foundation that this emerging transformation can rest upon and be held by. I add that we can even expand this thought: *"I deeply and completely accept the deeper intention of my family spirit . . . I deeply and completely accept the world as it is, and as it can become . . ."*

## How can I use this process to 'heal the heart of the world'?

I ask for an individual volunteer. Someone bravely comes forward, and we do the EFT work together on behalf of all of us, to transform the effects of a belief that was held in her family. Everyone else in the group participates too, from within their awareness of their own family patterns. In EFT this is called 'Borrowing Benefits', based on the thought that the group work generates an energy field that can be healing for everyone.

The volunteer's belief starts out being about *"You have to work hard to be successful".* This belief quickly morphs into being about her experience of her mother never letting her express any emotion. This young woman grew up thinking that her feelings must be bad—so she didn't feel them, she could only talk about them. I am noticing this. As she talks about herself, she doesn't seem to feel what she is feeling, although I can see and sense that the deep feelings are in there.

It turns out that her grandmother, her mother's mother, had also been a very repressive and judgmental person. That means to me that the great-grandmother must have had the same critical nature, and on and on . . . all these generations doing their best to survive their lives thinking the tools they were given were the only tools, thinking this was the truth. *"Life is hard. Don't make a fool of yourself",* the volunteer's mother had told her.

### A SMILING VISION OF APPROVAL

By the time our tapping work is complete, the room feels full of ancestors and light and angels. And suddenly the volunteer client has a vision of her other, dearly beloved grandmother giving her a big smile of approval!

I finish the session with some group EFT, using these thoughts:

- ☘ *Especially because I LOVE THAT I AM SO SENSITIVE, . . . I choose to deepen and expand my sensitivity in even more powerful wonderful ways.*

- ☘ *Especially because I LOVE THAT I AM SO SENSITIVE, . . . I hunger for deep and meaningful relationships so I make creating and maintaining a good and satisfying relationship with myself my first priority.*

+ *Especially because I LOVE THAT I AM SO SENSITIVE and I have a mission of bringing peace into the world, . . . I choose a mission of bringing peace into my own life. I deserve this!*

+ *I CHOOSE TO STAND UP FOR MYSELF, and express who I am with love and a light heart.*

+ *I love and appreciate and honor this world-changing soul quality that I have been so blessed with.*

+ *The world needs what I have to offer. I am ready to be more!*

## AUTHOR'S BIOGRAPHY AND CONTACT DETAILS

See 'Healing the Future with EFT' by Rue Anne Hass for biography and contact details.

REFERENCES:

1. Elaine Aron, 'The Highly Sensitive Person: How to Thrive When the World Overwhelms You' (Replica Books, 1999)
2. Isabel Briggs Myers & Mary H. McCaulley , 'Manual: A Guide to the Development and Use of the Myers-Briggs Type Indicator' (1985)
3. David Keirsey, 'Please Understand Me II: Temperament, Character, Intelligence' (Prometheus Nemesis Book Company, May 1998)
4. Rita Carter, 'Mapping the Mind' (University of California Press, 2000)

# The Bundling Baggage Technique

## FOR SIMILAR REPETITIVE EVENTS, TRAUMAS, OR ABUSES

### Lindsay Kenny, EFT Master, EFTCert-Honors

One of the first things I learned about EFT when I was a 'newbie' was how important it is to be SPECIFIC when dealing with an issue. When confronting anger, frustration, grief, stress, or whatever negative emotion, you are seeing the SYMPTOM, not the cause. With EFT it's important to address the core issue, and be specific about it in order to eliminate the resulting emotion. Just saying *"... this anger"* is not nearly as effective as saying *"... this anger and resentment at Bob for humiliating me at the wedding"*. Being specific when working with singular issues is vitally important in neutralizing the trauma, emotion or event.

## What do you mean by 'baggage'?

However, after many years of doing EFT with literally thousands of people, I realized there was another type of trauma that was more difficult to identify as a single incident. It consisted of REPETITIVE events, traumas or abuses that were related in some way, and had usually occurred during the formative years of life. I documented that over 90% of the people I worked with had experienced these SERIAL TRAUMAS OR SERIAL ABUSES, which I call 'childhood baggage'. Regardless of the presenting issue—whether manifested as fear, anxiety, depression, low self-esteem, addictions, chronic pain or a myriad of other symptoms—this baggage seemed to be at the core of their problems.

Allow me to explain further. I believe that the reason this childhood baggage is so impactful and relevant is that each negative event during the very impressionable time of childhood represents a huge percentage of our overall life experience.

For instance, you may have had an alcoholic parent who ignored you, didn't acknowledge your accomplishments, or was aggressive or abusive to you. Or perhaps your mom or dad repeatedly yelled at you or hit you, or fought with each other in front of you. These similar events would have been very traumatic and frightening to you, causing blockages in your energy system (resulting in negative emotions). Furthermore, if these traumas were also the first IMPACTFUL events of your life at that point they would represent 100% of your negative experiences at the time. That 'writes on the slate' of who you are, identifying who you will become.

Traumas, abuses or other negative events profoundly affect an impressionable child, resulting in anxiety, anger, fear, insecurity, a sense of unworthiness, self-loathing and much more. The bottom line is that most likely you would have begun to feel that something was wrong with you, that you didn't matter, that you were not OK, that you weren't safe, or that you just weren't good enough.

Left untreated, this baggage and its resulting blockages in the energy system can cause serious damage to our emotional and physical health. Later in life it can also manifest itself in numerous ways, including sabotaged relationships, low self-esteem, feeling stuck or unmotivated, unsuccessful careers, financial failures, fears, anxiety, depression and countless other tribulations.

## How does this 'baggage' affect our adult lives?

I have now treated hundreds of clients with numerous emotional or physical problems caused by the insensitive ways they were repeatedly treated in their childhood. While doing so I've developed the "Bundling Baggage Technique", a different but highly efficient and effective way to neutralize these serial events.

To be clear, being specific is still very important when dealing with a unique trauma, event or abuse. However, the 'Bundling Baggage Technique' is designed for 'serial' abuse or trauma.

Regardless of the specifics you may remember or the emotional 'charge' these events may still carry today, repetitive negative experiences in childhood can literally become PART OF YOUR IDENTITY. In fact, so much so that most people seek to replicate the experiences that defined them as a child throughout the rest of their lives! Bummer! It's as if some odd 'flaw' in our human psyche needs to repeat those childhood nightmares because they are 'familiar'. Those who were verbally abused as children will often grow up and marry someone who will verbally abuse them. Children of alcoholics will often marry someone with a propensity toward alcoholism, or become alcoholics themselves. And I know you've heard this one: children who were sexually abused will often grow up to become abusers themselves or marry someone who abuses them.

In effect, we simply pick up where our parents left off by continuing to abuse ourselves in adulthood. You might find that you often say things to yourself like *"I can't do anything right!", "What's wrong with me?", "Why can't I get out of this awful mess?"* and so on. It's as if you are stuck right where your parents put you . . . in a kind of permanent 'time out' in the corner of your own life.

Enough already! Let's break that cycle right now and heal that wounded child. In doing so you can profoundly change the way you function in your life today. Here's my guide for how to do that. You can do this! So stay with me here. The payoff is huge.

## What are the steps of the Bundling Baggage Technique?

STEP 1: Gather in your mind (then write down) the phrases, negative messages, abuses or traumas that you experienced repetitively as a child. You don't have to relive them, just get a sense of the impact from these accumulative multiple incidences. Then give those experiences or 'baggage' a short name such as: 'childhood traumas', 'my child abuse', 'alcoholic dad beatings', 'anger rampages from mom', 'brother's bullying', 'controlling dad abuse', or whatever phrase symbolizes your childhood experiences.

STEP 2: Next, give this collective bundle of baggage an intensity rating from 10 to 0 (that is how you felt at the time.) If you don't know, just guess. Most people find that their baggage is at least at a 9 or a 10. Note: You may feel differently now, either more intense or less intense. If you were numb as a child, you may feel more intense now. Be aware of the different SUDS levels, and keep track of both. My experience is that as you go through repeated rounds of tapping, the two SUDS levels will merge and become the same.

STEP 3:     Do a 'Reversal Neutralization' on your phrase. Because the subconscious tends to hold onto your identity from childhood experiences, it's best to do a reversal up front to deal with your subconscious head-on. This greatly expedites EFT's effectiveness. Here's the simple way to neutralize this type of reversal: On the karate chop point tap while saying:

   ✤ *Even though I DON'T want to get over this . . . . . . . . . . . . (fill in your personal phrase here), I do want to love and accept myself.*

   ✤ *Even though I DON'T want to get over this . . . . . . . . . . . . (fill in your personal phrase here), I do want to love and accept myself.*

   ✤ *Even though for WHATEVER reason, I don't want to let go of my 'childhood baggage' (use your phrase), I do want to accept who I am today.*

Saying it this way, in the negative is important in order to effect a shift in your subconscious's willingness to let go of your old problem or identity.

STEP 4: Now, using a setup point (on the sore spot or the KC point) say three times:

   ✤ *Even though, after all these years, I'm still affected by the (add your phrase here), I want to love and accept who I am now.*

STEP 5:     REMINDER PHRASE: *"these childhood traumas"* (or whatever your phrase is).

STEP 6: Do a second and third round using descriptive verbiage at each point that expresses your experiences from that time in your life. This allows you to vent your feelings about what happened then and can be very healing and cathartic. Don't worry about doing this 'right'. Do what works for you to help vent and release the pain. Here's an example, but use your own wording:

EYEBROW:        *Dad made me feel worthless*
SIDE OF EYE:    *He really hurt me*

UNDER EYE:      ***It wasn't even my fault***
UNDER NOSE:     ***I blamed myself***
CHIN:           ***I tried to be a good kid***
COLLARBONE:     ***I could never please him***
UNDERARM:       ***I needed to be hugged***
LIVER POINT:    ***I so wanted to be loved and accepted*** (The liver point, also called the BN or Below Nipple point, is a powerful meridian point, pertinent to stress, depression, cravings, anger and more. It's often avoided because of its inconvenient positioning—about 3 inches under a man's nipples, or under a woman's breasts and slightly to the side. If you're only tapping with one hand, tap on the right side.)
WRIST POINT:    ***Why couldn't they praise me once in a while?*** (The wrist is an optional point that I find valuable. It contains 3 important meridian points, dealing with stress, anxiety, grief and sadness. Simply bump the inside of your wrists together, where the hand meets the arm.)
HEAD:           ***I've been dragging this around too long*** (Tap on the Crown of your head using all of your fingers.)

Giving a VOICE to your feelings in this way helps collect different aspects of the problem dealing with them all at once. This 'stream of consciousness ranting' is very powerful and effective. Just let the words come out as you tap. Let your intuition guide you and you'll be just fine. If additional intensity comes up while tapping, do another round or two using the same method and words, or add more phrases and feelings. It's incredibly liberating to vent while tapping and often alleviates several aspects of the issue. Don't be surprised if the word *"hate"* comes up (among other things). Allow yourself the freedom to express how you felt at the time.

STEP 7:    Now reassess your feelings and assign a new intensity number. Typically it will have dropped to a 7 or 8. Occasionally it will have gone up because you may have gotten more in touch with the pain you experienced at the time. If so, just repeat steps 1 through 7 again.

STEP 8:    Do another setup phrase on your sore spot or KC point saying something like:

✦ ***Even though I'm still feeling the pain from my childhood (enter your phrase), a part of me really wants to let this go.***

| WRIST: | *I give myself permission to let it go now* |
| HEAD: | *I choose to begin my new, rejuvenated identity right now* |

STEP 19:   Do the third round alternating the negative and positive statements such as:

| EYE BROW: | *Any remaining childhood baggage (use your phrase)* |
| SIDE OF EYE: | *I choose to eliminate it now* |
| UNDER EYE: | *Any remaining anger, guilt (or whatever emotions you had)* |
| UNDER NOSE: | *I choose to let it all go* |
| CHIN: | *Any remaining hate and resentment* |
| COLLARBONE: | *I choose to bury it in a deep, dark hole* |
| UNDER ARM: | *Any remaining guilt, shame or negative emotions* |
| LIVER POINT: | *I choose to eliminate all of that at the cellular and molecular levels* |
| WRIST: | *Any shred of negativity from my childhood* |
| HEAD: | *I choose to eliminate it forever, right now* |

STEP 20:   When you really feel you're over the baggage, test yourself by trying to get upset. If you find that there's still a little bit, or you discover another aspect you hadn't dealt with yet, or that's still there, tap it away, just as you did the other issues. Start at STEP 16 unless the intensity level is more than a 3 on the remaining 'stuff'.

STEP 21:   This next sequence is my favorite part of this process because it leaves a person with a positive outlook, rather than just the elimination of the negatives. Feel free to use this sequence after the resolution of every tapping session. When you're sure your intensity is at a zero, continue with two more 'bonus' rounds using positive statements about yourself. As a guide use words or phrases that would be the opposite of how you felt as a child. Here's an example (no setup required):

| EYEBROW: | *I choose to acknowledge myself for surviving* |
| SIDE OF EYE: | *I choose to start recognizing my strengths and abilities* |
| UNDER EYE: | *I'm a good person* |
| NOSE: | *I'm more than OK* |
| CHIN: | *I'm smart and resilient* |
| COLLARBONE: | *I'm a good dad, mom (sister, son, friend, whatever is true for you)* |

UNDER ARM:    *I'm resourceful*

LIVER POINT:    *I'm creative and clever*

WRIST:        *I have a good sense of humor*

HEAD:          *I'm a good friend and people like me*

Keep going if you can, adding other phrases that are true for you, such as *I'm a survivor, I acknowledge myself for my kindness to others, I'm compassionate and caring, I choose to be confident and certain, I'm a powerful, intelligent, loving man (or woman).*

STEP 22:   Now, acknowledge yourself for doing a good job!

Good luck and Good tapping!

## AUTHOR'S BIOGRAPHY AND CONTACT DETAILS

Lindsay has been doing EFT since 2000 and has branded her own version of it as Progressive Emotional Release, or Pro-ER, an EFT cousin. She is also founder and director of the National Alliance for Emotional Health.

Lindsay offers private sessions as well as numerous workshops and tele-classes. She resides in the San Francisco Bay area and can be reached via e-mail at LKcoaching-LK@yahoo.com or by phone at 888-449-3030. Visit her website at www.LKcoaching.com for a wealth of tapping articles, downloads, links and more.

# Clearing Clutter for Clarity and Confidence

## USING AN ULTIMATE TRUTH STATEMENT

LINDSAY KENNY, EFT MASTER, EFTCERT-HONORS

## What causes us to collect clutter?

Messy homes, cars or offices are common issues today with our busy lives. True clutter, however, (and I mean really messy environments) is really a symptom of something other than a busy lifestyle. Most often clutter is a control issue. Being unwilling to let go of things is a way people can feel in control of their lives. Even though it appears that they are totally out of control, hanging onto 'stuff' gives people a sense of being in control. It's similar to how anorexics feel about food and their ability to at least control their weight.

Another common reason for clutter is fear. Fear of loss, rejection, failure and losing control are the most universal of these. But again, all of these fears and issues are just symptoms. Underlying these symptoms of clutter is a cause or core issue.

Clutter is often triggered by an event or a series of events that left the victim feeling traumatized, fearful and powerless. Hanging on to things gives some people a sense of commanding, or controlling at least a portion of their lives.

Determine the event that started the feeling of loss of power or loss of control and neutralize it. You are then halfway home to eliminating clutter.

## What do you really mean by clutter?

Let me define what I believe are the THREE LEVELS OF CLUTTER:

LEVEL 1:  Generally messy and disorganized at home; 'stuff' lying around on many or most surfaces

LEVEL 2:  As for Level 1, plus . . .
- a messy office, car and often (but not always) personal appearance
- an unwillingness to throw away outdated or useless things
- lack of desire or ability to put away clothing or items or to clean up behind one's self or others
- litter and disorganization everywhere

LEVEL 3: As for Level 2, plus . . .
- elements of complete disorder and filth, even to the level of pathology (meaning unsanitary conditions that create a health risk)
- complete organizational chaos; from dirty dishes overflowing the sink to unwashed clothing everywhere
- garbage accumulation (in or out of bags) on the floor or furniture, in the garage or car
- often there is animal excrement on the floor or furniture
- all accompanied by a feeling of being 'paralyzed' by an inability to do anything about the situation

It's the last two Levels that I want to deal with in this article.

## Case Study: Janice–Level 3

'Janice' came to see me with a Level 3 problem. Although she looked relatively clean, she assured me her home was beyond filthy. Boxes, stacks of magazines and newspapers, and junk lined her walls and floors so that she could only reach her bedroom or kitchen through a small path. She said you couldn't see her sofa, chairs, TV, or even her kitchen table. Dog poop was on the floors, in the spare bathroom tub and even on her bed. A loose parrot contributed bird *"pucky"* on everything everywhere. She said the smell when you walked in the door was *"staggering"*.

This was clearly more than just a messy house. And similar to a TV program where three tons of garbage was hauled away and a crew cleaned and sanitized a woman's house, six weeks later it was on its way to being the same pigsty it was before. That's because the reason for the 'clutter' was not dealt with.

For Janice, the age of the magazines (dated in the late 80s) was a clue to me. I asked her what happened 20 years ago. She had no problem remembering. A drunk driver had killed her only child, a much-adored 11 year-old daughter. Janice was still devastated and in shock when three weeks later her beloved husband of 15 years was killed. The mudslide that took away her husband eradicated their home and virtually everything else Janice had left. Photos, family keepsakes and personal treasures were lost, along with the two people she loved the most. Her whole life was turned upside down in a flash.

From that point Janice was virtually paralyzed with grief, sadness and a sense of abandonment. She became frightful and hyper-vigilant about everything. She didn't want to live, yet was terrified of dying. Janice became afraid to make a move, throw anything away, go anywhere or do anything. Her hoarding of the few things she recovered or replaced began her trend toward clutter. She didn't do it intentionally. She subconsciously had developed such a fear of loss that controlling her environment became her way of controlling (and protecting) her very life.

With this knowledge we first cleared out her grief and trauma about losing her husband and daughter. She said she had *"dealt with it"* through years of therapy. I knew that was doubtful, based on the results in her life.

## How did you help her to move on from the original trauma(s)?

We started with a reversal on the KC point:

> ⭒ *Even though I don't want to let go of the grief and trauma over losing my family and home . . .*

Then the Setup on her sore spot:

> ⭒ *Even though I'm still grieving at some level over the loss of my daughter and husband . . .*

We did several rounds just tapping on reminder statements of grief, sorrow, emptiness, sadness, anger, being afraid and alone. This brought a lot of tears, which surprised her.

On the 3rd round we gave voice to her feelings with phrases like:

*It was so unfair . . . I still miss them . . . I blame myself somehow . . . How could they leave me like that . . . Why me . . . ? It still hurts . . . My life isn't worth living . . .*

After a few rounds of venting like this her intensity dropped to a 6.

We did a few more rounds adding in positive phrases like: *I want to let this go . . . I want to move on . . . I'm ready to get over my grief . . . I'm ready to honor their lives by living mine to the fullest . . . Bob and Melanie wouldn't have wanted me to live like this . . .*

When the intensity was 2, we changed to the Choices Trio {see *The Choices Method*}, choosing to let go of the negative emotions around the loss of her family and choosing to live life to the fullest. She was responding very well and reached a zero in intensity at the end of this process (the first round of the remaining issue, the second round of positive choices to let it go and the third round alternating negative and positive statements at each consecutive point).

I asked her to really try to get upset about the loss of either of her loved ones. But she couldn't do it. She actually laughed about something funny she remembered her daughter had said.

With the cause of her clutter issue now put to rest, we could then move on to fixing the symptom of clutter problem. As always, I used the Ultimate Truth Statement to work toward a positive outcome. I could have started the whole process with this as well, but the underlying grief issue seemed so apparent that I wanted to eliminate that first.

## How did you help her to build an Ultimate Truth Statement?

I had Janice come up with a basic statement (I call it the Ultimate Truth Statement or UTS) as the goal she would like to achieve: *"I live in a neat and orderly environment"*.

We then filled in reasons she wanted this to be true: *"I could find things easily . . . I could have people come to my home without feeling shame . . . I would feel healthy, safe and comfortable having a clean home, car and office . . . My life would be easier and simpler . . ."*

We added some of those positive phrases to the UTS, so that it read something like this: *"My life is easy, comfortable and safe living in a healthy, neat and orderly environment."*

I then asked her to describe how that would make her feel when that statement became true. *"I would feel free and proud of myself . . . I would have clarity! I would feel good about myself and have more confidence . . . I would feel WONDERFUL and so happy . . . I would feel so much lighter . . . !"*

By compiling all of her phrases to her basic goal her 'Ultimate Truth Statement' looked like this:

*"I feel wonderful, light and safe living in a healthy, neat and
hygienic environment. My life is comfortable, easy and free
with my clean, well-organized, tidy lifestyle. I have clarity and
confidence again, and I'm happy and proud to invite people to my
beautiful, clutter-free home."*

This was a statement Janice could not only live with, but loved! She was
very excited about the possibility of achieving it. On a scale of 10 to 1, with 10
feeling and owning the statement right now, she was at a 5.

## How did you help her with her remaining fears?

She now had two major concerns. One concern was wondering how she could
possibly clear everything out and clean up the incredible chaos she lived in.
The second was fear. She feared letting go of things (control), feared she'd
throw something away she might need later (loss of control), and even feared
that she could never even get started, much less finish. In a way, holding onto
her fears, control issues, and clutter was her way of holding on to her family!

We put aside the UTS for the moment to work on the obstacle of the
fears in her way. We clumped her fears together and Janice gave them a 9.
We then did a Reversal Neutralization (I define a Reversal as a "Subconscious
Resistance to change,") saying:

- ⚜ *Even though I don't want to let go of these fears . . .*

- ⚜ *Even though these fears keep me safe or keep me from failing, they
  are part of my identity . . .*

- ⚜ *Even though I may not deserve to let go of these fears . . . because I
  don't really want a clean orderly environment . . . these fears ensure
  that doesn't happen . . .*

Just doing the Reversals gave Janice some relief, which surprised her. We
then simply tapped away the fears:

- ⚜ *Even though I have these fears about letting go of my filth, feces, and
  squalor . . . .*

**Note:** When dealing with something you want to eliminate, I've found it's far more impactful to paint it in the worst possible light. Using loaded words such as squalor and feces instead of just saying 'clutter' has much more punch. If you want to stop drinking Pepsi, call it 'this sugar and chemical-laden brown toxic stuff'. This is not, however, a good idea if you're letting go of a trauma or abuse issue.

After the setup statements we did one round just alternating the fears:

REMINDER PHRASES: *This fear of letting go . . . This fear of failing . . . This fear I might need something I throw away . . .*

On the second and subsequent rounds we added words to give voice to the fears:

REMINDER PHRASES: *What if I throw something away I really need? What if I can't even get started? I'd feel like even more of a failure. How will I ever get this all done? I'll feel so out of control and helpless. I can't do this. I need my stuff. I want to keep it*

After a round or so I then transitioned to the ridiculous.

REMINDER PHRASES: *I need my squalor. I love filth. It smells so good in there. Feces is my friend. I don't really need to find my cat. I need these fears. They help me keep my 'clutter and filth'. They are my friends. I don't want to let go of the fears OR the filth. Oh, ewwwwwwwww, yes I do! No I DON'T! YES I do! I'm tired of living this way. I want to have a clean, healthy environment. No, I love garbage. No I don't! I want to eliminate these fears, and this filth so I can be healthy again*

After arguing both sides of the issue, we reassessed Janice's number and her fear issue was at a 3.

We then moved to the Choices Trio with the setup of:

✦ *Even though I still have some fears of cleaning up my environment, I choose to let them go.*

After doing that two or three times we did the next three rounds with the Choices Trio:

- Round 1: Just the negative: *Remaining fears of letting go of clutter . . .*

- Round 2: All positive statements such as: *I choose to eliminate these fears . . . I choose to be fearless about cleaning up . . . I choose to have a neat an orderly home . . . I choose to let go of any remaining fears about it . . . I choose to feel good about being fearless . . . I choose to make this easy!*

- Round 3: Alternate the positive with the negative statements at every other point: r*emaining fears, I choose to let them go, remaining fear, I choose to be fearless . . .*

By now Janice's fear was completely gone on all levels and I tested her to make sure. It was truly at a zero for Janice. Now when looking at her UTS, her number had gone up to an 8 (with 10 being the target). She felt like she was almost there in feeling and believing in the veracity of her statement . . . in spite of the reality of a mess in her home. It's those positive feelings you want. That's what pulls you into the position in which you want to be.

## How did you help her to 'OWN' her Ultimate Truth Statement?

We then used the setup statement:

- ☩ *Even though there's still some reluctance or resistance in owning my UTS, and I don't even know what it is, I choose to let it go now. I choose to have a clutter-free, clean environment.*

We did slight variations of that three times, then:

- Round 1, on the negative: *remaining reluctance to owning my statement . . .*

- Round 2, on the positive: *I choose to eliminate this resistance to cleanliness . . .*

- Round 3, alternating remaining negatives with positive statements.

- Round 4, only positive statements pulled from the Ultimate Truth Statement, such as: *I feel great now owning my cleanliness . . . I love having a tidy, clutter-free home . . . I feel confident and comfortable having people over . . .*

At this point Janice was at a 10, meaning she could say her UTS with absolute conviction as if it were already true. I had her tap on this statement daily, just to reinforce her resolution. But she didn't need to for long. Within a week she was completely clutter-free.

## OK she's feeling much better, but how did you now help her to put all this into practice and start clearing the clutter for real?

It is here that most people say *"But how do I get it done?"*. Well if you really trust the Universe you can just allow it to happen; an idea will come to you, or a solution will be shown to you. With Janice we did a few more rounds to magnetize a solution.

Simply alternate these kinds of phrases on the tapping points: *I ask the Universe to clear this clutter for me . . . I want to be involved and I want it to be EASY . . . I choose to find a creative, fun way to have a clean, orderly environment . . . I know a safe, tidy home is on the way . . . And I want to have fun participating in it . . . Deep inside I already know how to eliminate this clutter.*

All of a sudden Janice stopped me and said *"I have a plan!"* It was a pretty good one too, and in a nutshell here's how she implemented it. She recruited three close, non-judgmental friends and assembled lots of boxes and bags. Trash was thrown into bags and immediately taken outside. Donation bags of unneeded but reusable items were labeled and set aside for charity. A set of boxes containing Janice's 'keep' items were numbered and recorded with their content.

Her friends generated a Master List of box numbers and their content so that Janice could find 'Shoestrings from 1989' in Box 82. Most of the boxes were stored in her garage so that in time, Janice would be able to reclaim what she really wanted and dispose of the rest.

## Did these positive effects really last for Janice?

To follow up Janice's story, three months later, when we spoke again, her home and car were still immaculate. She also hired a housekeeper to help her clean each week so she would never again have to experience a clutter problem.

Not surprisingly, Janice exclaimed how much better she was feeling; very focused, restored clarity, much higher energy, motivated, light, confident and happy. She also reported that she has more time to do the things she enjoys, she has often has friends over now, and her life is so much easier.

With those positive aspects to motivate her, Janice is maintaining an orderly, clutter-free life. And you can do it too.

Good Luck and Good Tapping!

## AUTHOR'S BIOGRAPHY AND CONTACT DETAILS

See 'Bundling Baggage Technique' by Lindsay Kenney for biography and contact details.

# Identifying and Neutralizing Reversals

LINDSAY KENNY, EFT MASTER, EFTCERT-HONORS

## How important are 'reversals'?

More than any other single element, reversals can impact the results of EFT. Broadly, a reversal occurs when energy flows in the opposite direction from your intention. Identifying and neutralizing reversals before you start tapping is one of the most effective ways to resolve issues quickly.

> If reversals are unrecognized or ignored, they can stop EFT in its tracks.

I break reversals down into two basic categories, Secondary Benefit Syndrome and General Polarity Reversals.

## What is Secondary Benefit Syndrome?

The first type of reversal I call the Secondary Benefit Syndrome or SBS. It's the most common type of reversal. SBS is simply 'a subconscious resistance to change'. This type of reversal occurs when the Subconscious Mind perceives that it is better or safer to keep an issue—like negative emotions, chronic pain, extra weight or a bad habit—than to eliminate it. Consciously, you might want to change, but your subconscious, which is far more powerful, is overriding your conscious choice. It's one of the reasons you find yourself saying: *"Why can't I just let this go?"* or *"Why do I keep self-sabotaging myself?"* or *"Why can't I lose this weight?"*

As the movie 'What the Bleep Do We Know' demonstrates, our bodies can actually become addicted to negative emotions or issues. Over time we become so accustomed to being angry, hurt, anxious, victimized and so on, that the body is reluctant to let go of these emotions.

---

> While negative emotions may be uncomfortable to our conscious mind, they may feel natural or familiar to the subconscious mind.

---

And it's that little anomaly that most often causes people to think that EFT doesn't work.

Incidentally, 'reversals' as I describe and use them, are different from the Psychological Reversals that Gary Craig describes in his manual and DVDs. The remedy, or neutralization, is also quite different.

I get hundreds of emails a week from strangers lamenting, *"EFT isn't working for me"*. They've read the many wonderful stories about EFT's one-minute-wonders, yet they aren't getting the results they want. The Secondary Benefit Syndrome type of reversal is most likely the reason and, in my opinion, the major cause when EFT doesn't work.

Since SBS is not a conscious choice, most people initially baulk when you tell them that subconsciously they don't want to get rid of their problem or issue. Naturally, most people don't consciously want to stay emotionally upset or in physical pain, but the subconscious is a powerful entity, usually exhibiting dominance over our conscious desires.

For someone who has carried around a trauma, chronic pain, anxiety, phobia or other issue for many years, the emotion becomes a part of his or her identity. How often have you heard phrases like: *"He's an angry young man . . ."* or *"She's just such an anxious person . . ."*? Or how many times have you said: *"Why can't just I get over this _____?"* Overcoming or losing that 'identity' can be very threatening to the non-rational subconscious mind.

For instance, the subconscious might be thinking: *"If I get over this issue . . .*

> *. . . it might be scary*
> *. . . I may not know who I am anymore*
> *. . . I won't have an excuse anymore for my life not working*
> *. . . it may not be safe*
> *. . . I won't get the attention or sympathy I get now*
> *. . . I won't know how to act as a functional, non-victim person*
> *. . . I'll feel afraid if I let go of this*

For example, if someone has been trying to lose weight for a long time and hasn't been successful, they are almost certainly reversed on it. Consciously, they want to lose weight, but their dominant, stubborn subconscious may be saying, *"Wait a minute here. If I lose weight my clothes won't fit and I'll be deprived of the foods I love. And what if I lose that 40 pounds and I still don't get that promotion I need; the guy I'm lusting after; the friends I want? Maybe if I lose that weight I'll be so attractive to men that I'll be abused or harassed again. Or what if I get skinny and my life still sucks?"*

Once again, remember, this is the subconscious mind wielding control over what we consciously want. It is very difficult, under most circumstances, to consciously override the more powerful subconscious mind. If you doubt that, I highly recommend 'The Biology of Belief' by Bruce H. Lipton[1]. It's a powerful documentary about why we are the way we are, the power of perception and the subconscious mind.

---

As long as the Subconscious is unwilling to let go of a problem (i.e. a reversal!), it's very hard to resolve an issue, with or without EFT.

---

A good clue as to whether or not a person has an SBS reversal is if their SUD (Subjective Units of Distress) intensity level remains the same after a couple of rounds of tapping. The intensity or SUDs level is a way to gauge the emotional charge of an issue on a scale of 0-10.

If you've had a problem for over a month, then you are probably reversed on it. If it's a highly charged issue, such as fear, anger, grief or guilt, you are probably reversed on it. If there's something you want to accomplish and just can't seem to get there, you are probably reversed on that. If you consistently do something you know you don't want to do, such as smoking, drinking, gambling or internet porn, then you are probably reversed on letting it go. When I hear someone say, *"I've had this _____ for years and have tried everything"* the phrase *"They're reversed"* immediately comes to mind.

There are many others reasons, of course, why an issue can be difficult to resolve. But the main reason, by far, is the wicked reversal!

## So how can I resolve SBS?

The good news is it's very easy to fix Secondary Benefit Syndrome. It's so easy that people find it hard to believe. Here's how: Simply tap the Karate Chop Points at the bases of both little fingers together, while saying a reversal phrase such as:

- *Even though I don't want to get over this anger (or trauma, chronic pain, grief, etc)*
- *Even though it may not be safe to get over my (issue) . . .*
- *Even though I may not deserve to get over (this issue) . . .*
- *Even though I won't know how to act if I get well . . .*
- *Even though I won't have an excuse for my life being messed up . . .*
- *Even though I don't want to forgive the people that ruined my life . . .*
- *Even though I don't know how to be 'normal' . . .*
- *Even though I'm afraid I'll lose my identity . . .*
- *Even though for whatever reason, I don't want to overcome this problem . . .*

I almost always use at least the first and last of these phrases, which usually catch everything in between. 'Not deserving' to get over something is also a biggie; just pick three or four and say them while bumping the Karate Chop points together.

You'll know the reversal neutralization worked when you start doing EFT again and your intensity number starts going down. Reversals can be huge stumbling blocks, but they are easily remedied so don't let them stand in your way.

> Remember, fixing a reversal does not fix the issue. It only
> eliminates an impediment to fixing the issue. You still need to do
> EFT as usual after fixing a reversal.

Just as a footnote, in addition to Secondary Benefit Syndrome, there can also be a conscious resistance to letting go of a problem. People with disabilities, for instance, might fear that if they become whole-bodied again, more will be expected of them. They will lose their blue handicapped tag or license plate, they'll lose their disability income, they won't get special attention and so on. That's NOT a reversal; that's a 'Secondary Gain' issue.

Please don't imagine that I believe everyone who has a debilitating issue feels that way, or that I would judge him or her for it. I'm only mentioning it because I've seen it happen many times. I'll ask someone, *"Do you WANT to let got of this problem?"* and once in a while someone will admit that they don't want to get over it because medical benefits or other compensations might be lost if they healed. These are not reversals, they are conscious choices.

## What are General Polarity Reversals?

A General Polarity Reversal (or GPR) simply means that the electricity or energy in the body is 'agitated' or 'going in the wrong direction'. Therefore, polarity is reversed. A simple way to look at our body's energy field is to think of batteries in a tape recorder, flashlight or other battery-operated device. The batteries that run the gadget must be installed with the positive and negative poles seated in the correct direction. If not, the device simply won't work. It's very much the same way in our energy system.

Since your body has its own 'electrical system', your 'batteries' need to be positioned correctly for you to function properly. If your polarity, or direction of flow, is scrambled up, you have a General Polarity Reversal. While GPR is not common, it does happen, and it is unlikely EFT will work until the reversal is corrected.

You know those days when you just feel off? Your timing is out of whack, you're dropping your keys or pens, bumping into doorframes, fumbling for words or phrases, falling off curbs, and so on? Chances are your polarity has become reversed, literally causing you to be out of balance.

Think of the experiment in grade school where you used a magnet to attract tiny particles of metal on a piece of paper. The positive end of the magnet pulled the particles toward it, lining them up neatly, all going the same direction. The negative end of the magnet, when directed toward the metal shavings, caused the particles to repel, scattering them into all different directions. In a sense, that's what happens to our body's energy when a negative force, like those listed below, is introduced into the system.

## Can you give me some examples of common causes of GPR:

- NEGATIVITY—chronic negative thoughts or negative behavior

- ELECTRICAL FORCE FIELDS—being around electrical devices for long periods of time (cell phones, computers, MP3 players, TVs etc.,) can scramble the body's energy system

- ADDICTIONS—addictive personalities or addictive substances in the body

- DRUGS—prescription or illegal, including alcohol or tobacco

- CHRONIC PAIN—can cause a disruption in your entire energy system, which can put your body in a 'spin'.

- TOXINS—substances (chemicals, paint, solvents, etc.), allergies (food, perfume, dust) and sensitivities (pollution, noise, light)

- DEHYDRATION—water is a primary conductor of electricity so if you are dehydrated, the energy moving through your system can be greatly impeded.

The good news is that Polarity Reversals are easy to fix, especially if you can discover the cause.

## So how can I remedy GPR?

- RECTIFY THE CAUSE: If you're dehydrated, drink more water. Remove yourself from electrical fields; do what you can to eliminate the cause of the Reversal.

- JUST TAP! A simple, effective way to fix the most common GPR problems is to perform this simple procedure: Bump your hands together at the Karate Chop Points. You don't even have to say anything. 15 to 20 seconds will generally rebalance your meridians and fix a simple 'general' reversal.

Also, performing the standard set-up procedure (rubbing the sore spot or tapping on the Karate Chop point while saying the set-up statement) will fix some types of GPRs. Addictions or toxin-related GPRs, however, are not usually eliminated just doing the set-up statement alone; the irritating substance needs to be eliminated from the body in most cases.

Reversals are only one stumbling block to a successful EFT treatment, but they are often the one that causes people to say: *"I tried EFT, but it just didn't work for me"*.

Fortunately, though, they are relatively easy to remove once you recognize that they are there!

Good luck and Good tapping!

## AUTHOR'S BIOGRAPHY AND CONTACT DETAILS

See 'Bundling Baggage Technique' by Lindsay Kenny for biography and contact details.

REFERENCES:

1. Bruce Lipton, 'The Biology of Belief' (2004)

# Creating a Bridge to our History

MAIR LLEWELLYN, EFT MASTER, EFTCERT-HONORS

## Part 1: A bridge to our history

In 1980, when I first started working as a hypnotherapist with physical issues such as hay fever, migraine, asthma and IBS, I noticed that if I took my clients back in time while in a trance state, we were able in many cases to connect to memories of a time prior to the onset of their current illness or symptoms {see *Using Personal Resource States*}. It appears to be consistently true that our memories of healthier times remain intact, even after an accident, trauma or the onset of illness.

Later, I realised that I could use the same procedure with smokers to help them to quit smoking. Instead of creating a void by taking away cigarettes, we accessed early memories of the way they were before they began to smoke. This routine enabled clients to enjoy experiences of belonging and completeness without smoking, and the majority reported little or no cravings.

During the last nine years of using EFT, I have noticed that these same memory archive mechanisms can be accessed through the tapping procedure.

## What about loss of mobility due to an accident?

For example, a client attended for help with loss of function after an accident. Following tapping on connecting to healthy memories from before the event, we discovered that it was possible for her to access more mobility via EFT than she had so far experienced through other therapeutic approaches.

> It would appear that connecting to the memory and beliefs prior to the accident helped her to bypass tail-enders and link to an increased positive expectancy.

## What about eyesight?

A number of clients have been able to improve their eyesight with tapping suggestions to access memories of clear eyesight from before the onset of their eyesight deterioration[1]. In some cases these recollections have been going back to the memories of five and six-year-olds, before glasses or contacts needed to be worn, enabling crystal clear visual memories to be tapped into.

## What about strokes or spinal injuries?

By contrast, there appears to be little added benefit in accessing earlier memories with clients who have had a stroke. Perhaps in these circumstances, the memory in the brain has been damaged by the haemorrhage. However, this is not the case with spinal injuries which do appear to benefit from re-connecting to the memory before the injury. And in all examples it is helpful to do traditional EFT on the trauma, frustration, loss and fear.

## What about other physical conditions and infertility?

Stress symptoms such as hay fever, migraine, IBS and asthma appear to improve faster by this method than for example by working on specific upsetting events and tapping to neutralise them individually.

A further very interesting part of my work is to provide support in working with infertility. This is particularly the case in circumstances where a client has undergone a termination, or following a miscarriage. Bridging a client's historical beliefs about their ability and worthiness in becoming pregnant is very beneficial. This is consistently the case when, for whatever reason the client has guilt connected with conception. On these occasions, for instance, if they feel (however illogically) that their original birth control method was detrimental to their conceiving, re-activating earlier memories of positive expectancy of the natural order of things can be an enormous help.

These observations reflect my experience in my own practice; I have not yet had the opportunity to conduct any controlled trials to test the results against other approaches. However, I feel that this method provides a very powerful way of (quite literally) tapping into the excellent resources we have stored in the archives of our minds

This raises an intriguing possibility regarding a mechanism on how EFT works and why we tap on the negative. Maybe tapping removes the negative layer, thus exposing the original positive area below . . . ?

## Part 2: How to build a bridge to our history with EFT

*THE IMPORTANCE OF PREFRAMING:*

When we introduce our clients to EFT, we create a bridge from their existing knowledge of therapy or personal empowerment to EFT. When I introduce the benefits of accessing earlier memories of a behaviour or skill, I create a bridge too. I ask if they have learned a skill such as cycling or skiing, most clients have. I ask clients if they have ever spent short or longer periods of time when this skill was not in use—most have done that too, especially if they have a forgotten bike hanging up in their garage or they have to travel to another country to find snow. Then I usually suggest, when appropriate, that the transformation they are now wanting from our time together is possibly already held in the archives of their mind to literally tap into.

Another useful analogy could be an early word processing programme on our computer, which is still there even though it may not have been in regular use for a long time. In much the same way, our history of physical comfort and/or emotional well-being is still there to tap into.

*GIVING THE MOVIE A POSITIVE TITLE:*

Clients already familiar with using a movie title to connect to specific negative events will possibly need very little introduction regarding connecting to specific POSITIVE events. These would be experiences, memories, images, sounds and feelings which they are wanting to reactivate. Asking clients to create a movie of that experience or memory and think of a suitable title strengthens their pleasant associations. Then, when a client taps while narrating their movie of physical or psychological well-being, it's an even more powerful reconnection. Asking how long and how many euphoric crescendos were experienced is even better!

Throughout this whole time of choosing a movie title and tapping when talking and remembering the positive experience, it is very possible that any 'yes-buts' and tail-enders will have been successfully neutralised. Frequently I notice this happens even before we get to the stage of weaving in the positive suggestions with a more structured setup or reminder phrase. Perhaps when we move on to implementing this we are doing even more than we really need to, and the reconnection is already happening. Despite this, I am all for being thorough and I have always liked the idea of using 'belt and braces' (as we say in England). Or as Gary frequently puts it: "*Undersell and over deliver*".

*USE OF TRANCE:*

Asking a client to think of a movie title for a positive past experience tunes them out from the here and now (their pain or trauma) and links them to the feelings, images, smells and sounds of that wonderful experience. When we daydream, or drive from A to B on a familiar route we tune out, yet we drive safely whilst we are thinking of something else. In a daydream, trance state, it is easier to gather information. Throughout any one day we drift in and out of this state frequently—at school we were told to pay attention by our teacher when we were daydreaming in a lesson. Within our minds, it is possible for us to experience our 'past', 'present', and 'future'. Daydreaming with intention can connect us to our previous healthy state, and tapping while using appropriate language facilitates this reconnection.

## Can you give me a worked example?

In the example below, I have included language to help my client connect to the free feelings he remembers before he started smoking. This focused, specific tapping usually happens after feelings of being totally free have been accessed, as described in an earlier paragraph. My client decided on a movie title for that time. The movie was called 'Complete Freedom'. In all circumstances it is important to use your client's own movie title. Each therapy session is an energetic dynamic exchange. The setup and reminder phrase which come to mind in that moment reflect a client's wants and worries. In this way, it is tailor-made for the client.

When (and only when) the setup and reminder phrases resonate for the client, the conscious and unconscious mind connects to and recovers a healthier programme:

⚜ *Even though I've been smoking for forty years, and I think I cannot stop, I deeply and completely love and accept myself anyway.*

⚜ *Even though I started smoking to be part of the gang, I respect my teenage needs at that time—I was doing the best that I could.*

⚜ *Even though I've been smoking since I was fourteen and I'm not listening to that teenage logic now because—I'm making healthy choices of 'Complete Freedom'.*

| | |
|---|---|
| EYEBROW: | *As a teenager I wanted to belong to a group* |
| SIDE OF EYE: | *It's different now* |
| UNDER EYE: | *Now, I want healthy choices* |
| UNDER NOSE: | *I cannot give up* |
| CHIN: | *I can* |
| COLLARBONE: | *I really want to somehow* |
| UNDER ARM: | *What if I could do this really easily now* |
| TOP OF HEAD: | *What a difference that would make* |

⚜ *Even though I don't see how giving up cigarettes can happen –I've been a heavy smoker for 40 years now and I just cannot stop, I deeply and completely accept and forgive myself anyway.*

⚜ *Even though cigarettes bring no genuine benefit to me—old habits are hard to change that's why I don't ever learn any new ones*

⚜ *I choose to recover my 'Complete Freedom' now.*

⚜ *Even though cigarettes have controlled me for 40 years—I choose to make today a really positive milestone and embrace my freedom again.*

EYEBROW:        *I cannot remember being free of cigarettes*

SIDE OF EYE:    *I do remember—my movie title choice is 'Complete Freedom' and that's how being completely free of cigarettes feels*

UNDER EYE:      *What if I connected to this 'Complete Freedom' programme again?*

UNDER NOSE:     *It's my birthright*

CHIN:           *What a difference that would make*

COLLARBONE:     *Connecting to my health and vitality*

UNDER ARM:      *Asking, receiving and easily making the connections*

TOP OF HEAD:    *'Complete Freedom' is the way my lungs are intended to be*

⚡ Even though I don't know how I can do this, I do have this inner wisdom which I deeply and completely respect.

⚡ Even though in the past I thought cigarettes were my friend, I choose to create a more constructive feedback loop to optimum health and 'Complete Freedom'.

⚡ Even though it's hard for me to consciously remember being completely free, my unconscious mind does remember, is my faithful servant and connects to the way I was meant to be right here and now.

EYEBROW:        *Recapturing my birthright*

SIDE OF EYE:    *I really want my health instead of cigarettes*

UNDER EYE:      *Whatever will I do with my hands?*

UNDER NOSE:     *My hands remember being free*

CHIN:           *I ask to be completely free*

COLLARBONE:     *The way I was intended to be*

UNDER ARM:      *Recovering my birthright*

TOP OF HEAD:    *I'll be amazed and grateful at how good that feels and that good feeling gets better every day and in every way!*

## Part 3: Further bridges to our history expanded

Let's now look at how this approach may be used with pain and physical problems. Any setup or reminder phrases which are used need to resonate with the client's own experience as well as relate to his desired objectives. I often say to my client: *"I want to know what you are wanting, not my perception of what you are wanting"*.

I believe that part of the art of delivery in working with EFT is being totally PRESENT with where your client is, right now—this includes what they are wanting from being with you in therapy. I have found that the technique of using NLP Time Line Therapy facilitates the process of accessing past wellbeing, whilst EFT provides an effective bridge to any shortfall here. In addition to this, accessing positive anchors or triggers strengthens the focus towards what clients are wanting. The combination of these client-centred approaches, together with aiming the setup to reactivate memories of wellbeing, provides a winning combination. To facilitate this healing we need to get ourselves out of the way. This applies to working on ourselves as well as working with clients. The following paragraphs briefly describe these concepts.

## Why use time line therapy?

We exist in the past, present and future. On a moment to moment basis we are affected by memories, positive or negative. These memories can be from the past, or what we are experiencing in the here and now, as well as any possible future consequences of our current actions. That is why the healing work of EFT can create an awesome reframe when working on our history. This not only manifests change in the here and now but also brings benefits in the future.

The combination of using the NLP timeline technique together with EFT can be a profoundly effective bridge from past wellbeing to present and future emotional and physical contentment.

## Why use NLP anchors?

Positive NLP anchors (associations or triggers)[2] provide a way to connect to a previously resourceful state so that that state may be cued at some possible time in the present or future. Cueing creates a link to past wellness, and is intended to reclaim and re-presence an earlier positive state of being. Re-connecting to the earlier state, to how we remember being, is our emotional, physical and spiritual birthright. When we re-ignite positive remembered anchors during the process of the EFT setup and reminder phrase, it often neutralises the 'yes-buts' and 'tail-enders' too.

## Why get myself out of the way?

I have frequently found that when I have cleared my own 'tail-enders' to the limitless possibilities of true freedom, things happen. Getting myself and my preconceived ideas out of the way allows divine healing energy to flow freely. I encourage you to tap on yourselves for your own 'tail-enders' before doing this type of work with your clients.

## Can you give me an example of these principles in action?

In this example a client we will call Pam described how EFT was helping her with her discomfort. The aim of working with this was to enhance the help that she was already receiving from EFT and to magnify it.

As Pam describes it: *"For myself, I am dealing with arthritis, which some-how fortunately is at a low level. I'm sure I have EFT to thank for that. It certainly helped to nip the last attack in the bud quickly."*

⚜ **Even though I find that EFT can nip an attack in the bud, what if I could amplify the benefits even more somehow. I respect myself profoundly, I am doing the best that I can.**

⚜ **Even though EFT helped to nip the last attack in the bud, what if I could go back before it ever began somehow, what a difference that would make—I honour my body for giving me these messages and I'm open to the possibility of building a phenomenal bridge to my healthy past somehow.**

⚜ **Even though I don't know how, I do know that my unconscious mind remembers comfortable joints and ease of movement because they are all in the archives of my mind—I ask, receive and allow that comfortable experience in again right now, and I'm willing to listen with even more respect to my body's messages.**

Pam goes on: *"I do have to deal with an ache in my hips that comes while sleeping and actually wakes me regularly (that's about the worst discomfort with it). The remedy is to roll over onto my back and allow my hips to release, then I can fall back asleep again. I would love to be able to access my pre-arthritis body!"*

The following setups were used to link with this mechanism of 'rolling over' and her desire to access her 'pre-arthritis' body, while at the same time expanding on her experience of a physical release:

- ✢ *Even though I would love to be able to access my pre-arthritis body and I'm excited about the possibility but I don't know how—what if that experience is there right there for me to receive—how amazing that would be!*

- ✢ *Even though I have learnt physical remedies which serve me well—of rolling over onto my back and allowing my hips to release—what if my mind could release whatever it needs to let go, naturally enabling me to receive added benefits? I know that in asking, I receive. I respectfully ask now—just as I roll over and ask physically—thankfully and with positive expectancy allowing these added benefits to unfold.*

- ✢ *. . . I accept myself completely, and naturally allow the abundance of added benefits to unfold, and I'm open to the possibility of being even more in tune with my mind body and spirit.*

I recommended that Pam ask a for a layperson's description on her next official assessment with her conventional medical consultant. Understanding what happens within her body when it flares up, as well as when it settles down can be helpful. Gaining another person's perspective of a physical problem, as well as insight into how her joints would work if they were working well can be key to using EFT on the problem and connecting to relief.

When applying these approaches to your own life or the lives of your clients, the following points are valuable:

- When working with pain, medical check-ups are essential to rule out any issues which need to be addressed medically.
- Then, when you are ready to work with EFT, tune into how the discomfort feels for you physically and emotionally.
- Ask what was happening around the time the problem was manifesting.
- Ask what or who the feeling or discomfort reminds you or your client of.
- When the discomfort and emotional drivers have been adequately addressed, think of possible choices.
- Plan and use time line work to connect to freedom of movement and comfort.

- Create positive anchors of these remembered experiences.
- Throughout all of this work use EFT creatively and persistently.
- Aim setup statements and reminder phrases at current experiences of comfort, and build on them.
- Acknowledge each incremental step of improvement however small with thanks. When we do this it is like putting in a blueprint or signpost into the brain, directing the mind and body with the help of EFT towards more of the same.
- Use persistence to transform 'tail-enders' into understandable rational disbelief. You cannot lose anything by doing this and you stand to gain far more than you would even dare to ask for or imagine.

## Part 4: Connecting to our birthright of fertility

We will now see examples from portions of sessions with two clients wanting help with improving their chances of fertility. These specifically highlight our endeavour to access their more positive mind-body connection. It is important to note that these two examples followed working in-depth on core issues. After your client reports emotional freedom on related issues, this is the most helpful time to make a reconnection to wellness.

Confirmation of freedom from trauma or negative issues can be assessed for you and your client in a number of ways:

- reaching a zero on the SUDs scale
- using a muscle test
- or even by testing SUDs in the real world.

Many therapists round off their sessions by using Pat Carrington's Choices. Following choices is an ideal time for your client to aim EFT at their future— and or to reconnect to their birthright of balance and harmony. When these approaches are used at this time, it frequently enhances the energy flow to associations of wellbeing.

### How can I apply this process to infertility?

Fertility treatment is complex and often involves working with a group of health care professionals to discover what may be going on. Conventional specialists often refer clients to me to help with possible emotional components of infertility.

## Case Study 1: Ann

Ann (not her real name) was one such client. She and her husband had been receiving many forms of fertility treatment without noticeable results. They were both feeling very stressed because it was not only costly financially but also emotionally. It was beginning to jeopardise their relationship.

I asked Ann the following question: *"If you were to guess at a reason why this is happening—however illogical it might seem—what would you say?"* (This is a question I often use) Ann replied, as many do, almost immediately. The answer appeared to come to her unexpectedly and spontaneously from her unconscious. She said: *"I don't believe that I will ever conceive because I have many feelings of shame surrounding becoming pregnant".* Logically she knew that wasn't necessarily true. However, because her unconscious mind was running the show, not conceiving was what felt true for her at this point in time. Our initial sessions of therapy focused on using EFT to work on core issues surrounding this shame.

Ann believed that these core issues were the major block to her ability to conceive. After freeing her of these limiting beliefs, we could have felt at this point that it was a done deal. However, I always remember Gary's motto: *"undersell and over deliver".* The following sessions of EFT with Ann included aiming EFT at the future as well as reconnecting to her inner wisdom prior to her trauma. Here are some of the setup statements which we used:

- ⚘ **Even though I know it was natural for me to conceive before my trauma, I deeply and completely welcome a reconnection now to my birthright during our loving oneness together.**

- ⚘ **. . . I deeply and completely honour my body's patience in allowing my mind to become ready to accept and nurture, so safely and completely, our baby within.**

- ⚘ **Even though I don't know consciously how, I do trust the inner wisdom of my mind and body to naturally do what it needs to do to welcome and cherish our loved baby.**

In addition to using setup statements and reminder phrases, I frequently encourage my clients to visualise their dreams, to include wonderful feelings and senses, and to tap whilst doing this.

Doing EFT whilst in a positive daydreaming state picks up any unspoken fears, and at the same time enhances the joyful positive expectancy of receiving.

## Case Study 2: Di and Jim

In another case, Di and Jim (not their real names) were a couple who had been recommended to come to me by a fertility clinic some four hours' journey away. They arranged to stop over in our clinic and have intensive therapy over a three day period. During our introductions, Di told us that she had a somewhat reduced chance of conceiving due to the fact that she had had one of her ovaries removed in her early 20s.

The fertility clinic had assured Di, during assessment three years ago, that despite this they were very optimistic that she would conceive naturally. After three years of trying for a baby without result, they now felt concerned that their time clock was ticking and had returned to the fertility clinic for reassurance and guidance. Further tests were run and these provided reassurance that all was well, physically.

Even though Jim and Di came together, Di asked if I would talk to her on her own first of all. Jim talked and did EFT with Tam whilst Di and I spent some time alone. During our conversation she confessed that she had become drunk one night at a club and the following day as a precaution she had taken the 'morning after' pill. Five years later she was diagnosed with ovarian cancer. Di said that from that day until this one, she had always blamed herself for getting the cancer because of her recklessness.

While Di told her story, we tapped continuously on her distressing emotions. Afterwards, she explained that she had needed to discuss this with me on my own because Jim had always said: *"You were only young Di doing what teenagers do—give yourself a break"*. It wasn't that Jim belittled what had happened but intuitively Di knew that this guilt appeared to be a stumbling block to her conceiving. She said: *"I don't believe that I deserve to be a mother"*. For a short while, we took the edge off these distressing emotions.

We intentionally take time out to 'break' state. This enhances the integration and consolidation of the positive cognitive shifts. These well-chosen breaks provide a great way of connecting to the here and now. Tam and I both feel that this whole process is particularly healing and centring.

After a relaxing lunch break, a considerable amount of EFT tapping was done with both Di and Jim on their painful emotions and limiting beliefs until Di said she felt truly ready to welcome their baby and be a loving mother.

During the second morning Di and Jim enjoyed time alone. After lunch they took time out to prepare setup statements that related to exactly what they were wanting. I have included some of the setup phrases that we used.

- *Even though Jim was ok with what had happened and I wasn't until now, we deeply and completely respect one another's individual needs.*

- *Even though we don't consciously know how conception happens, we now both totally believe in our body's ability to bond my egg and Jim's sperm perfectly together because we are at one in our love.*

- *Even though we have waited for many years, we are now experiencing positive expectancy, happy in the knowledge we can be welcoming this baby into our lives with so much love.*

REMINDER PHRASES: *Receiving this love into our lives. Allowing our bond of love to conceive this little one*

On our third day, Di and Jim wanted support and guidance to follow up and strengthen what they had already done with some positive imagery, using their words and making connections to their already great feelings. I have found that when clients use their own words to plan and dream their dreams, they really connect to their inner wisdom and their vital force flows freely. Di wanted to enjoy her feelings as well as to picture her body healing completely and her ovary brimming full of energy and vitality and ovulating naturally. Whilst Di did this Jim gently tapped Di through the EFT sequence over and over again. There was tremendous energy, emotional excitement and joy flowing after this magical tapping procedure. They both reported their positive imagery and liberating feelings as we took time for a break together.

After our lunch break I asked them if they felt it would be helpful to build on this imagery and the good feelings as well as tapping along the way. They were both very enthusiastic about continuing this whilst they were in this wonderful state of flow. I took Jim and Di through an imaginary experience of truly loving oneness, with beautiful synchronised orgasms thrilling their body, mind and spirits. As they enjoyed the afterglow of imagined love in action, I continued to guide them through their perception of the joy of conception and a strong healthy egg softly and comfortably embedding safely in exactly the right place for their baby to grow. During the time of their beautiful experience, I added suggestions of continued benefits from their earlier EFT tapping routine, and of continuing to do this on their return home.

We discussed the power of their dreams, connecting to feelings and having a positive focus. They were both very happy to take home the CD recordings which we had made for them. These audios included what they were wanting, their dream journeys and positive tapping along the way. We heard two months after their visit that their healing and uplifting journey continues to be a support and inspiration to them both.

Trauma can create distorted writing on the walls of our minds. We are truly blessed now that we have EFT which erases these misperceptions which limit our lives. Tapping also has the potential of reconnecting to our birthright and life enhancing perceptions.

This was succinctly put by Bruce Lipton[3], (a cellular microbiologist and Stanford researcher) when he taught that 'our perception of life informs our biology'. How our cells respond to life is based on what we believe. 'Perceptions' lie between the environment and cell expression. If our perceptions are accurate, the resulting behaviour will be life enhancing. If we operate from 'misperceptions', our behaviour will be inappropriate and will jeopardize our vitality by compromising our health.

## Part 5: Reconnecting to freedom in breathing

### Case Study 3: Jamie

Jamie visited me last summer with streaming itchy eyes and other typical hay fever symptoms. Summertime for Jamie had been really miserable for the past twenty years. He had received little benefit from anti-histamine medication and he was finding his symptoms were getting progressively worse. This seems to occur mainly due to the fact that with practise we get better at doing most things. An example of this is riding a bike—with repetition we become more adept at cycling. Unfortunately, because of this, reactions or patterns of behaviour that we do not want—or which no longer serve a useful purpose can become habitual and we become 'better' at performing them.

Fortunately we can make traumas and limiting beliefs vanish as if by magic when using EFT to neutralise the emotional roots. I asked Jamie a few questions about his symptoms and also asked him what was happening around him at the time that he first noticed them. He said his first recollection of feeling tightness in his breath was when he was six years old, during an extended family camping holiday on a farm. Towards the end of this family holiday, his breathing became so difficult that his parents rushed him to the local village doctor. The doctor listened to his chest and sent him on his way with a prescription for anti-histamines. Every summer since that time, Jamie had been on anti-histamine medication.

During our first consultation, as we delved deeper into Jamie's memory of that breathless panic attack, he realised that it had happened well into the second week of the holiday. Throughout the whole of their time on the farm, the combine harvester was working in nearby fields. Despite this, Jamie's 'allergic' reaction only appeared later on into the holiday. I asked him if he was enjoying his holiday before his breathing problem showed up. He recalled the holiday as being an absolutely great time because there were lots of cousins and friends to play with. Jamie said he had celebrated his sixth birthday around a week before he experienced his breathing trauma.

I became aware, as he talked about his memories, that he was experiencing some distressing symptoms. So, straight away, I asked him to follow me through the EFT routine. This period of tapping focused upon his current presenting symptoms and also connected him to the holiday experience. Open ended questions such as *"My hay fever symptoms happened because . . . . . . . . . . . . . . ."* were also used. After a considerable amount of tapping Jamie had noticed a slight reduction in his discomfort. Throughout this session we made an audio CD to jog his memory of the EFT routine. This recording also included suggestions of homework. This homework was aimed at him using EFT with more specific descriptions of any discomfort he was feeling. I highlighted the tremendous value to him of really noticing any changes in the quality or level of symptoms occurring. Jamie was happy with the idea of chasing these symptoms especially after discussing the concept the of 'chasing the pain' technique. Just before he left, he also wrote down some setup statements to work with such as:

- ⁊ *Even though it was a great holiday with all my family—it just hasn't been fun having this reaction which is still bothering me right now.*

- ⁊ *Even though I don't understand why I got this reaction part way through my holiday—I'm open to the possibility of discovering why, somehow.*

In addition to doing this tapping homework, I also asked him to ask his parents if they could throw any light on any earlier sensitising events to help us open other possible doors to his freedom.

On Jamie's return a week later he reported short bursts of improvements but then his symptoms quickly returned. Unfortunately, no one in the family had been able to shed any light on the problem at all. In our second session, we explored doing the EFT tapping procedure and Jamie just guessing at what might have happened on this fateful holiday. Whilst he talked about imagined events and feelings, he did the EFT tapping as if he was telling his story. Following this, there appeared to be some improvement in his symptoms. When I asked him what these symptoms reminded him of when he was younger, he looked blank. As his guessing had so far been fruitful, he was happy to tap and at the same time to make up imagined memories of what it reminded him of. There was no way of telling if his guesses were close to the truth or not. However, after this he reported a measurable improvement in the comfort of his throat and eyes which appeared to point to the possibility of his unconscious guesses being close to the truth.

Towards the end of this second session I asked him if he could tell me the story of this holiday again and do the EFT tapping as he did so. I recommended that he begin at the very start of the holiday describing just how he felt at the beginning of this holiday. He described his feelings of total and complete summer freedom and happiness. He had been involved in turning the hay as it dried in the sunshine. His family and friends had spent many hours during the first week living outside and picnicking in the fields. It occurred to me that as he talked in this very animated way, his breathing and eyes looked much clearer. It seemed as if he was re-living this freedom as he spoke—I asked him how much he wanted to live, breath and feel these easy feelings every summer from now on. Jamie did not need to answer my question; his enthusiastic nodding and energetic happy tapping answered that for me.

On Jamie's third visit he reported a vast improvement in his hay fever symptoms. He also said that normally he would have tended to keep out of the garden and especially avoid times when he knew that his son was mowing the lawn. Instead, he chose to test the benefit of the tapping homework that he had done. Despite facing potentially difficult situations, no undue discomfort had occurred. I asked him if he was willing to go through telling his holiday story right from this lovely summer freedom experience to his difficulty in breathing, as well as visiting the doctor. I urged him to let me know if he experienced any emotional discomfort whilst he was doing this so that we could really use EFT to hone into some important issues.

As before, in telling his story he was very animated, telling how he was enjoying being involved in the haymaking and baling process. He said some of the older cousins made hay houses out of the bales and they all played in these tiny houses. At this point of the story his breathing became much more laboured so I tapped on him at the same time as he was tapping on himself. Later, when he calmed and we progressed through his story—stopping and clearing as we went—it became evident that one of the bales of hay had fallen on him creating a considerable amount of dust and fragments of straw which obviously hampered his breathing and frightened him.

Towards the end of the third session together, Jamie re-told his story without any undue disruption in his energy system. We completed our session with Jamie once again talking about the very beginning of his holiday. He described his total summer freedom and at the same time tapped himself continuously. At the peak of his joyful freedom experience, we created a positive kinaesthetic anchor for those wonderful images and feelings. The following week I was thrilled when he rang to say that he wouldn't need another appointment because he still felt exactly the same freedom of mind and body that he remembered feeling before the hay bale incident.

> EDITOR'S NOTE:
> 'Anchor' refers to a physical position (e.g. left hand on right wrist) which can be used by the client at any time in the future to help him re-associate with the positive images and feelings.

Jamie also told me something else which fascinated me and is another interesting twist to his story. When he related his hay bale story to his Mother and was telling her about what had happened on that holiday, she look really shocked. Then, she immediately told Jamie her story. Apparently, when he was only two days old, they had had to call an ambulance to take him to hospital because he was fighting for his breath. When they arrived at the accident and emergency department the doctor there used a special tube to clear a blockage of mucous from his mouth and throat.

Jamie wisely tapped on himself as his mother recounted this trauma to him. His mother said, at the time she was sure that her little two day old baby was going to die. She said Jamie had turned blue and the only thing she could think to do whilst she waited for help was to rub his back whilst he lay with his head hanging down over her knees. Her distress at her powerlessness and the emotional charge within her in telling her story was very obvious to Jamie so he asked his dear mother to just follow him through the tapping routine as she talked.

Co-incidence maybe—I think not. I believe this frightening experience whilst playing in the hay, reminded his unconscious of nearly dying as a two day old newborn baby. At six years old, once again his unconscious mind was understandably triggered by the hay bale falling and his difficulty in breathing. This created an extreme reaction and association to the powerlessness that he felt as a little baby fighting for his breath and the six year old's difficulty in breathing.

I had a Christmas card from Jamie last Christmas, also signed by his mother, in which they said how much happier they both felt after neutralising this extremely fearful memory from the archives of their minds.

## AUTHOR'S BIOGRAPHY AND CONTACT DETAILS

Mair has thoroughly enjoyed her full time self employment in private practice as a psychotherapist/hypnotherapist since 1980. In 2000 she was thrilled to do her Energy Psychology training with the developers of EFT, TAT & BSFF. Since receiving her training, Mair and her husband Tam have been teaching EFT, BSFF & TAT in the UK and throughout the world. In 2005 Mair was honoured to receive EFT Master Practitioner status from Gary Craig, the developer of EFT.

website:   www.TickhillClinic.com
email:     MairLLLL@aol.com
phone:     01302 743113

REFERENCES:

1. Hogan, Kevin, 'Through The Open Door—Secrets of Self-Hypnosis', (Pelican, 2000) (chapter 16 was my earliest reported interventions for my own eyesight improvements)
2. O'Connor, Joseph & Seymour, John, 'Introducing Neuro-Linguistic Programming—The New Psychology of Personal Excellence', (Aquarian Press, 1990)
3. Lipton, Bruce, 'The Biology of Belief', (Hay House, 2008)

# Finding the Root of the Problem

## Tam Llewellyn, EFT Master, EFTCert-Honors

### What do you mean by the 'root of the problem'?

When we use EFT it is essential that we tap on the correct problem. This may seem obvious, but it is very easy to miss the major aspect of the problem—the one which is really driving the discomfort.

In its standard form, EFT requires a 'setup statement' where the problem is brought up and stated as accurately as possible before the tapping begins. Finding the correct setup statement is essential. When EFT fails to solve the issue, I find that by far the most likely reason is that we have chosen the wrong aspect of the problem or even the wrong problem.

Often the problem is 'obvious', but in these cases we should be especially on our guard. If it is so obvious, why was it not identified and treated long ago? I will give two of my own cases to illustrate this, and how careful we must be.

### Case Study: Crunchie Bars As A 'Reward'

The first case was a middle aged woman, who had a number of both physical and emotional problems but they all appeared to relate to her being grossly overweight. The cause of her excess weight was 'obvious'—she ate too much and exercised too little.

We worked on various aspects of her over-eating, found that these were related to incidents in her past, soon dealt with them using EFT and her weight dropped a little. However, she eventually admitted to being 'hooked' on Crunchie Bars (a chocolate bar available in the UK). Her craving for them was removed using EFT to the extent that the smell and very idea of them revolted her. The job appeared to be done and I left a month's gap until her next appointment expecting her to have lost a considerable amount of weight by then and to be ready for me to work on a few outstanding problems.

A month later she returned still over weight and still eating Crunchie Bars. She hated the smell and taste of the Crunchie Bars but was still eating four or five a day! We spent a long session exploring this aspect and I eventually discovered that many years ago she had been in a 'Weight Watchers' Club' using a strict diet plan. Crunchie Bars were included in the diet as a reward if the dieter had complied with the diet. They had become associated in her mind as a reward, and she still felt happy and rewarded eating them, even though they tasted awful!

We could have tapped on the weight problem and other consequent problems forever with little result, but as soon as the link between Crunchie Bars and the feeling of reward was tapped away, the weight and problems disappeared.

CASE STUDY: TRAINED TO 'TAKE IT' WITHOUT RESISTANCE OR EMOTION

The second case involved a younger woman who had suffered physical abuse from her father and sexual abuse from an older brother. She was also raped by a stranger as a young adult. As a result, she had no confidence in herself and would not venture out alone. She was even very tense when she was outside and escorted.

Again the problems were 'obvious'. The abuse by father and brother and the rape were all vivid individual events and all appeared to be legs under the table top which represented her problem. All were ideal problems for EFT and easily worked on by tapping on the specific events which she could vividly recall. The only difficulty was that she had very little emotion when recalling the events. She had had a lot of therapy and I put her lack of strong emotion regarding the events down to the partial success of earlier therapy.

It was difficult to raise her emotion regarding the events. Being provocative and pushing her very hard could bring tears to her eyes which could easily be tapped away. After a number of sessions she could recall the various events clearly and without emotion, and she had forgiven the perpetrators. However, the fear of being outside alone remained huge and steadfast.

When discussing forgiveness there was always some reluctance in forgiving herself. This is often a factor when women have suffered a sexual assault. There is often a feeling that the victim is in some way responsible, however illogical that may be. When we worked on this aspect, she was always willing to forgive herself and certainly understood that there was, in truth, nothing to forgive and that she was in no way the cause of the physical and sexual abuse she had suffered. Still there was always a feeling that there was more to it, and always the problem crept back.

We had almost a full session on this area and the truth finally surfaced. She had been beaten by her father and was beaten until she stopped crying (as her father thought any sign of emotion needed knocking out of her). Her elder brother had received the same treatment but had rebelled. His rebellion had caused the father to increase the beatings until the brother was seriously injured and left home. This had taught her to take the beatings without emotion or resistance and this proved to be a very successful strategy {see *Healing the Future with EFT*}.

In later life when she was raped, the same strategy sprang into play and she did not resist, nor did she show any emotion after the event. In view of this, her family and the authorities while accepting her story that she had been raped did not take the matter too seriously and the case was not pursued. Consequently, she thought of herself as a natural victim, and was afraid to expose herself to any risk, as she knew she was trained to accept any abuse without resistance or emotion. Not wishing to be abused, she simply did not go out without protection.

Now that we had found the real problem, we knew where to work. It was not an easy case, as we had to remove a life-long tactic of submission and withheld emotion, and show that she could be safe outside and could assert herself. However, once the real problem was identified the task became possible.

## How can I avoid the pitfall of the 'obvious'?

Now that we have seen how the 'obvious' aspect may not be the 'real' aspect requiring work, let's look at tactics we can take to avoid this pitfall.

The first important one is to OBSERVE, and observe closely. The client will, often subconsciously, point out the problem area. In the first case above there is an obvious inconsistency in that the client continued to crave something that revolted her. In the second case the inconsistency was not so obvious, but there was a pointer in that the client's forgiveness of herself was not fully implemented and the problem crept back.

Sometimes the inconsistency is identified by LEAKAGE (such as a tapping foot or a tight throat) or sometimes there is inconsistency between word and action (such as saying 'yes' and shaking the head).

If you study Gary Craig's more recent examples of EFT you will see that he is far less reliant on a slickly worded concise setup statement, but wanders around the problem statement—"spouting garbage and gold", as he puts it. This may seem undirected and random, and the actual wording probably is, but look at Gary's eyes. As he chats on he is observing his client's every movement and reaction. As he mentions the real problem in his ramblings he notes the client's reaction and focuses in on the issue causing the problem, even if the client does not recognise it until much later.

Gary sometimes moves on from the obvious problem by asking the client: *"What does it remind you of?"* You will note that he does not stop tapping while the client thinks, as during the thinking the client will be turning over in their minds the true problem basis, and needs to be tapped on as different things pop up. You will also note how closely Gary looks at his client while they think—looking for that subconscious indication that they have realised what the real problem is.

Another useful tactic, when neither the setup statement nor the reminder phrase is hitting home is to drop them altogether for a round or two and just tap. The client will often understand the real root of the problem, even if they do not realise it, and tapping without reminders will sometimes bring it out.

In summary, watch your client and understand their tiniest reaction. If you are not getting results, have the client tap without words, and allow the problem to surface.

## AUTHOR'S BIOGRAPHY AND CONTACT DETAILS

Dr Tam Llewellyn-Edwards is the non-executive Chairman of the AAMET, and holds the Chair of Homeopathy & Energy Studies at Calamus International University. He is a Master EFT Practitioner awarded that status by Gary Craig and holds Gary's EFTCert-Honors Certification. He also practices and teaches a number of other Energy Therapies.

    Website:  www.TickhillClinic.com
    Email:     TLlewellyn@aol.com

# A Conversation with Your Body

CAROL LOOK, LCSW, EFT MASTER, EFTCERT-HONORS

## Introduction

Whenever we have been traumatized, hurt, betrayed or scared, our body records the feelings on an energetic and cellular level. As the well-known trauma specialist Bessel van de Kolk says: *"Your body keeps the score."*

When we have a car accident, the bruises or broken bones are evident, physical, visible to the eye and painful when touched. When we cut ourselves with a knife or burn ourselves in the kitchen, the scars can last indefinitely—proof that yes, we endured yet made it through a hardship of some kind. But when we've been screamed at, abandoned, or threatened, we have no visible scars to see or show others. However, our bodies do indeed make and keep excellent records of these incidents in our energy fields.

## What is the 'freeze response'?

According to traumatologist and neurologist Dr. Robert Scaer[1], the necessary ingredients for a trauma are when we experience both helplessness and terror from our life being threatened. When we experience these feelings, we 'freeze' and all the incoming data gets downloaded into our bodies until some later date when we are allowed the time, space or safety to discharge this freeze response. The problem is that we rarely have the time, and are rarely given the opportunity to discharge the freeze response, which then leads to a continuum of experiences that can be categorized as Post-Traumatic Stress Disorder (PTSD).

The reason talk therapy is useful only up to a point is because of this body-oriented freeze response . . . talking just does not get to the bottom of the trauma that has been encoded into our physiology.

Enter EFT . . .

## So if talking won't help, what will?

EFT is my energy technique of choice to address all emotional conflicts and trauma at multiple levels—emotional, spiritual, physical, and electrical. So when you were reamed out by your coach, the 'trauma' can't just be talked out in traditional talk therapy without leaving an electrical trace. Impressions have been made beyond the rational processing of the mind, and when your friend or colleague says: *"He was having a bad day"* or *"He does it to everyone"*, this doesn't help erase the electrical impression that was made by the incident. If we seriously want to rewire ourselves, EFT is our tool.

Think of the positive reframe of the phrase, 'rewiring our brain'. We don't need a new brain, we don't need to be fixed because we're not broken. We have all the necessary parts, we just need to do some rewiring so the electrical impulses are firing in response to the right stimuli. We have all the ingredients now, we just need to make new connections, perceptions and interpretations.

EFT's Discovery Statement says: 'THE CAUSE OF ALL NEGATIVE EMOTION IS A DISRUPTION IN THE BODY'S ENERGY SYSTEM'. Let's continue to clear those disruptions and embrace the deep level healing that is available to us.

The first step is to develop 'rapport' with your body.

## How do I develop this 'rapport with my body'?

First and foremost, you need to do it in a genuine and loving way, as you might with a friend or new client coming for an appointment. Be kind, listen deeply, be open, and make time to communicate. Too many people ignore the messages from their body, or don't even recognize that their bodies are communicating with them to begin with!

The following points help me approach my clients when they want to work on emotional underpinnings of physical issues. (Keep in mind that I am not a medical doctor, so I am not treating the illness, but the underlying emotional and vibrational conflicts that contribute to the illness.)

1. PAIN IS A SIGNAL: Pain is a brilliant, loud, information-rich signal. We need to hear it or we will risk the signal becoming amplified to get our attention. Pain is often an unconscious process. Conflicts are manifested through the body (soma) from emotional tension in the mind (psyche) which is why we develop psychosomatic illnesses. The illnesses or headaches are real; however the origin is psychological conflict, not germs, viruses or bacterial causes.

2. METAPHORICAL CLUES: Often the body has stored information in particular organs for metaphorical reasons. Our body is far more intelligent than we ever give it credit for, and sometimes it tries to get our attention in a humorous or obvious way. It's not unusual for shoulder problems to be connected to experiences of carrying the weight of the world, with legs, knees and feet being connected to moving forward, or skin issues reflecting deep irritations and issues bothering us 'below the surface'.

3. TRAUMAS AND CONFLICTS DRAIN OUR IMMUNE SYSTEMS: These repressed, suppressed, 'frozen' or avoided hurts, resentments and conflicts naturally siphon off energy and strength from our immune systems, making us susceptible to illness or structural vulnerabilities. Although still potentially highly functioning, we remain in inner turmoil and eventually develop a physical challenge because we have no more psychic room in which to store it.

4. CURE VERSUS CAUSE: It is my personal opinion that we spend way too much time looking for cures and ignoring the cause of our physiological ailments. EVERY ILLNESS HAS A VIBRATION. We would spend less time and money and gain more health and vitality if we looked at the vibrations or causes of our problems and treated them with EFT. This does not mean we don't need a doctor when we have a serious issue. It means throwing pills or surgery at our body will succeed—but only temporarily—if we don't address the underlying vibration.

*EDITOR'S NOTE:*
This is one of the principal themes of this book.

## Can I establish rapport with my body by asking questions?

I love asking myself or clients questions to stimulate energetic connections that may have gone unnoticed by the conscious mind. I also like 'fill in the blank' statements such as the ones listed below. Make up your own, write quickly, and you may be surprised by what pops up for you. Below are some samples and favorites:

1. If my _____ could talk, it would tell me that I have been neglecting this emotion: _____.
2. My sore _____ represents the conflict I have over _____ (or in this relationship.)
3. Romantic love conflicts and hurts seem to be stored in my _____.
4. Money worries always seem to show up in my _____.
5. Anger issues have traditionally caused me to develop pain or inflammation in my _____.
6. Fears seem to manifest physically through my _____.
7. When I feel underappreciated, my _____ hurts.
8. When I'm threatened on the job and feel competitive, I tend to have tightness in my _____.
9. When I'm exhausted and overworked, I notice discomfort in my _____.
10. When I encounter problems with my family, my _____ always flares up.

Remember, I believe we would be far more efficient if we spent time and energy on the vibrational cause of the problem, (its core) rather than the cure (what happens afterwards), and then address this vibration with EFT, so that we can stay healthy longer! Problems are caused by vibrations, and since we have the power to change our vibrations (which we do through thoughts and feelings), why not put more focus where we have more power?

## The Past—Holding onto traumatic events

In this section, I will be addressing ways to approach illness and pain that has been stored in the body from traumas from an energetic perspective. Please note, I am not a medical doctor, and am not in any way suggesting you do not seek appropriate medical care for physiological issues. I am offering an additional perspective and a powerful way to use EFT in combination with medical options.

We hold the memory of past events in our bodies as much as we do in our minds and our energy fields. Past events have a particular 'vibration'. This is why they need to be cleared at all levels, and I have not yet found a technique more elegant and complete than EFT for this clearing process.

## How can I discover what my body is trying to tell me?

After you have seen your doctor and heard the diagnosis, does it make sense? Can you trace it to emotional contributors? What is your body trying to say? And, more importantly, are you willing to listen?

We all have experienced mild to severe past traumas (actual events such as car accidents, falling, being hit, mugged, etc) or have been holding ongoing emotional conflicts that remain unresolved.

Pick a part of your body where you tend to have a vulnerability to stress. Maybe your tummy acts up over work stress, maybe your lower back bothers you when you're having marital conflict, maybe your skin erupts when a problem is festering. Assume that your body has made connections for you. I invite you to be a detective to find out what you need to release in order to bring physical comfort back into your life.

1. What trauma is being stored in this body part and why is it trying to get your attention?
2. Have you been neglecting something?
3. Have you been ignoring making a commitment or a decision?

## Can you give an example of how to do this?

A client comes in complaining of severe back pain. She assumes it started after having a sports injury, but the MD/GP found no concrete structural damage left after her medical treatment. There is no more treatment available other than rest, pain relievers, or a risky surgery that has a poor track record. You are not a doctor, so you are not licensed to treat the illness or injury, but you may start asking questions:

1. Did you ever have back pain before the sports injury?
2. Why do you think it is still going on after all these years?
3. Who or what is represented by this pain?
4. If there is no damage visible on the x-rays, what 'information' about the injury/accident is still being stored in your back?

The pain was physical as well as emotional, but the wounds are still 'active' even though the injury was years ago. What message might be in her back pain? What does she need to 'hear'? Try these setup phrases and tapping sequences as a guide:

- ⸙ *Even though I have been ignoring this message in my back, I choose to pay attention now*

- ⸙ *Even though I'm scared to listen to the message in my back, I am open and willing to listen now*

- ⸙ *Even though I know there's something I need to hear from this pain, it's not just about the injury, I accept that I was scared and that I am now open to the information.*

| | |
|---|---|
| EYEBROW: | *I feel scared of listening to the message.* |
| SIDE OF EYE: | *I know my back has stored that trauma since 19__.* |
| UNDER EYE: | *I feel so worried about bringing it up again.* |
| NOSE: | *I know my back is trying to get my attention.* |
| CHIN: | *I don't want to 'go there'.* |
| COLLARBONE: | *My back is taking me there.* |
| UNDER ARM: | *I can handle dealing with this trauma again.* |
| HEAD: | *I want to know why my back is 'talking' to me.* |
| EYEBROW: | *I feel open to the information here.* |
| SIDE OF EYE: | *I'm ready and willing to listen.* |
| UNDER EYE: | *I'm scared but I know I can handle the information.* |
| NOSE: | *I know what emotions I am storing, but I wanted to ignore them.* |
| CHIN: | *No wonder my back is hurting.* |
| COLLARBONE: | *I am willing to express and release the trauma.* |
| UNDER ARM: | *I don't need to store the pain anymore.* |
| HEAD: | *I am free to give it up if I choose.* |

## How can I use this process for allergies?

Allergies are rampant in our society. When the body has an allergy, it believes there is an outside force attacking, and it musters all its forces (the runny nose, watery eyes etc) to fight off the attacker. Suppose you looked at your life for other perceived or real 'attacks' that may be manifesting in allergies. While you may use the fact that the pollen count is high as a way to legitimize your allergies, I encourage you to look for underlying emotional causes and conflicts. Do any other 'attacks' come to mind?

⚘ *Even though I'm allergic to so many things, I choose to accept my body is trying to protect me.*

⚘ *Even though the allergies remind me of an earlier attack, one I wanted to forget, I choose to accept my body's response.*

⚘ *Even though I remember what attack my body is truly responding to, I accept the allergies and accept my body's response.*

| | |
|---|---|
| EYEBROW: | *I was attacked many years ago.* |
| SIDE OF EYE: | *I'm still holding that fear in my body and allergies.* |
| UNDER EYE: | *I had forgotten about that attack, but my body remembers.* |
| NOSE: | *I have been fighting that attack with my allergies.* |
| CHIN: | *It has been a long time and I'm willing to feel the pain.* |
| COLLARBONE: | *I remember the attack as if it were yesterday.* |
| UNDER ARM: | *I was so scared.* |
| HEAD: | *No wonder my system wants to protect me.* |
| EYEBROW: | *I am ready to release the need for protection.* |
| SIDE OF EYE: | *I'm ready to protect myself now.* |
| UNDER EYE: | *I am safer than I was back then.* |
| NOSE: | *I choose to protect myself in new ways.* |
| CHIN: | *I appreciate how my body was trying to take care of me.* |
| COLLARBONE: | *I am ready to release the allergies.* |
| UNDER ARM: | *I know why I needed them.* |
| HEAD: | *I don't need them anymore.* |

## How can I use this process to facilitate *letting go*?

Take another physical event such as a car accident. Why is the pain still there after 20 years? Regardless of the original diagnosis, think of it in energetic terms. Why might you still be holding on to it?

It is very common to hold on to physical pain for emotional reasons. We all have done it, but it is possible to separate this tangle and move on with EFT.

I have had several clients who were involved in car accidents who were afraid to 'let go' or forget the trauma of the accident. They believed the pain helped them stay vigilant on the road --- it reminded them what could happen if they didn't pay attention.

⚡ *Even though I've been holding on to the pain from this accident for too long, I'm afraid to give it up, I deeply and completely love and accept myself anyway*

⚡ *Even though the doctors said I would be in pain for the rest of my life, I'm willing to consider that I don't need to be.*

⚡ *Even though I'm holding onto this physical pain for emotional reasons, I accept who I am and how I feel about what happened.*

| | |
|---|---|
| EYEBROW: | *I am afraid to give up the pain, I don't want anyone to forget what happened.* |
| SIDE OF EYE: | *I was traumatized by the accident* |
| UNDER EYE: | *I need to remember and be careful* |
| NOSE: | *The accident was so overwhelming* |
| CHIN: | *I'll never forget the accident, and neither will my body* |
| COLLARBONE: | *I don't want to let it go* |
| UNDER ARM: | *It's been with me so long* |
| HEAD: | *I'm afraid of letting go of the pain even though I want to* |
| EYEBROW: | *I might be able to let it go now* |
| SIDE OF EYE: | *I'm listening to my body and I know what I need* |
| UNDER EYE: | *What if I could let some of it go?* |
| NOSE: | *I don't need to remember the pain* |
| CHIN: | *I'm willing to work through the trauma and fear* |
| COLLARBONE: | *I know my body is better now* |
| UNDER ARM: | *I don't need to hold on any longer* |
| HEAD: | *I feel open to releasing this old pain from the accident* |

## The Past—Storing bad news

In this section, I will address numerous examples of how past emotional conflict and 'bad news' may be stored in your body, ailments, aches and pains.

Let's begin with emotional traumas that don't involve cuts, scrapes, bruises or any other obvious physical problem. Suppose you felt abandoned by your parents when they divorced. They were so involved in their fighting that they left the kids alone and without resources to talk through the fear and sadness. Maybe you were pre-adolescent, not quite angry yet, and the shock of the news of your parents' divorce was never aired with them, a counselor or your peers—this is extremely common.

- Do you remember where you were when you heard this news?
- Do you remember what you were wearing, what the temperature was, whether you were sitting or standing?
- Where was the news stored in your body? If there isn't a clear answer, just guess.
- What conclusions about yourself and life (e.g. It's not safe to love . . . ) did you make as a result?

For example:
> "I felt like I was punched in the stomach when I heard that."
> Q: How's your stomach now?

> "It hit me like a ton of bricks."
> Q: Where did the ton of bricks land?

> "It really threw me for a loop."
> Q: What was the effect of being thrown for a loop?

Our bodies are storage places for verbal, emotional, and spiritual betrayals. This is why we need to clear our energy system of leftover conflicts. It is more than probable that many people aren't even aware of how particular shocks were stored, how bad news has been held, or how old wounds were covered up instead of being healed.

## Can this process help if I feel betrayed or unsupported?

As I mentioned earlier, it should come as no surprise that the ailments and complaints of adults can be symbolically traced to an early emotional pain or conflict. Suppose you were stunned to hear that you were betrayed, and lost the support of a trusted friend, mentor or boss. One convenient place to store this information and trauma is in your knees and legs . . . . symbolically representing 'feeling supported' etc. (If this following example doesn't resonate for you, choose your own, and fill in your own words.)

- ✢ *Even though the bad news has apparently been stored in my knees, I choose to release it now.*

- ✢ *Even though I didn't know where else to store the bad news, I accept who I am and how I feel about it.*

- ✢ *Even though I've been keeping this bad news in my body, I choose to release it now.*

| | |
|---|---|
| EYEBROW: | *I don't want to remember this bad news.* |
| SIDE OF EYE: | *I know I've been storing it in my legs.* |
| UNDER EYE: | *I feel protective of this bad news.* |
| NOSE: | *I didn't feel supported.* |
| CHIN: | *I don't want to open up these old hurts.* |
| COLLARBONE: | *I feel hurt from the bad news.* |
| UNDER ARM: | *I still feel shocked and frozen.* |
| HEAD: | *I have been storing the bad news in my legs for years.* |
| EYEBROW: | *I'm not ready to let it go.* |
| SIDE OF EYE: | *Maybe I am.* |
| UNDER EYE: | *I don't want to remember the bad news.* |
| NOSE: | *I might be able to let this go from my legs.* |
| CHIN: | *It was a long time ago.* |
| COLLARBONE: | *It's time to be free of this burden.* |
| UNDER ARM: | *I'm willing to let some of it go from my legs.* |
| HEAD: | *I don't need to hold it in my body anymore.* |

## What if I've received bad news?

Bad news is often a shock to us and of course, therefore, to all the cells in our body. It represents a trauma and we 'freeze' when we hear it. Telephone calls often deliver bad news of an accident, a death, results of a medical test, or a major life change. Think of a phone call you received that was a shock to you (or your client.)

- Where is the shock of this news stored for you?
- Does it feel like it's frozen in your body?
- Did time stop for you back then?
- What physical problems have you encountered since then?
- Have you ever been able to let it go?

   ↳ *Even though this information came as a shock to me, and I've been storing it in my neck, I accept who I am and what I did with it.*

   ↳ *Even though I didn't see it coming, I accept where I chose to bury this information.*

   ↳ *Even though I wasn't prepared to hear the bad news, and it lodged in my neck, I accept who I am, where I put it, and how I feel about it now.*

| | |
|---|---|
| EYEBROW: | *I still remember how I felt when I heard it.* |
| SIDE OF EYE: | *I froze up inside.* |
| UNDER EYE: | *I feel so sad when I remember the phone call.* |
| NOSE: | *I remember being so shocked, and a part of me still feels shocked.* |
| CHIN: | *No wonder I have a stiff neck.* |
| COLLARBONE: | *I was caught off guard and didn't know what to do.* |
| UNDER ARM: | *I've been holding onto the shock and fear in my neck.* |
| HEAD: | *I didn't know what to do with the information.* |
| EYEBROW: | *I am considering releasing the shock from my neck.* |
| SIDE OF EYE: | *I'm willing to let go of some of the emotional trauma.* |
| UNDER EYE: | *I WAS caught off guard, and that's ok.* |
| NOSE: | *I didn't see it coming, how could I?* |
| CHIN: | *It's ok to let my guard down again.* |
| COLLARBONE: | *I didn't know what to do, but now I can let go.* |
| UNDER ARM: | *I choose to release the shock from my neck and body.* |
| HEAD: | *I feel relieved already as I release these feelings from my neck.* |

## What if I blame myself for the 'bad news', or for not predicting it?

Suppose you were suddenly fired from your job or your marriage . . . and didn't see it coming. Where did you 'put' that information (bad news) while you tried to compose yourself? Many people are completely caught off guard when their spouse or partner announces that they are leaving. They berate themselves for not seeing the warning signs, and assume that they 'aren't good enough'. These conclusions along with the shock of the 'news' gets stored in the body.

- ✤ *Even though this came as a total surprise, and I'll never forget it, I accept who I am and how I feel about it*

- ✤ *Even though I blame myself for being left, I accept who I am and what I did with the information*

- ✤ *Even though it's my fault, I deserved it, I am still in shock and don't know what to do about it.*

EYEBROW: *I still feel the shock and frozen response in my back.*
SIDE OF EYE: *I know I've stored it in my back.*
UNDER EYE: *I feel so sore about the bad news.*
NOSE: *My back has never been the same.*
CHIN: *I can feel the pain of the abandonment in my back.*
COLLARBONE: *I have been storing this pain in my back.*
UNDER ARM: *I don't want to let it go.*
HEAD: *I'm still so angry.*
EYEBROW: *I feel shocked even after all these years.*
SIDE OF EYE: *I couldn't control what happened.*
UNDER EYE: *I feel so helpless even now.*
NOSE: *Why didn't I see it coming?*
CHIN: *I feel angry about being told in this way.*
COLLARBONE: *I wish he/she had handled it differently.*
UNDER ARM: *I don't know how to process the bad news.*
HEAD: *I have been holding onto the shock for all these years.*

When in doubt, add some positive rounds to help you or your client accept what happened and consider moving on.

EYEBROW: *I am ready to work through this conflict.*
SIDE OF EYE: *I'm willing to consider that it wasn't all my fault.*
UNDER EYE: *What if it was all for the best anyway?*
NOSE: *I'm not ready to let go.*
CHIN: *I still feel hurt and abandoned.*
COLLARBONE: *I don't know how to release the pain in my back.*
UNDER ARM: *I'm willing to relax and accept myself.*

| HEAD: | *I feel almost ready to accept who I am and how I dealt with the bad news back then.* |
| EYEBROW: | *I appreciate my back and who I am.* |
| SIDE OF EYE: | *I'm ok with how I stored the information in my back.* |
| UNDER EYE: | *I did the best I could back then.* |
| NOSE: | *I'm still doing the best I can.* |
| CHIN: | *I appreciate my body.* |
| COLLARBONE: | *I'm grateful to my body for protecting me.* |
| UNDER ARM: | *I appreciate my body.* |
| HEAD: | *I feel good about letting go of some of this pain.* |

## The Present—What's under your skin?

In this section, I want to address issues that manifest through our skin, the largest organ in our body. For the purpose of these illustrations, I will assume that the irritations are from current life stressors, not from past traumas as illustrated in earlier sections.

People, places, and situations get under our skin, and when we feel irritated, it shows on our face or bodies. Our skin is in touch with both our inside world and our outside world, and absorbs all the information from our environment. I believe it would do us a great service to pay attention to what our skin is communicating to us through eruptions, ailments, conditions etc. When we feel overloaded, and our feelings aren't being expressed and heard, they tend to spill into our bodies. Our skin is a perfect place to express our conflicts, stress and feelings of being overwhelmed. It is not surprising to hear someone say *"My skin is acting up since that job change . . ."* or *"He is so under my skin these day s . . ."* or *"He's like a bad rash . . ."*

### What if my skin is inflamed or showing 'eruptions'?

Suppose you or your client has been given some kind of diagnosis about skin inflammation, and the MD/GPs have done all they can do to offer medical remedies. The next step is to explore what might be causing this in your current situation:

- If your inflamed skin reminded you of someone, who would it be?
- If the inflammation had a name, what would it be?

- Who or what is causing you to feel itchy?
- If the dry itchy patches had a message, what would it be?
- If your skin rashes were trying to get your attention, what do you need to focus on?
- If you could trace the 'eruptions' with a current stressor in your life, where would you end up?
- If your skin represented 'you' and what you need, then what do 'you' need right now?

If our skin is showing conflict, find out why, where, and who is being expressed through irritations, rashes, and itching!

> ✢ *Even though he really got under my skin this time, I accept who I am and appreciate my feelings*

> ✢ *Even though I'm afraid to admit how strongly I feel about this issue, I accept myself and my feelings about what happened*

> ✢ *Even though I let this problem get under my skin, I choose to release this irritation.*

| | |
|---|---|
| EYEBROW: | *I feel so irritated by this situation.* |
| SIDE OF EYE: | *I let him get under my skin.* |
| UNDER EYE: | *I have many issues underneath the surface.* |
| NOSE: | *I'm afraid to go beneath the surface.* |
| CHIN: | *I don't want to look at what might be causing these 'eruptions'.* |
| COLLARBONE: | *He/she is so under my skin!* |
| UNDER ARM: | *I'm holding onto this irritation in my skin.* |
| HEAD: | *I don't want to let go yet.* |
| EYEBROW: | *I will consider releasing this conflict in my skin.* |
| SIDE OF EYE: | *I'm almost ready to let it go.* |
| UNDER EYE: | *Part of me really wants to let it go.* |
| NOSE: | *The other part of me wants to hold on to it.* |
| CHIN: | *He/she really got under my skin this time.* |
| COLLARBONE: | *I'm so irritated by what happened.* |
| UNDER ARM: | *I don't need to hold it in my skin anymore.* |
| HEAD: | *I feel ready to release some of this conflict and soothe my skin.* |

I also find it incredibly productive to use a few rounds expressing gratitude for your body. It reminds us how strong we really are, and allows us to temporarily focus on something positive, in spite of the problem.

| | |
|---|---|
| EYEBROW: | *I'm so grateful for my skin.* |
| SIDE OF EYE: | *I appreciate my skin.* |
| UNDER EYE: | *I love how flexible my skin has always been.* |
| NOSE: | *I appreciate all of my skin.* |
| CHIN: | *I'm grateful for what my skin has done for me.* |
| COLLARBONE: | *I appreciate my skin.* |
| UNDER ARM: | *I'm grateful for all of me.* |
| HEAD: | *I feel so grateful for my skin and my body.* |

## What if I'm feeling overwhelmed or stressed?

And if the skin problems seem to be caused by overwhelmed feelings and stress in general, I would try something along the lines of the following setups and phrasing:

- ⚕ *Even though the stress from my job is coming out in my skin, I choose to express my feelings and take care of myself*

- ⚕ *Even though the stress from my work and family is spilling over into my skin, I accept who I am and how I feel*

- ⚕ *Even though I can't handle the stress so it's irritating my skin, I accept who I am and how I feel about my life.*

| | |
|---|---|
| EYEBROW: | *I feel so stressed out.* |
| SIDE OF EYE: | *I know the stress is coming out in my skin.* |
| UNDER EYE: | *I feel so exhausted and stressed from my life.* |
| NOSE: | *I have so many feelings inside that need to come out.* |
| CHIN: | *I have so much stress in my current environment.* |
| COLLARBONE: | *I want to relax and soothe my skin.* |
| UNDER ARM: | *My poor skin can't take any more stress.* |
| HEAD: | *I just want to feel calm and soothed.* |
| EYEBROW: | *I know I'm expressing my feelings through my skin.* |
| SIDE OF EYE: | *My entire family expresses feelings through their skin.* |
| UNDER EYE: | *I don't want to express these scary feelings.* |

| NOSE: | *I'm afraid to express these strong feelings to anyone else.* |
| CHIN: | *I am so itchy about all of this.* |
| COLLARBONE: | *I feel so irritated.* |
| UNDER ARM: | *There's no place else for it to go.* |
| HEAD: | *I feel so itchy about these issues.* |

I would always end with a positive round to give the person some options about soothing their skin.

| EYEBROW: | *I know I have other outlets besides my skin.* |
| SIDE OF EYE: | *I choose to express myself clearly.* |
| UNDER EYE: | *I appreciate my feelings and will allow them to come out.* |
| NOSE: | *I accept who I am and how I feel.* |
| CHIN: | *I understand why my skin is full of conflict.* |
| COLLARBONE: | *I feel less irritated already.* |
| UNDER ARM: | *I can finally let go of some of this inflammation.* |
| HEAD: | *I no longer feel itchy about these issues.* |

The above examples are a good start. Do your own homework about the places in your body you store your conflicts, and keep tapping.

## The Present—It's not about the germs

Again, since I have already addressed past traumas and betrayals showing up in ailments, for the purposes of this section I will assume that current stressors are contributing to the aches and pains of our daily life. While there are always past stresses, let's focus on your present life.

We are all exposed to germs and bacteria every day. I have clients coming into my office coughing and spewing all over the place, I ride the New York City subway system, and I work in an apartment building. So why would I catch a cold or get the flu on a random Tuesday? What happened this time to make me a 'favorable host' to the germs?

Our immune systems are incredibly strong and adaptable. However, they can take just 'so much' before slowing down or fighting infection inadequately. The only time I catch the colds, despite how many I am exposed to, is when I am stressed out, tired, upset, or not feeling supported in my life. Clearly, it's not about the germs . . .

Suppose you feel a cold coming on, but it hasn't quite taken hold yet. While it may be too late to 'stop' it, I find it useful to explore the timing.

- What's been bothering you recently to upset you?
- What do you need to cry about?
- What has been overwhelming you recently?
- Why now?
- What's the upside of getting the cold/flu this week?

## Could it be that I need to take a break?

As we all know, some illnesses 'allow' us to take a break when we don't take enough 'time out'. This goes back to the theory of self-care ... if you don't take good care of yourself, your body will start screaming out loud to get your attention. I don't know anyone who hasn't seen this pattern in their life at one time or another.

- ✢ *Even though I'm ignoring something I need to address, I accept that my body is feeling run down*

- ✢ *Even though this virus is trying to tell me something, I accept who I am and how I feel*

- ✢ *Even though the flu is expressing something for me, I choose to be open to expressing my feelings now.*

| | |
|---|---|
| EYEBROW: | *I feel weak and run down.* |
| SIDE OF EYE: | *I feel this cold coming on.* |
| UNDER EYE: | *I feel so tired I just want a break.* |
| NOSE: | *I don't know why I'm getting sick now.* |
| CHIN: | *Maybe I'm just overtired.* |
| COLLARBONE: | *I need to rest my body.* |
| UNDER ARM: | *I wonder why I got this illness right now.* |
| HEAD: | *I don't want to be sick right now.* |
| EYEBROW: | *I choose to express my feelings.* |
| SIDE OF EYE: | *I'm going to listen to my body right now.* |
| UNDER EYE: | *I'm willing to listen to my symptoms.* |
| NOSE: | *I know I've been ignoring my health.* |
| CHIN: | *It's time to listen to my body.* |

| | |
|---|---|
| COLLARBONE: | *It's time to take care of my health.* |
| UNDER ARM: | *I choose to appreciate who I am.* |
| HEAD: | *I feel ready to hear what my body is trying to say.* |

## What if I *keep* getting ill?

If you keep feeling susceptible to germs, colds and the flu, keep tapping away at your fears of being 'infected'. From a medical perspective, most doctors will be exploring the germs. I'm not a doctor, so I am exploring the energetic causes and vibrations around illness. I have seen enough patterns to believe it's not about the germs, it's about you and your vibration . . .

- ⚡ *Even though I'm afraid to get sick again, I choose to feel strong and happy in my body*

- ⚡ *Even though I'm convinced the germs will get to me, I accept who I am and how I feel*

- ⚡ *Even though I'm feeling susceptible to germs, I accept who I am and how strong my body is.*

| | |
|---|---|
| EYEBROW: | *I feel vulnerable to germs.* |
| SIDE OF EYE: | *I've always been afraid of getting sick.* |
| UNDER EYE: | *I've always been afraid of germs.* |
| NOSE: | *I don't want to get sick.* |
| CHIN: | *I think about it all the time.* |
| COLLARBONE: | *I don't want to be so fearful.* |
| UNDER ARM: | *I feel so weak.* |
| HEAD: | *I think I have a weak immune system.* |
| EYEBROW: | *I want to feel strong.* |
| SIDE OF EYE: | *I'm ready to get over these fears.* |
| UNDER EYE: | *I choose to feel strong.* |
| NOSE: | *I AM stronger than I think.* |
| CHIN: | *It's time to feel strong again.* |
| COLLARBONE: | *My body knows what to do.* |
| UNDER ARM: | *My body knows how to be healthy.* |
| HEAD: | *I feel ready to be strong and healthy now.* |

## What if I get ill (or develop a pain) at specific times or dates?

In this case, we won't deal with germs, but with a chronic condition that flares up when you are out of sorts. Suppose your back 'goes out' approximately every 6 months and you have experienced this pattern for years. The doctors tell you there's nothing to do about it.

- Why now?
- Why this week?
- Is the feedback from your back worth listening to?
- What needs to change?
- What is your back wanting from you?

  ⚶ *Even though I just couldn't take it any more and needed a break, I choose to love and accept who I am and how I feel*

  ⚶ *Even though I couldn't take the stress in my life anymore, I accept who I am and how I feel*

  ⚶ *Even though I'm holding the stress in my back, no wonder it acted up this week, I accept who I am and choose to listen to my feelings.*

| | |
|---|---|
| EYEBROW: | *I feel so overwhelmed.* |
| SIDE OF EYE: | *I don't know why my back went 'out'.* |
| UNDER EYE: | *I feel so stressed out and can't get a break.* |
| NOSE: | *I need rest.* |
| CHIN: | *I don't know how to take time for myself.* |
| COLLARBONE: | *I don't know how to give myself what I need.* |
| UNDER ARM: | *I don't even know what I need right now.* |
| HEAD: | *I'm grateful for the quiet time and rest.* |
| EYEBROW: | *I am willing to listen to my back.* |
| SIDE OF EYE: | *I'm willing to pay attention to my feelings.* |
| UNDER EYE: | *I'm not sure why my back went out NOW . . .* |
| NOSE: | *I am willing to be open to the information.* |
| CHIN: | *It's time to make some changes.* |
| COLLARBONE: | *I don't even know what to change.* |
| UNDER ARM: | *I want to change because my life's not working.* |
| HEAD: | *I feel ready for a change.* |

When someone has to stay in bed with an illness or pain, it provides time for reflection. I always make good use of the time! What do I need to change? Something isn't working, and I try and pay attention to the recent conflicts about balancing life, love, work and family. Again, add a round expressing gratitude to your body for how strong it is.

EYEBROW:  *I totally appreciate my back.*

SIDE OF EYE:  *I'm grateful for the strength of my back.*

UNDER EYE:  *My back has carried me all these years.*

NOSE:  *I am so grateful for my back.*

CHIN:  *I appreciate the strength in my back.*

COLLARBONE:  *I feel deep gratitude for my back.*

UNDER ARM:  *I appreciate my whole body.*

HEAD:  *I appreciate my back and my body.*

## The Future—Anxiety about my life

A great deal of energy is spent worrying about our future that hasn't arrived yet. We live with chronic anxiety which of course drains our immune system and may set us up to be vulnerable to stress-related illnesses.

These worries take energy; they are 'expensive' to our health. However, tell someone with chronic anxiety that they should stop worrying, and they have no idea what you are talking about, much less how to accomplish this!

I recommend that if you find yourself 'in the future' a great deal of the time, do regular tapping sessions about your fears and anticipatory anxiety, and watch and enjoy an overall peace come into your daily life.

Suppose you are worried about your job, possible promotions, whether you're 'cutting it' or not. Worry keeps you up at night, causes you to feel exhausted and to be irritable with your spouse and kids. Sooner or later, you develop a pain, an irritation, an annoying problem with your health that gets diagnosed as a 'stress condition'. This is a typical cycle with chronic anxiety. Then the diagnosed ailments or undiagnosed pains are cause for more worry.

Imagine trading some of the current and chronic worrisome thoughts with more peaceful, gentle thoughts about your life. Maybe you could even reduce the amount of time you worry about your future. The gift of EFT for people who suffer from chronic anxiety is nothing short of astonishing.

Chronic anxiety underlies numerous health issues and sleep irregularities, so regular periods of tapping are a must for my anxious clients.

Common symptoms of chronic anxiety are stomach problems, overall digestive complications, skin irritations, insomnia, heart irregularities, internal thermostat problems etc.

- Where does your worry 'live' in your body?
- What physical conditions do you suspect may be a direct result of your anxiety?
- If you didn't obsess/worry about your future, what would you be focused on?
- What resources are your worries draining from your body/mind?
- Who will you be if you aren't a worrier?
- Who will do the family worrying if you don't?

## What if I have digestive problems?

Below, I will illustrate EFT setup phrases and tapping sequences for digestive problems, as they are so common in our culture. Before overdosing on those over the counter remedies for indigestion and gas, I recommend seeing if you can answer the above questions. You may also wish to examine your eating habits and their relationship to stress and anxiety.

For example:
- Do you watch stressful television shows or news while you eat?
- Do you tend to have arguments at the dinner table?
- Is there tension present in the kitchen in your home?
- Is there a key past event that happened during a holiday meal?
- Do you talk about unpleasant subjects during meals?

I recommend keeping these questions in mind and watch what happens during your meals. Many people don't even realize how much stress they have in their life while they are trying to eat and digest.

- *Even though I keep worrying about the future, and it unsettles my digestion, I accept who I am right now*

- *Even though I know my stomach is torn up by the worries I have, I accept who I am and how I feel anyway*

✢ *Even though my anxiety is showing up in my stomach problems, I
deeply and completely love and accept who I am.*

EYEBROW:        *My worries go right to my gut.*

SIDE OF EYE:    *I can feel the anxiety inside.*

UNDER EYE:      *I feel so worried and my stomach knows something's wrong.*

NOSE:           *I feel the worries in my gut.*

CHIN:           *I am worried all the time.*

COLLARBONE:     *I know I need to feel more peaceful.*

UNDER ARM:      *I feel out of control with my worries.*

HEAD:           *I should give my stomach a rest.*

EYEBROW:        *I will consider releasing my anxiety from my stomach.*

SIDE OF EYE:    *I'm willing to let go of some of this stomach upset.*

UNDER EYE:      *I want to be free of this worry.*

NOSE:           *I choose to be free of this anxiety about my future.*

CHIN:           *I want to release the future right now.*

COLLARBONE:     *I want to stay in the present instead.*

UNDER ARM:      *I accept who I am and how I'm feeling.*

HEAD:           *I feel better already.*

EYEBROW:        *What if I could relax my gut.*

SIDE OF EYE:    *I want to relax my gut.*

UNDER EYE:      *I choose to be free of my future worries.*

NOSE:           *I choose to relax my gut right now.*

CHIN:           *I feel free about releasing my anxiety.*

COLLARBONE:     *I choose to stay in the present instead.*

UNDER ARM:      *I accept my feelings and release and relax.*

HEAD:           *I choose to relax about my future.*

## What if I'm a *chronic worrier*?

The challenge is that the behavior and habit of worrying provides a certain
security for chronic worriers. When they are fussing about others or themselves, they feel better than when they aren't worrying. Part of it is habitual,
but the other part is what we call 'magical thinking'. They believe that if they
worry sufficiently about others, they can magically 'control' certain circumstances. At the very least, they don't have to suffer being caught off guard by
what might happen.

I think it's essential to give worriers the OPTION to keep worrying. If you take away their 'job' they will feel utterly empty, at least in the beginning. Remember, we need to feel safe with the changes from EFT {see *Is It Safe to Change?*}, or we will revert back to our old behavior.

⸙ *Even though I'm reluctant to let go of my worrying, I choose to feel calm about my life anyway*

⸙ *Even though I'm not ready to let go of my worrying, because I still think it's useful, I accept who I am and how I feel*

⸙ *Even though I don't want to give it up yet, it doesn't feel right, I accept who I am and how I feel.*

| | |
|---|---|
| EYEBROW: | *I feel reluctant to let go of my worrying.* |
| SIDE OF EYE: | *Don't make me give it up.* |
| UNDER EYE: | *Who will I be without my anxiety?* |
| NOSE: | *How will I feel in control without my anxiety?* |
| CHIN: | *Who will worry if I don't?* |
| COLLARBONE: | *I'm not ready to let it go from my stomach.* |
| UNDER ARM: | *Don't ask me to let it go yet.* |
| HEAD: | *I'm not ready to let it go.* |
| EYEBROW: | *I refuse to let go of my worrying.* |
| SIDE OF EYE: | *I'm not ready to feel free yet.* |
| UNDER EYE: | *I don't know who I'll be without it.* |
| NOSE: | *I don't want to give it up.* |
| CHIN: | *It helps me in so many ways.* |
| COLLARBONE: | *I won't give it up yet.* |
| UNDER ARM: | *I refuse to stop being anxious.* |
| HEAD: | *I feel scared about giving it up.* |

*EDITOR'S NOTE:*
All habits exist at some level to alleviate anxiety—even the habit of worrying! That is one reason why in the absence of tapping therapy, removing habits can be so challenging—because it does not initially feel safe (see 'Is It Safe to Change?')

Once you give them permission to continue worrying, then their stance loosens a bit and they become able to release a small part of the behavior. Remember, worriers have used their habit for years, sometimes decades, so to remove it with EFT will not feel safe. Once you've done a few rounds on allowing them to 'refuse' to let it go, and admit they're not ready to release it, then you have room to make some alternative suggestions. You also allow their bodies to reduce the chronic tension and stop the cycle of pumping stress hormones through their systems.

EYEBROW: *I will consider letting some of my anxiety from my stomach.*
SIDE OF EYE: *Maybe it's not as useful as I thought.*
UNDER EYE: *I wonder what it's doing to my health and my digestion?*
NOSE: *I still don't want to give it up.*
CHIN: *It helps me in so many ways.*
COLLARBONE: *Maybe I don't need it anymore.*
UNDER ARM: *Maybe it's time to consider relaxing my digestion.*
HEAD: *I still feel apprehensive about letting it go.*

When in doubt, even if there are no physical symptoms present in the body, worrying is a huge stress on the body. I recommend using **EFT** for regular health maintenance and self-care, so you have as much energy available to you to live your life with peace.

## The Future—Fear of other people's reactions

Many people spend time worrying about other people's reactions, and this always interferes with their ability to be free to attract abundance. It's not that we don't want the success or happiness we keep talking about, it's that we fear what 'they' will say, or how 'they' will react in response to our success. While these may seem like obvious fears we all have about making changes in our lives, they actually represent deeper limiting beliefs and I believe they cause quite a drain on the immune system.

Sometimes people sabotage themselves with an illness in order to appease someone in their life who might be jealous of their success. Sometimes people regain the weight they worked so hard to lose or start smoking again in order to make others feel more comfortable. Other times clients suddenly get sick in order to slow down their success—this has the effect of warding off negative reactions from family members or colleagues.

If you have put aside time to talk to your body, you will be able to 'hear' the answers to some important questions. All fear gets lodged in our bodies somewhere. In fact, I think all feelings of every kind cause changes and shifts in our chemical make-up.

For instance, say these limiting beliefs out loud:

- I'm convinced if I become successful, they will leave me.
- I know that if I'm not perfect, they won't love me.
- If I stand out again, they will try and hurt me.
- If I'm too successful, I won't be able to trust anyone.
- If I get that job, they will hurt me with their jealousy.

Do any of these statements ring true to you? Check your gut for the true 'charge' you have on these limiting beliefs.

Now read the list of statements again and locate where they surface in your body. Does the statement of trust land in your gut? Does the jealousy issue get stuck in your throat? Where does the statement about being perfect get stored in your body?

Another critical question to ask yourself and your clients is *"What happened the last time you were successful?"* There was usually a negative consequence (or perceived problem) that occurred the last time someone was 'successful'. This event needs to be cleared from your energy system and body, or you will sabotage your success in hundreds of ways to remain 'safe' from this happening again.

## What if my emotions show up in my throat?

A singer was teased and mocked by her classmates for landing the biggest part in the school play. They didn't think it was 'cool' and were probably jealous as well. Ever since that time in junior high school, she has suffered throat problems. This of course is no surprise to an outsider, but she never made the emotional and energetic connection with why her vulnerable point in her body was her throat. Every time she got sick, the illness was connected to her throat in some way. She didn't realize how expressing herself through singing had caused a conflict for her:

 ✦ *Even though they ridiculed me for standing out, I choose to voice my feelings once and for all*

 ✦ *Even thought their teasing me really hurt, and I let it stay in my throat, I accept who I am and how I feel*

 ✦ *Even though they teased me and it stayed in my throat all these years, I accept who I am and how I feel about it.*

| | |
|---|---|
| EYEBROW: | *I don't feel free to express my feelings.* |
| SIDE OF EYE: | *The hurt got caught in my throat.* |
| UNDER EYE: | *I feel so hurt about their nasty comments.* |
| NOSE: | *I wanted to sing and sing freely.* |
| CHIN: | *I thought it was a good thing to express my voice.* |
| COLLARBONE: | *My throat is so vulnerable.* |
| UNDER ARM: | *I'm tired of getting a sore throat.* |
| HEAD: | *I want to feel free and express what I feel.* |
| EYEBROW: | *I deserve a voice.* |
| SIDE OF EYE: | *I'm ready to voice my feelings.* |
| UNDER EYE: | *I couldn't tell them I was hurt back then.* |
| NOSE: | *I couldn't express my feelings back then.* |
| CHIN: | *It still hurts sometimes in my throat.* |
| COLLARBONE: | *I just want to scream and sing and shout my feelings.* |
| UNDER ARM: | *Why can't I sing?* |
| HEAD: | *What's the matter with my throat?* |

The throat always represents our ability to communicate, so there were many layers of tapping for this client. Once she cleared the original trauma stored in her throat, she could work on the fear that 'they' would ridicule her again in the future.

## What if I consistently sabotage myself?

A business man was the target of nasty gossip after he was promoted over a more senior employee. What did this leave for him in terms of energy and fear? Every time he got close to being promoted again, he sabotaged his success. When I asked him *"What happened the last time you were successful?"* he was able to identify this painful time in the office, and made the energetic connection to his sabotage behavior. In his case, he sabotaged himself by suddenly putting his back out and needing to stay at home in bed. Doctor's orders were to stay in bed, so this was a legitimate reason to stay away from work. This always happened around deadlines for critical projects at work, and the boss of course could no longer rely on him.

> ⚡ *Even though I'm afraid to be successful because of what they might say this time, I accept who I am and how I feel*

✢ *Even though I'm afraid to be successful again, I remember what happened last time, I accept my feelings and who I am*

✢ *Even though I'm afraid to be successful again, they won't like it, I accept and appreciate who I am and how I feel.*

| | |
|---|---|
| EYEBROW: | *I feel afraid of being successful again.* |
| SIDE OF EYE: | *Don't you remember what happened last time?* |
| UNDER EYE: | *I feel so afraid of standing out.* |
| NOSE: | *I don't want them to be mean to me.* |
| CHIN: | *I don't want to stand out again.* |
| COLLARBONE: | *I remember what happened last time.* |
| UNDER ARM: | *I am afraid of being seen as successful.* |
| HEAD: | *I don't want to shine again.* |
| EYEBROW: | *I'm storing this fear in my back.* |
| SIDE OF EYE: | *My back feels so vulnerable.* |
| UNDER EYE: | *I've never felt very supported by my colleagues.* |
| NOSE: | *I don't want them to be mean to me again.* |
| CHIN: | *I don't want to stand out again.* |
| COLLARBONE: | *I remember what happened last time.* |
| UNDER ARM: | *I am afraid of being seen as successful.* |
| HEAD: | *I don't want to shine again, so I take it out on my back.* |
| EYEBROW: | *I am willing to release that pain.* |
| SIDE OF EYE: | *I'm going to release the hurt from that experience.* |
| UNDER EYE: | *Their feelings were about them.* |
| NOSE: | *I choose to be successful again and enjoy it.* |
| CHIN: | *I want to be successful and feel strong in my body.* |
| COLLARBONE: | *I already am successful.* |
| UNDER ARM: | *I don't need to hide any more.* |
| HEAD: | *I feel free and ready to move forward.* |

Again, the process of clearing has several steps. First, clear the original incident or event, then clear the fear of 'it' happening again in the future, and finally, clear the symptoms in the body.

If any of these stories resonate for you, continue tapping along with the suggested sequences and then make up your own to better fit your situation.

I hope this CONVERSATION WITH YOUR BODY has been useful for you. Remember, we all store feelings and conflicts somewhere in our body, so make time to listen and hear yourself and your body's needs. Our immune systems need care, our feelings need airtime, and our bodies need rest and relaxation from the stress of the past, the present and the future.

## AUTHOR'S BIOGRAPHY AND CONTACT DETAILS

Carol Look's specialty is inspiring clients to attract abundance into their lives by using EFT and the Law of Attraction to clear limiting beliefs, release resistance and build 'prosperity consciousness'. Before becoming an EFT Master, Carol was trained as a Clinical Social Worker and earned her Doctoral Degree in Clinical Hypnotherapy.

A leading voice in the EFT community, Carol is well known for her 4 seasons as an internet radio show host and as the author of the popular books, 'Attracting Abundance with EFT', 'Improve Your Eyesight with EFT', and 'It's Not About the Food'. She has also released audio CD programs called 'The Vibration of Abundance', 'Weight Loss with EFT', and 'Clearing Clutter with EFT'. Her popular DVD programs include 'A Vibrational Approach to Healing Pain and Illness' and 'Attracting Success and Abundance with EFT and the Law of Attraction'.

Carol's primary professional focus and passion is teaching EFT workshops and retreats around the world on the topics of Attracting Abundance, Pain Relief, and Clearing Addictions.

Visit Carol through www.AttractingAbundance.com or by email: carol@carollook.com.

REFERENCES:

1. Robert C Scaer, MD, 'The Body Bears the Burden', (Hayworth Medical Press, 2001)

# Is It Safe to Change?

CAROL LOOK, LCSW, EFT MASTER, EFTCERT-HONORS

## How does 'safety' relate to making changes?

In the early days of EFT and TFT, the topic of 'safety' was considered one of the subjects practitioners would treat as a cause for 'energy reversals'. Being 'reversed' meant that your energy system was temporarily upside down, confused, or not working efficiently, and either your system would not 'take' the treatment to begin with or the treatment would not 'stick'. There were and still are many complicated ways to address and treat this problem. However, treating the real issue—*being afraid to change*—with the basics of EFT has always worked for me in my practice and workshops.

If someone was apparently reversed—meaning energy therapies weren't working on them—practitioners concluded that there were some emotional reasons for not wanting to change. Safety, not deserving, being unwilling to do what it takes, not being able to accept yourself unless you change—all of these conflicts were considered tappable issues using the standard reversal setup statements.

> Feeling safe enough to change is the bottom line, regardless of what technique you are using, whether traditional talk therapy or EFT.

If your body and mind are not congruent with the consequences of releasing the old patterns, you will not feel safe to change and nothing permanent will come of the therapy. If your energy system is reversed because it feels emotionally threatening on any level to make the changes, you will eventually regress to the original behavior, habit, or fear.

So you need to take a good honest look at what might not feel safe to you if you change in order to find the tappable issues. By the way, it isn't 'bad' if you don't (or your client doesn't) feel safe, it is merely feedback from your organism. We all feel unsafe to varying degrees about moving forward or releasing old habits and conflicts. Sometimes the reasons are irrational and illogical because of what and how we learned certain lessons from our childhood. Sometimes the reasons make perfect sense to us on a conscious level. It doesn't really matter. The point is, if you don't feel safe, you won't change.

---

The first clue that SAFETY may be blocking your forward movement is that your treatment is neither working very well nor sticking in the long term.

---

Below are important questions, explanations, and suggested tapping sequences for possible reasons you might not feel entirely safe to move forward in your personal, professional, or physical life.

Remember, the reasons we don't feel safe need to be heard and respected before the tapping will make any headway. Otherwise these reasons continue to operate behind the scenes.

## What if symptoms return despite repeated tapping?

If your symptoms continue to return, make sure to ask your practitioner (or yourself) if you are being too global or general in your statements. Make certain there is a good emotional match between therapist and client. If you don't feel safe enough to change because you are on your own, it may be time to seek out a qualified EFT practitioner. I highly recommend a session or two for a jumpstart. If you can't find the core issues, or don't feel safe enough with your particular practitioner, discuss this as openly as you are able to. A skilled practitioner will help you feel heard, and then know where to take the next EFT session.

Occasionally there are energy toxins (this is rare but can happen) that interfere with your energy system and block treatment. More commonly there are multiple aspects (different angles to the same problem) that have not been adequately addressed. Again, make sure you are working with a qualified practitioner and that you are feeling heard and understood before proceeding. If your emotional or physical symptoms continue to surface or return, some detective work is required.

Maybe you actually feel ambivalent about changing—a part of you really wants to change, while another part is determined to stay the same for safety reasons on an emotional basis:

- *Even though I can't 'hold on to' my changes, I deeply and completely love and accept myself anyway.*

- *Even though I feel ambivalent about changing, I accept how I feel.*

- *Even though I don't feel safe enough to change right now, I choose to come back to this another time.*

EYEBROW:    *I can't seem to hold on to my changes.*
SIDE OF EYE:   *What's wrong with me?*
UNDER EYE:   *I'm not entirely sure I want to change.*
NOSE:   *I just don't feel safe enough YET.*
CHIN:   *I don't really want to change.*
COLLARBONE:  *I can't hold onto my changes.*
UNDER ARM:   *I don't feel safe enough.*
HEAD:   *I feel too afraid to make these changes.*

## What if sabotage is a big theme in my life?

If the term self-sabotage rings all sorts of bells for you, this is another reason you might want to look at the issue of safety. Everyone is convinced that sabotage comes from not feeling worthy, and that's true.

But if you felt *safe* deserving success and feeling worthy, you wouldn't sabotage your progress!

So approaching sabotage from another angle is often the medicine you need:

۞ *Even though feeling deserving of success feels foreign to me, I accept myself anyway.*

۞ *Even though I am determined not to feel deserving of success, that's ok, I accept my feelings anyway.*

۞ *Even though I am afraid I'll just sabotage my success anyway, I accept who I am and how I feel.*

۞ *Even though I'm a master at sabotage, I accept who I am and how I feel.*

۞ *Even though I don't feel safe deserving success, I accept all of my feelings.*

EYEBROW: *I always sabotage my progress.*

SIDE OF EYE: *I don't deserve success.*

UNDER EYE: *I never have.*

NOSE: *I don't deserve success because I'm not worthy.*

CHIN: *I always sabotage my success because I don't deserve it.*

COLLARBONE: *I can't stop the sabotage patterns.*

UNDER ARM: *Yes I can.*

HEAD: *I just don't feel safe enough yet.*

## What if EFT seems to work on everyone else but me?

All human beings have an energy system, so there is no logical reason why EFT wouldn't work for everyone. Now, if you do not appreciate the technique, do not believe in the foundational principles of acupuncture, do not 'buy' that there is an energy system in the human body, then your beliefs may be blocking treatment. You need to ask yourself whether you should try another type of therapy that might be more in alignment with who you are or whether you should continue to work with EFT. If EFT seems to work on everyone else, then EFT is not the problem. However, if you want EFT to work, believe it can work, have seen it work for others, you must look to safety issues as the cause of impeded progress.

What is fascinating to me is how many EFT practitioners have come to me for sessions or workshops because apparently EFT doesn't work for them, even though they conduct exceptional sessions for their clients!

Oftentimes the reason EFT doesn't 'work' for someone is connected to energetic issues, not the inadequacies of EFT.

Try the simple tapping sequence below to get you started:

⚡ *Even though I'm frustrated because EFT doesn't work on me, I choose to be open to it working now.*

⚡ *Even though EFT works on everyone else but me, I choose to accept the blocks I must have.*

⚡ *Even though EFT doesn't work on me, and I can't figure out why, I deeply and completely love and accept myself anyway.*

EYEBROW:       *I can't figure out why it won't work on me.*
SIDE OF EYE:   *It's typical that something won't work on me.*
UNDER EYE:     *Nothing ever works on me.*
NOSE:          *What's the matter with me?*
CHIN:          *Maybe I don't want it to work.*
COLLARBONE:    *Maybe I'm too different.*
UNDER ARM:     *I don't feel safe enough to allow it to work.*
HEAD:          *I feel anxious about making these changes.*

## What is the best way to discover what's keeping me stuck?

Most of you who have been reading my articles and books know by now that my favorite question in EFT therapy is: "WHAT IS THE DOWNSIDE OF GETTING OVER THIS PROBLEM?" Answering this question is the fastest way to come up with the reasons you don't feel safe moving forward. What are possible downsides to your progress? What would be negative about you getting over it? Ask yourself this question gently and often until you get a glimpse of what might be in the way of your (or your client's) progress:

⚡ *Even though a part of me doesn't really want to change, I accept myself and my feelings.*

⚡ *Even though there are some 'negatives' to my changing, I accept myself and who I am.*

✣ *Even though I don't really want to get over this problem, I accept and love myself anyway.*

✣ *Even though I'm not aware of the DOWN SIDES yet, I accept who I am and what I am feeling.*

| | |
|---|---|
| EYEBROW: | *I don't feel safe letting go of this problem.* |
| SIDE OF EYE: | *Apparently there are some downsides to releasing this problem.* |
| UNDER EYE: | *I'm not entirely sure I want to change.* |
| NOSE: | *I just don't feel safe enough YET.* |
| CHIN: | *I don't know what the downsides are yet . . .* |
| COLLARBONE: | *I feel my resistance but can't stop.* |
| UNDER ARM: | *I don't feel safe enough to make these changes.* |
| HEAD: | *I feel too afraid to change yet.* |

## What if I feel that someone might be jealous or upset if I no longer have this problem?

Always ask yourself about your closest family members, friends and co-workers . . .

Who might have a difficult time if you are no longer a failure, no longer overweight, no longer suffering with chronic pain?

These feelings from others don't come from bad intentions, they are just rarely expressed openly and honestly . . . we often hear or feel a 'zinger' from someone who is jealous! Humans get accustomed to things being a certain way . . . and change causes any underlying discomfort and envy to surface. If hearing about or experiencing these feelings from others makes you afraid, you won't change:

✣ *Even though I'm afraid of their reaction, I deeply and completely love and accept myself anyway.*

✣ *Even though they might be too jealous if I get better, I accept my fears of their reactions.*

+ *Even though I won't feel safe if they find out about my success, I deeply and completely love and accept myself anyway.*

| | |
|---|---|
| EYEBROW: | *I know they won't like it.* |
| SIDE OF EYE: | *I'm afraid of their reaction.* |
| UNDER EYE: | *I won't feel safe changing if they hear about it.* |
| NOSE: | *I don't want to upset them.* |
| CHIN: | *I think it's my job to protect them.* |
| COLLARBONE: | *I'm afraid of their reaction.* |
| UNDER ARM: | *No wonder I don't feel safe enough.* |
| HEAD: | *I don't feel safe making these changes because of their reactions.* |

## Won't people expect more of me if I change?

You can see why changing starts to seem like a risky business! Many of my clients and workshop participants uncover this conflict about changing—someone in their life will suddenly have enormous expectations of them now that they have 'gotten over' their problem, whether it is fear of flying or shyness. A client who finally cleared her agoraphobia after years of not leaving her home was afraid to tell anyone lest they ask her to make up for lost time and travel all over the countryside! Sometimes this fear is hidden away, but ask yourself who will have higher expectations of you if you make headway with a particular conflict you have been working on:

+ *Even though I don't want them to want anything more from me, I accept who I am and how I feel.*

+ *Even though I'm afraid of their expectations, I deeply and completely love and accept myself anyway.*

+ *Even though I'm afraid of my own expectations, I deeply and profoundly love and accept myself anyway.*

| | |
|---|---|
| EYEBROW: | *I can't take their expectations.* |
| SIDE OF EYE: | *I don't want them to want more.* |
| UNDER EYE: | *I don't want them to find out.* |
| NOSE: | *What if they expect more of me?* |
| CHIN: | *What if I expect more of me?* |

COLLARBONE:  *I can't take the pressure.*
UNDER ARM:   *I don't want their pressure.*
HEAD:        *I'd rather stay the same.*

## How can I tell if there are safety issues underneath the surface?

Many people enter therapy claiming they will 'do anything' to change a problem they have been wrestling with throughout their life. Then when you give them some minimal homework, they 'forget' and don't follow through! This is evidence that there are safety issues underneath the surface.

---

Remember, safety issues are to be respected and honored. Then you will have a window into the complexity of the conflict.

---

- ✤ *Even though I have obvious conflicts about making this change, I accept who I am and how I feel.*

- ✤ *Even though I can't figure out why I won't follow through, I accept who I am and how I feel.*

- ✤ *Even though I refuse to change for some reason, I deeply and completely love and accept where I am.*

EYEBROW:      *I must have some ambivalence.*
SIDE OF EYE:  *I feel so confused.*
UNDER EYE:    *Don't I want to change?*
NOSE:         *I just don't feel safe enough YET.*
CHIN:         *Maybe I really don't want to change.*
COLLARBONE:   *I seem to be refusing to change.*
UNDER ARM:    *I don't feel safe to change right now.*
HEAD:         *I want to feel safe enough to change.*

## What if I change and I'm still not happy?

This presents an enormous risk to people who outwardly state that they feel convinced they will be happy WHEN and only WHEN they change. A tiny voice inside tells them that actually, even after they make the change they have been struggling with they will still be unhappy. From this point of view, it is safer to stay the same and not risk this outcome. It would be far too risky to land on the other side and find out you are still unhappy, and that the weight, the phobia, the fear, or the relationship was not the cause of your unhappiness to begin with!

Remember, if you feel threatened by anything emotional or physical, there won't be any permanent change.

---

> The mind reads the risk as foolish or unsafe on a primal level, and returning to the original behavior seems to be the best choice.

---

If a smoker is deathly afraid of the grief that might surface if he puts down his cigarettes, trust me, he will sabotage the best of EFT, NLP, hypnosis, or any other therapeutic tool to quit smoking:

* *Even though I don't want to change if I'm still going to be unhappy, I deeply and completely love and respect who I am.*

* *Even though I fear I might still be unhappy, I accept these fears and feelings.*

* *Even though I'm afraid changing won't really make me happy, I choose to feel good about me right now.*

| | |
|---|---|
| EYEBROW: | *I need to be happy.* |
| SIDE OF EYE: | *This better work for me.* |
| UNDER EYE: | *What if I go to the trouble and I'm still not happy?* |
| NOSE: | *I just don't feel safe enough yet.* |
| CHIN: | *I don't want to change and still be unhappy.* |
| COLLARBONE: | *What if I'm still not happy?* |
| UNDER ARM: | *Maybe I should stay the same.* |
| HEAD: | *I feel too afraid to make these changes.* |

## What if I am just a tough case?

Trust me, people who get a thrill out of being a 'tough case' are terrified to change. They don't want to be different, they won't feel safe losing this exterior of being a 'tough case' and they will go to any lengths to make it difficult for the practitioner to reach them and their issues. I highly recommend that practitioners ask questions around (1) safety, (2) staying the same, (3) the upside of being a tough case, and (4) the possibility of NOT CHANGING to trigger emotional conflicts and jumpstart the therapy. Of course in many cases, these clients won't change because the investment in staying stuck and being hopeless is just too great—they may be living out some abusive situation from their past or some internal beliefs that need to stay intact so they don't feel destabilized in this world:

- *Even though I'm a tough case and nothing works on me, I deeply and profoundly love and accept myself.*

- *Even though I'm sure nothing will work on me, I deeply and completely love and accept myself anyway.*

- *Even though I'm quite special in many ways, I accept that I have not been able to change yet, and I accept exactly who I am right now.*

| | |
|---|---|
| EYEBROW: | *I've always been a tough case.* |
| SIDE OF EYE: | *I'm really quite challenging.* |
| UNDER EYE: | *I don't want to change and I can't.* |
| NOSE: | *I just don't think anyone has really understood me yet.* |
| CHIN: | *I don't think anyone 'gets' me.* |
| COLLARBONE: | *I'm a tough case.* |
| UNDER ARM: | *I could change but I'm too tough for EFT.* |
| HEAD: | *Nothing works on me . . . because I'm different.* |

## Could my 'real reasons' actually be preventing change?

I once asked a smoker *"What are the real reasons you want to change?"* and he replied: *"To get my wife off my back."* Well, I sent him home and wouldn't work with him. He was in no way, shape, or form ready to quit, and we both knew it. I taught him EFT as a tool for cravings, and encouraged him to come up with his own reasons to quit and come back when he was ready.

Another client came into therapy to 'find a husband'. She was clearly looking for a relationship to shut up the loneliness and childhood pain she experienced constantly, which would account for some of the poor choices she made. Being alone was excruciatingly painful for her, and her skills at evaluating a boyfriend were non-existent. Sometimes she used food and alcohol too, but mostly, dramatic and tumultuous relationships were the distraction she craved from her feelings of inadequacy. So her 'real' reason to change *("I don't want to be single anymore so I don't have to focus on myself")* was not going to actually help her change; it was going to get her into even more trouble:

- ✧ **Even though the truth is I have no interest in changing, that's ok, I accept myself as I am.**

- ✧ **Even though I have never wanted to give up this problem for the right reasons, I accept their feelings and my feelings.**

- ✧ **Even though I'm not ready to change, and it's relieving to admit it, I deeply and completely love and accept myself anyway.**

- ✧ **Even though I want to distract myself from my feelings, I accept who I am.**

Another client said she wanted to lose the weight to fit into a dress for her 20th high school reunion. There's nothing wrong with wanting to look good on social occasions such as these, but your progress will not last if this is your top reason:

- ✧ **Even though I'm only willing to do some of what I need to do to change, I deeply and profoundly respect myself anyway.**

- ✧ **Even though only a part of me wants to make this change, and I can't wait to go back to normal, I accept who I am and how I feel.**

- ✧ **Even though I feel this urgency but know it won't last, I accept these feelings and choose to love myself anyway.**

| | |
|---|---|
| EYEBROW: | *I want someone else to fix me.* |
| SIDE OF EYE: | *I want to fix someone else.* |
| UNDER EYE: | *I'm not ready to do the deeper work, and that's ok.* |
| NOSE: | *I don't want to focus on myself.* |
| CHIN: | *I don't really want to change.* |
| COLLARBONE: | *I can't handle my own feelings.* |
| UNDER ARM: | *I can't tolerate the pain.* |
| HEAD: | *I feel too afraid to look at myself.* |

## What if I'm scared of losing relationships if I change?

A client's marriage was already on the rocks, but she knew if she felt confident enough to lose her extra weight, there was no turning back, and she would leave her husband. Another client knew he would no longer 'hang out' with his drinking buddies if he handled his emotional issues, and was afraid to make the necessary changes to move his life forward. What else might change? Job positions? Titles? Weekend activities? What other losses might there be if you change this big issue?

---

> If a person doesn't feel safe about changing because it might 'rock the boat' in their family or social circles, there will be constant sabotage.

---

> ⚜ *Even though I know they will leave me if I change, I accept who I am and how I feel.*

> ⚜ *Even though I'm afraid I might leave them if I make this final change, I accept my anxiety and accept all of me now.*

> ⚜ *Even though I can't handle any more losses, I accept these feelings and appreciate who I am right now.*

| | |
|---|---|
| EYEBROW: | *I don't want to lose anyone.* |
| SIDE OF EYE: | *I don't want to face this challenge.* |
| UNDER EYE: | *I'm not entirely sure I want to change.* |
| NOSE: | *I don't feel safe about this conflict.* |
| CHIN: | *I don't really want to face these issues.* |
| COLLARBONE: | *I know I'll leave her/him.* |
| UNDER ARM: | *I don't feel safe enough yet to make this change.* |
| HEAD: | *I feel too afraid of the consequences.* |

## What will happen if I don't change?

This is also an essential question to ask yourself. So what if you don't change? Will it really be so bad? Are you the one who really wants to change? What if you give up the battle on this issue?

- *Even though I might never change, I deeply and completely love and accept myself anyway.*

- *Even though I don't want to accept myself unless I change, I am willing to consider accepting myself anyway.*

- *Even though I don't feel worthy of respect and love unless I change, I choose to accept who I am right now.*

EYEBROW:    *What if I never change?*

SIDE OF EYE:    *What will happen if I stay the same?*

UNDER EYE:    *I'm not entirely sure I want to change.*

NOSE:    *I don't want to accept that I might not change.*

CHIN:    *I don't really want to change all that much.*

COLLARBONE:    *I can't believe I might stay the same.*

UNDER ARM:    *I won't feel worthy unless I change.*

HEAD:    *What if I could feel worthy even if I don't change?*

Whether you are working with an EFT practitioner, using EFT on your own, or a clinician noticing constant relapse and sabotage in your practice, I invite you to get to the core issues underlying resistance to change --- the fears, the dangers, the threats, and the "yes, buts" --- and you will be able to tolerate and absorb the magnificent changes made possible with EFT, the most powerful healing tool available today.

## AUTHOR'S BIOGRAPHY AND CONTACT DETAILS

See 'A Conversation with Your Body' by Carol Look for biography and contact details.

# EFT and the Law of Attraction

## A PERFECT MATCH

## CAROL LOOK, LCSW, EFT MASTER, EFTCERT-HONORS

### What is the Law of Attraction?

You've written down your wish list, you know what you want and what date you want it by, and you've been waiting patiently for the 'stuff' to fall into your lap. So where is it? What's the missing piece, and why hasn't it come to you yet? According to the popular philosophy of the Law of Attraction, you haven't yet 'allowed' it into your life. How do you allow what you want into your life? You relax, feel more joy, appreciate what you have and choose positive thoughts instead of dwelling on fear or scarcity. All of this serves to raise your vibration. YOUR ONLY JOB IS TO RAISE YOUR VIBRATION.

### How can I focus on joy and appreciation when my life is full of pain, strife, angst or past memories that scare me?

You use EFT! We've all done plenty of asking, plenty of telling the universe who and what we want in our lives. The missing piece is that we don't know how to get out of our own way and open the door. Enter EFT . . .

The Law of Attraction is ALWAYS working for us. For those of you who've seen The Secret, What the Bleep Do We Know, or been following the Abraham-

Hicks work, (just to name a few) you know what the Law of Attraction is—the popular term to describe why we have what we have or experience in our lives. It means 'like attracts like', no matter what. If you vibrate in fear, you will be delivered more experiences that cause fear. If you vibrate in a joyful place, you will bump into more experiences that bring you joy. Pretend your thoughts and vibrations are like slow moving boomerangs . . . they always come back to you.

## So it's my 'vibration' that does the communicating, not my words?

Yes. The theory of this metaphysical 'Law' of the Universe states that whatever we are feeling or vibrating (*not* what we are saying) is what is communicating our energetic 'position' or posture to the Universe. The Universe then 'hears' this vibration we are emitting, and matches it by returning to us similar experiences to produce more of the same feeling and vibration. (This is why I have been obsessed with using the Gratitude List and Gratitude Walk that I talk about in my book[1]. When I use these tools along with EFT, I immediately improve my vibration which in turn magnetizes into my life the desires I have been focused on.)

Many people misinterpret the principles behind the Law of Attraction, and think they can 'fool' the Universe by pretending that they are joyful. This is not possible, as the Universe reads your vibration, not what you say or do.

The key points of this article are:

(1) The Law of Attraction is *always* operating

(2) The Universe 'hears' your vibration/energy, not your words

(3) Knowing about this Law allows you to have more power in your life and feel/ be less of a victim

(4) You DO have control over your vibration if you make choices about your thoughts and focus

(5) EFT is one of the fastest and easiest ways to change your vibration

So when you use EFT to release any negativity and conflict in your energy system, you will naturally be vibrating in a more positive, uplifting space. Then the Law of Attraction, which is always working, will bring you more of the positive things that you have been asking for. It's a perfect match.

## Where does EFT fit in?

Think about all the pieces of EFT—(1) choosing a specific problem, (2) affirming that you deeply and completely love and accept yourself no matter what, and (3) tapping on the points in your energy system and relieving the stress, tension, and conflict that has been stored there. What a wonderful way to raise your vibration!

What do you want to attract in your life? Professional success, money, love, friendships, joy, peace, spiritual depth, happiness? It's all available, but you need to know how to control your 'vibration' which is in direct communication with the Universe. We need to use the Law of Attraction to our advantage since it's working 24 hours a day for us anyway.

In his 'Serious Diseases' DVD series, Gary Craig described how the hurtful or traumatic events in our lives drain and reduce the effectiveness of our immune system over time. This makes perfect sense. When we have negative feelings and don't find ways to relieve or express them, we eventually run our immune systems down and we end up in a compromised physiological place. Then we are a favorable 'host' for the flu bug or cold virus circulating in our environment. The same is true for our vibration. When we run ourselves down by focusing on negative thoughts, painful experiences, or upsetting what if's, we lower our vibration which the Universe then answers. (Remember the image of a slow moving boomerang . . . )

## So are you saying it's my fault if things go wrong for me?

No, certainly not. The theory behind the Law of Attraction is NOT a system of blame! It is an explanation of responsibility and an opportunity to take back control of our lives and stop being victims. We have all attracted negative things into our lives from time to time, some more than others. When people argue, *"but I didn't want that bad thing to happen . . ."* you can bet that at some point, and definitely over time, they were inadvertently focusing on negativity, resentment, and probably fear. We all do it, we all attract negative things into our lives, and we are all afraid much of the time . . . it comes with being human. However, we have many more tools at our disposal now to reduce the fear, transform the powerlessness, and increase our genuine joy. IT'S AN INDIVIDUAL DECISION WHETHER WE WANT TO PICK UP AND PRACTICE USING THESE TOOLS OR NOT.

## Is it true that 'thoughts become things'?

It's more helpful to see the Law of Attraction working in a 'big picture' way. You don't have a resentful or fearful thought at 10:00 in the morning, and get a flat tire at noon. It's about your *overall vibration* on particular subjects, your accumulated vibration, and this is something you can change and influence in a very short period of time. So consider being patient, believing that what you want is on its way to you, and work on raising your overall vibration.

Everyone oversimplifies the issue and manages to turn it around again into victimhood. *"Why did the universe send this to me???"* they ask ... Because they were pulsing, vibrating, communicating that same level of vibration that was returned to them on some subtle level in their energy system by focusing on resentment, pain, hurt, anger or feeling powerless. We all do it, we all have done it, and we all will continue to do it in our lives. But now we can CHOOSE to do it less, relieve the feelings, take back our power, and harness the incredible power of the Law of Attraction. Remember, this 'law' works as often and as predictably as gravity, so it's up to you what targets you want to offer to it. The Law of Attraction has perfect aim.

## If the Law of Attraction has perfect aim, why do I get so much of what I don't want?

*"I wouldn't have asked for the flu"* you protest ... No, you wouldn't have and neither did I last winter, but I did communicate resistance, tension, fear, and irritation for a long time before I weakened my immune system enough to allow myself to react to the flu bug. In other words, I had to be ready, or a favorable 'host' for it. (I also still 'expect' to get sick at some point in the winter ... another vibration I can work on changing.)

Remember, WE ALL DO IT. If any of you are hearing blame, you are not hearing me and what I am saying in this article. We all use the Law of Attraction in our daily life, why not use it for our benefit, rather than to hurt us or slow our progress down?

## So are you saying I need to focus more on what I DO want?

Yes! If you want more in your life to be grateful for, focus on the appreciation you already feel for what and who you have in your life. Try the gratitude list or gratitude walk I talk about in my newsletters, or my gratitude tapping sequences from other articles.

All you need to attract outrageous success and abundance into your life is:

1. The Law of Attraction
2. EFT, and
3. An Attitude of Gratitude

Try a marathon of gratitude tapping and measure how you feel afterwards, and what tail-enders surface. Start by addressing the genuine mood or feeling state you feel right now, then move into appreciation and gratitude:

⁍ *Even though I feel a little down right now, I choose to focus on positive emotions.*

⁍ *Even though I don't feel very positive right now, I accept who I am and how I feel.*

⁍ *Even though I'm wallowing in self-pity right now, I accept all of me and how I feel.*

| | |
|---|---|
| EYEBROW: | *I'm always afraid of what might happen.* |
| SIDE OF EYE: | *What if something bad happens to me?* |
| UNDER EYE: | *I feel the fear in my vibration every day.* |
| NOSE: | *I can feel the fear no matter what I do.* |
| CHIN: | *I don't feel safe unless I'm feeling worried.* |
| COLLARBONE: | *I'm afraid to let go of my fear.* |
| UNDER ARM: | *I don't know how to feel any other way.* |
| HEAD: | *What if I can't let go of my fear?* |
| EYEBROW: | *I'm always afraid of what might happen.* |
| SIDE OF EYE: | *What if something bad happens to me?* |
| UNDER EYE: | *I feel the fear in my vibration every day.* |
| NOSE: | *I can feel the fear no matter what I do.* |
| CHIN: | *I don't feel safe unless I'm feeling worried.* |
| COLLARBONE: | *I'm afraid to let go of my fear.* |
| UNDER ARM: | *I don't know how to feel any other way.* |
| HEAD: | *What if I can't let go of my fear?* |

After you have relieved the sensation of chronic fear in your mind and body with EFT, move towards more positive and appreciative thoughts and statements:

| | |
|---|---|
| EYEBROW: | *I love feeling grateful.* |
| SIDE OF EYE: | *I choose to feel good no matter what.* |
| UNDER EYE: | *I feel appreciation for being alive.* |
| NOSE: | *I love who I am and how I feel.* |
| CHIN: | *I'm grateful for my life.* |
| COLLARBONE: | *I appreciate so much in my life.* |
| UNDER ARM: | *I'm grateful for the clarity in my life.* |
| HEAD: | *I love feeling so joyful.* |
| EYEBROW: | *I love feeling good.* |
| SIDE OF EYE: | *I appreciate feeling so grateful.* |
| UNDER EYE: | *I appreciate who I am.* |
| NOSE: | *I love who I am becoming.* |
| CHIN: | *I'm grateful for all my feelings.* |
| COLLARBONE: | *I appreciate the guidance I am getting.* |
| UNDER ARM: | *I'm grateful for who I am.* |
| HEAD: | *I love feeling such joy.* |

## EFT makes you focus on the negative; won't that make you attract more negativity into your life and make things worse?

Good question! This is one I find myself answering a dozen times every week through emails, and hundreds of times in my Law of Attraction workshops. I have studied, experimented, pondered and come to the conclusion that the answer is a resounding "NO!" After 10 years of doing EFT, I can safely say that my personal and professional experiments have determined that EFT and the Law of Attraction are a perfect match.

> We need to STOP TRYING TO RESIST OUR REAL FEELINGS. EFT allows us to name them, feel them, and release them. Once this step is done, we are in a vibrational position to allow into our life (or 'magnetize') what we want.

When you use EFT and target an emotion you have (which I call 'the truth'), you have pinpointed the feeling that is causing your vibration anyway ... you are *already* feeling that way, so why not call it what it is? EFT is effective in direct proportion to the 'truth' you are able to tell and

the bull's-eyes you are able to hit. So instead of saying *"I'm upset with her"* I recommend you say words that more deeply resonate with the truth: *"I feel so angry about what she did because it wasn't fair"*. This allows you get more of a 'hit' and more of a positive result with EFT, as you have nailed it on the head. EFT is the fastest tool I have ever come across to identify, address and clear an issue and find immediate relief. The event itself doesn't change, but your expe-

*EDITOR'S NOTE:*
This precise naming of how you feel is critical to great success with tapping therapy. We are often taught to use polite or less intense language, and there are times when doing this is appropriate and helpful—but not when working to release an emotion with tapping.

rience, memory, and perception of it and emotions about it change. What more could we ask for?

## So the key thing we're looking for is that feeling of 'relief'?

YES! WHEN YOU FEEL RELIEF, THE LAW OF ATTRACTION IS 'LISTENING' AND ALLOWS INTO YOUR LIFE (BY SENDING YOU) MORE OF WHAT YOU WERE ASKING FOR, WHETHER IT IS RELATIONSHIPS, MONEY, OPPORTUNITIES OR CLIENTS.

When the real feeling (the one you've been trying to hide in your daily life) is finally addressed with EFT and soothed in your thoughts, mind, and body, you free yourself to vibrate in a more grateful, peaceful, joyful place, to which the Law of Attraction then responds and adds more joy and more reasons for gratitude.

Consider this ...

1. People think that because they're pretending not to hate their boss, they're not exuding anger or vibrating negativity and resistance. Humans are very transparent. Our feelings 'show'.

2. People think a few seconds of EFT where they focus on a 'negative' feeling is an eternity. They ignore the fact that they have spent 23 hours of the day pushing hard against a feeling of fear, then worry about a few minutes of EFT. When they are asked to focus on the negative feelings, there is a direct connection to their vibration. This allows the deep feeling to finally be relieved. It's very quick ... there is no wallowing in EFT ...

3. EFT allows you to clear the decks, which makes space for peace and joy in your life.

So once again, it's all about relief. Even saying well-formed setup phrases allow people to feel more joyful and relaxed.

When you feel relieved, the 'stuff' you have 'asked for' receives an invitation to show up for you, through many unusual channels. When you use EFT to get relief, you instantly vibrate in a better place, and voila! . . . the manifestations start to appear. What stuff? Relationships, money, career opportunities, love, peace, coincidences, guidance, serendipity etc., you name it. I have actually had to stop some of my own experiments as I haven't quite caught up yet energetically with what I am receiving.

---

So stop pretending you aren't hurt by what happened. Stop pretending that you've forgiven everyone when the truth is you're seething mad inside. The Universe hears your vibration, not your words.

---

Use EFT to target the feelings and release them once and for all, and allow peace into your life.

## How can I put all this into practice?

Once you have cleared the negativity with EFT, you can be assured you have opened the door a little more to let into your life whatever you have been asking for, writing about, and visualizing.

- ⚕ *Even though I have been too embarrassed to admit my hurt, I accept who I am and how hurt I really was by him.*

- ⚕ *Even though I didn't want to admit I was hurt, so I pretended I wasn't, I choose to express it now.*

- ⚕ *Even though I felt devastated, I accept who I am and how I feel about it.*

EYEBROW:         *I was so hurt by what happened.*
SIDE OF EYE:     *I've been pretending I wasn't hurt.*

| UNDER EYE: | *I've been so hurt all along.* |
| NOSE: | *I thought I was supposed to forgive him.* |
| CHIN: | *But I wasn't ready.* |
| COLLARBONE: | *I still feel hurt.* |
| UNDER ARM: | *I feel hurt by what happened.* |
| HEAD: | *I need to admit my hurt.* |
| EYEBROW: | *I was deeply hurt and couldn't get over it.* |
| SIDE OF EYE: | *I kept trying not to be hurt.* |
| UNDER EYE: | *It feels so good to say it out loud.* |
| NOSE: | *The truth is I've never gotten over it.* |
| CHIN: | *It feels so good to admit the truth.* |
| COLLARBONE: | *I can finally say it out loud.* |
| UNDER ARM: | *I'm ready to release it.* |
| HEAD: | *It's time to release the hurt after all these years.* |

Using EFT in this way allows you to release the real pain instead of spending all that energy *trying not to feel hurt*! Now you will be in an emotional and energetic position to feel more grateful and allow yourself to feel relief and joy.

## How can I use this process when I'm feeling afraid or fearful?

Fear definitely keeps you in a lower vibration and delays the magnetization of what you want. I find that EFT is the easiest way to relieve this feeling and change your focus. Remember, when you change your focus, you vibrate in a different place, and attract different (more positive) things into your life.

A client of mine was very afraid of her negative thoughts but she spent most of her waking hours using tricks and affirmations to try and help her *push away the fear* and push away these thoughts. This always backfires, as she spent all her energy actually *focused on the negativity* rather than on something positive by trying so hard NOT to think about these feelings. This of course means she was ultimately focused on her fears anyway, as all her waking hours were spent *trying not to be fearful*!

(You might want to try and substitute *"I'm afraid of my negative thoughts"* for the sentences below if you related to the above story.)

✣ *Even though I'm deeply afraid of what might happen, I accept who I am and how I feel.*

⤋ *Even though I live with these fears every day, I am willing to consider relieving them now*

⤋ *Even though I'm afraid not to feel fear, I accept who I am and how I feel*

| | |
|---|---|
| EYEBROW: | *I'm always afraid of what might happen.* |
| SIDE OF EYE: | *What if something bad happens to me?* |
| UNDER EYE: | *I feel the fear in my vibration every day.* |
| NOSE: | *I can feel the fear no matter what I do.* |
| CHIN: | *I don't feel safe unless I'm feeling worried.* |
| COLLARBONE: | *I'm afraid to let go of my fear.* |
| UNDER ARM: | *I don't know how to feel any other way.* |
| HEAD: | *What if I can't let go of my fear?* |

Now that you have voiced the real feelings, you are able to gently guide the client and can make the easy transition into more positive statements and vibrations. If the client objects to 'positive' statements, they will hear 'tail-enders' surface such as *"no I'm not"* or *"that's not true"* or something that counters the positive statements. THIS IS GOOD NEWS! You now have more information and targets for tapping. When their tail-enders surface, be happy you are getting to the core issues! But try a positive round first to see where it lands.

| | |
|---|---|
| EYEBROW: | *I will consider letting go of my fear.* |
| SIDE OF EYE: | *I'm afraid to let go of my fear.* |
| UNDER EYE: | *I intend to be freer and lighter.* |
| NOSE: | *I love feeling peaceful more often.* |
| CHIN: | *I'm ready to let go of my fear.* |
| COLLARBONE: | *I love feeling grateful about my life.* |
| UNDER ARM: | *There is so much to feel grateful for.* |
| HEAD: | *I appreciate who I am and how I am living.* |

## Finally, what about when I'm feeling powerless?

Of course the feeling of powerlessness is overwhelming and lowers our vibration immediately. Usually it is perceived powerlessness, rather than actual powerlessness, but it doesn't matter, it's the feeling that counts, not the reality of the situation! For those of us who suffer from feelings of powerlessness, we need to find ways to feel more powerful, and using EFT is a wonderful tool for this.

- ✣ *Even though I have no control in this situation, and it makes me anxious, I deeply and completely love and accept myself anyway.*

- ✣ *Even though I feel powerless, AGAIN, I choose to feel calm and peaceful.*

- ✣ *Even though I feel out of control and powerless, I love and accept all of me anyway.*

| | |
|---|---|
| EYEBROW: | *I feel powerless.* |
| SIDE OF EYE: | *I feel out of control.* |
| UNDER EYE: | *I hate feeling powerless.* |
| NOSE: | *I want more control.* |
| CHIN: | *I'm afraid of what might happen.* |
| COLLARBONE: | *I'm afraid of not having control.* |
| UNDER ARM: | *I want to feel more power in my life.* |
| HEAD: | *I don't want to feel so weak* |
| EYEBROW: | *I still feel powerless.* |
| SIDE OF EYE: | *I want to feel strong.* |
| UNDER EYE: | *I hate feeling weak and powerless.* |
| NOSE: | *I hate feeling so down about it all.* |
| CHIN: | *I want to feel better.* |
| COLLARBONE: | *I still feel powerless.* |
| UNDER ARM: | *I want to feel better.* |
| HEAD: | *I will consider feeling better.* |

Now you and your clients are in a position to take in the gratitude tapping:

| | |
|---|---|
| EYEBROW: | *I love appreciating who I am.* |
| SIDE OF EYE: | *I love receiving what I want.* |
| UNDER EYE: | *I am so grateful for my life.* |
| NOSE: | *I appreciate all my feelings.* |
| CHIN: | *I feel better already.* |
| COLLARBONE: | *I love feeling so confident and strong.* |
| UNDER ARM: | *I love the clarity in my life.* |
| HEAD: | *I appreciate the guidance I am receiving.* |

In closing, ask yourself how quickly you want to manifest more of your desires, small and large. If you are eager to manifest them sooner rather than later, then I highly recommend using EFT to clear the blocks and neutralize the limiting beliefs. This will allow all that you have been asking for to come in your front door. Remember, the Law of Attraction is always working, and with EFT, we help it work for us and not against us.

## AUTHOR'S BIOGRAPHY AND CONTACT DETAILS

See 'A Conversation with Your Body' by Carol Look for biography and contact details.

REFERENCES:

1. 'Attracting Abundance with EFT' by Carol Look, pp 104 and 139, Crown Media & Printing Inc., 2008

When you realise what you have been up to, maybe an unconscious decision made in the heat of an emotionally charged incident, it can be a very empowering experience. A client of mine once said *"I decided that the only way to stop myself from being hurt is to keep people at a distance"*.

When you really get it, and you understand why you did it, and how inappropriate it is for whom you now choose to be, it won't come back.

## What if my client is sceptical about the idea of an emotional cause of physical pain?

The concept that emotional issues are often the real reason for physical pain is sometimes hard to get across. So saying to someone: *"Could there be any emotional reasons for this pain?"* could be met with astonishment at the very thought.

It's important to maintain rapport, so I needed to set up an appropriate information gathering exercise that would bypass the limits of the conscious mind. Then I fell back on an old NLP (Neuro-Linguistic Programming) exercise to gauge the submodalities of physical aches and pains. I added an additional question at the end with a surprise element to it, so that the answer I got was an unconscious response. To make sure this unconscious answer wasn't dismissed as too surreal, I asked for the answer that first came to mind. Let me illustrate this with an example:

One day whilst working with a lady called Margaret who was suffering from hip pain, I asked her to close her eyes and move her awareness down to the area where it was most painful. I asked her to guess what colour the pain would be if it had one. Margaret replied that it was dark green. Then I asked if it was bigger or smaller than her hand. It was smaller. Further questions quickly revealed that it was solid and moving around.

Then I asked the surprise question—if it had a feeling or an emotion what would it be? Margaret said it felt like anger. I asked what she thought the anger might be about and she said her parents never gave her a chance to prove herself. Instead, they diverted all their attention to her older brother.

Margaret had said earlier that she felt stuck in a job that was unfulfilling, but was afraid to move forward for fear of failing. The anger was a definite ten plus, but it quickly reduced and turned to

sadness. Margaret then remembered that her parents had given financial support to her brother which brought yet more anger, which we
then tapped away.

Eventually, all the emotions were released—including her fear of
failing in a new career. I then checked on the colour of her hip pain,
which was now clear, as was the pain.

## So what is the 'Colour of Pain' technique?

This following list of questions helps people get to the root of their problem
by neatly sidestepping conscious belief filtering. Make a note of the answers
as you go along so you can refer back to them later. Lower your voice and
speak calmly and slowly, and if you need to, tap any remaining emotions
away.

STEP 1:    Ask your client to close their eyes and move their awareness to the
           area where they feel physical discomfort. Then ask:

  1. *"If it (the painful area) had a colour what would it be?"*
  2. *"Is it bigger or smaller than your hand?"*
  3. *"Is it moving or still?"*
  4. *"Is it solid or transparent?"*
  5. *"If it had a feeling or emotion . . . what would it be? . . . Just guess . . . .the
     first thing that comes to mind . . ."*

STEP 2:    Do a number of rounds of EFT using what I call the '1-2-3 of EFT'
           in which every round MUST include the following:

  1. An emotion e.g. anger, sadness, fear
  2. A specific reason for the emotion e.g. *"He let me down"*
  3. The emotional score from one to ten

Write these three down so that you can re-check after each round whether
the emotion and the specific reason for it are still the same. In some cases, clients don't notice changes in emotional aspects, and using this process prevents
aspects from switching without the client knowing. For example, the emotion
may still be sadness, but the reason for it may be different; perhaps sadness
because of a similar incident from earlier in their life. Continue with the 1-2-3
of EFT until all the emotions have been released.

STEP 4:    Ask your client to close their eyes again and move awareness back to the painful area. Then repeat STEP 1. Often, you may find that the colour changes from dark to light, moves when before it was stuck, and so on. More often than not your client will say that the pain is less intense or has gone altogether. Sometimes the pain can move to other areas of the body and then it is necessary to 'chase the pain' by going through the procedure again.

STEP 5:    Of course with physical pain, you may need to be persistent and give your client homework with the instruction to tap several times a day and as required.

## Can you give me another example of the process in action?

At the first EFT Masterclass in London in October 2006 I was invited to talk about the Colour of Pain technique. While people were booking in, I took the opportunity to look for volunteers with any physical aches and pains.

> One lady, I'll call her Michelle, had hip and lower back pain. I asked her how long she had been in pain? She replied 'about five months'. I then asked her to close her eyes and to move her awareness down to where the current pain was. When she nodded I asked her to guess if the pain had a colour, what would it be? She said it was red. I asked if it was bigger or smaller than her hand—she said it felt bigger. It felt like it was moving a little and felt solid. I then asked if it had a feeling or an emotion, what would it be? She replied that it was apprehension. I asked what it could be apprehension about and she thought it might be because she was due to make a parachute jump for charity in a few weeks' time.
>
> She looked surprised that her pain could have anything to do with this. I asked her when she thought about the parachute jump, what exactly was she thinking about? At this point she started to get upset, so I started tapping on her.
>
> Several rounds of EFT later there was still no change, so I asked if the feeling felt reminiscent of an earlier time. She said that when she was three years old she developed pneumonia. Because of this she was sent to hospital and was placed in an isolation ward away from her family, where her anxiety led to her wetting the bed. Instead

of showing any kindness or sympathy, the nurse told her off as she plucked her roughly out of her bed and put her into a bath of cold water.

Reliving this incident, Michelle looked shocked and upset, but we were able to release the emotion very quickly. I then asked her to imagine jumping out of the plane again. This time she said that she felt OK about the parachute jump.

Just to make sure, I asked her to imagine, in vivid detail, the lead up to making the jump, the moment she would jump out of the plane and the descent. By this time she was smiling and even had a look of peace about her. When she opened her eyes she said her only concern now was about wetting herself when she jumped out of the plane.

Michele's calmness as she said this surprised me. I thought it was the likely connection between the two incidents, which is why the emotion about her jumping out of the plane didn't release at the first attempt. We had to resolve the hospital memory before we could collapse her fear of the parachute jump. After one round of tapping on her concern about wetting herself as she jumped out of the plane, the emotion released completely. I joked with her that people have probably done a lot worse, which lightened the mood.

Once Michelle felt relaxed about the prospect of her parachute jump, I asked her to close her eyes again and move her awareness back to her hip area. I asked her to report on the colour of her pain now. She said that it had changed from red, to clear . . . . and the pain had now gone.

I later wondered about the cause and purpose of her hip pain and what it all meant. I remembered her saying that the pain had been getting steadily worse since deciding to do the jump weeks before. With a few weeks to go before the event, the pain could have gotten a lot worse. It would have provided her with the perfect excuse not to jump had we not resolved her fear . . . .the cause of her pain.

Some weeks later I received the following email from her:

"Hi Paul,

An update—following our session at the EFT Masterclass. During this session you tapped away my fear of doing my forthcoming skydive jump, which I was holding in my very painful hip. Since then I have had no problems at all with either my hip or any anxiety about doing the jump. The jump, which was for the Breakthrough Breast Cancer charity, was on Saturday 18th November. I have attached a photo of me free

*falling from 13000 feet up over the Oxfordshire countryside . . . . it was*
*absolutely amazing! I loved it. Thanks so much for helping me with this.*
*I could do it again tomorrow—no problem!"*

## What are we really tuning into with this process?

I am under no illusions. The colour of pain is just an elicitation technique that enables us to clear the pathway to understanding the cause of an illness. What still surprises me is that the colour perceptions change from dark to light. I often wonder what we are tuning into. If the mind is the creator of disease, then it must also be the healer. Maybe we are opening an intuitive part of ourselves that holds answers to the questions we don't dare ask . . . sometimes, until it is too late.

Today we live in a society that seems to treat the human organism in much the same way as a mechanic treats a car. Over the centuries we have handed over the responsibility for our wellbeing to physicians. But are we expecting too much of them?

As human beings we are constantly evolving. Sometimes, being fallible, intuition and feelings give way to thoughts and desires. But instead of being honest with ourselves and admitting this, we power on down the wrong path. Every locked door has a key that fits though, and EFT provides us with a chance of getting to that key if we are brave enough to take it.

---

Sometimes, the toughest thing to do is look at ourselves with new eyes. and admit to what we've been trying to ignore in the hope that it will go away. People will do anything but look at the true causes of their difficulty.

---

One lady said to us a while back: *"I've decided to cancel my appointment. My doctor's advised me to try a new course of anti-depressants. He said it's going to take a long time to get over this".*

## Where do we go from here?

We often joke with our trainee EFT therapists that we should be called 'The Last Resort' rather than 'The Heart Centre'. Because one of the bravest things we can do is trace our footsteps back to the cause our problems. Just being able to say to yourself *"I've got a problem"* is liberating in itself.

One of the great delights of being an EFT therapist is the look on the face of someone who has just released anger from a childhood memory. They look lighter, they feel lighter. That change is reflected in their body too. Because they feel better about themselves, their family and friends will benefit too. Like ripples in a pond, the healing reaches those around us.

Science is catching up with what we already know in our hearts—that emotional disharmony can lead to physical disorders. One day I'm sure we will live in a society that is geared more towards prevention than cure.

## AUTHOR'S BIOGRAPHY AND CONTACT DETAILS

Authors of the best-selling book 'Emotional Healing in Minutes' (Thorsons) EFT Master Paul Lynch and his wife Val were amongst the first therapists in the UK to spot the tremendous healing potential of EFT. In 1998 they opened their Heart Centre practice, and are now highly respected consultants in the EFT community for their innovations and training expertise. The Colour of Pain is just one of the advances that Val and Paul have introduced over the years. Other techniques include 'The 1-2-3 of EFT', 'The Gesture-lation Technique', 'Pandora's Box' and 'How old do you feel emotionally?' Val and Paul were the first to demonstrate EFT live on UK TV, successfully collapsing phobias in front of an audience of millions. They have also been featured in the national press, with articles in The Times, Daily Mail and Telegraph newspapers.

Web Site:   www.theheartcentre.co.uk
Email:        theheartcentre@btinternet.com
Telephone: 01323 505263

# The Imagineering Technique

GWYNETH MOSS, EFT MASTER, EFTCERT-HONORS

## Why was Imagineering developed?

When using EFT with a physical symptom, the obvious place to start is with
the pain. But what if there is no pain? Sometimes when people come to us for
help with a physical symptom they tell us how painful it has been and how
they anticipate further pain, but they don't currently experience it. When you
ask them *"On a scale from 0 to 10, where 0 is no pain at all and 10 is as bad as
it can be, what number would you give it now?"*, their response will come back
*"It doesn't hurt just now"*. So where do we get started with EFT when someone
has a painless condition with no visible symptoms?

It was for these painless, invisible conditions that I developed the EFT
Imagineering Technique and then found it had many other applications.

## What is Imagineering?

Using imagination, we create a metaphor for the real physical issue. Using EFT
on various aspects of the metaphor generally results in change to the metaphor
which, in turn, translates into change in physical reality.

Our imagination can use our full consciousness to create these metaphors
of reality. Our conscious mind resides in the left hemisphere of the cortex—the

thinking part of the brain which seeks meaning and causality and processes sequentially. Our imagination, in the right side of the brain, is the process of awareness via images, sounds and felt senses. It processes spatially, or simultaneously in response to emotion generated in the limbic (or emotional) brain. Does this sound too complicated? Let's try again:

Our words are:
- connected to images, that are
- connected to emotions, that are
- connected to our body

In Imagineering we make use of this chain of connections to gain access to the roots of dis-ease in a gentle and indirect manner. This is a technique we can add to our collection of EFT 'gentle techniques'. We know that our physical symptoms have emotional roots. At times a person is not able to handle those emotions and therefore avoids recall of those emotional experiences. This may be precisely how a physical symptom comes into place. Imagineering allows an indirect and metaphorical access to the emotion locked in the symptom and gives an opportunity for the calming and clearing effects of EFT to get to work. The core issues can then come safely into awareness.

## Can you give me an example of Imagineering in operation?

THE CASE OF WENDY'S FINGER

Wendy is an artist. She tells me that she has arthritis in her finger joint which has been getting painful and preventing her from holding a paintbrush. When she comes to me to learn EFT she says: "It doesn't hurt right now but it can get really bad".

Knowing that she is an artist I confidently expect that she will enjoy the Imagineering Technique with EFT, so I ask her first to imagine that she holds a small light in her hand, it may be a bulb or a flame or just a bright little light. Wendy imagines a small and powerful flashlight. Next we try it out. I ask her to imagine that she shrinks the light down so that it is very, very small and very, very bright and that she sticks it into her ear and imagines that she goes with it right inside her head. I ask her to tell me what it's like in there. She tells me that she is in a beautiful cavern and that there is a soft humming sound and the cavern is vast and spacious and the walls are sparkling, and soft colours.

I ask what it's like to be in there. She says it is warm and there are all sorts of things floating about like old friends and her father's dog and her school desk and she is weightless and feels like giggling. I ask her to come back out and we talk about her pleasant experience. Then I ask her to put the little bright light into her finger joint and to go inside with it. When she brings the light out again she tells me that inside it is cold and dim and there are jagged spikes of broken glass and screeching glass sounds. It feels lonely in there.

*Even though there are jagged spikes and broken glass in my finger joint . . . .*

*Even though it's lonely in my finger*

I ask her what the 'lonely' is like, and she tells me that sometimes her husband travels for his business. Even if it is only for one night it feels desperately lonely, and that's like when she was little and her father, who was a ship's captain, would go to sea for months. So we tap with:

*Even though I know he's coming back but I get sad like when daddy went away to sea . . . .*

We then tap using The Movie Technique with a specific memory from her childhood.

I ask her to take the light back inside the finger joint. She tells me that it is warmer in there and the glass is now ice and is dripping and melting, the screeching sound is fading and more distant. We do more tapping:

*Even though there is dripping ice in there . . .*

When she next goes inside the finger with her little light, the ice has melted and there is a clear blue pool, a soft humming sound and she feels calm. She looks different too, her face has softened and there is a sparkle in her eyes.

Later that year she told me that she had far less bother from her arthritis through the winter, physically the pain is much less frequent and her finger seems to move more easily and does not interfere with her painting. Whenever her finger did bother her she shut her eyes for a while, sat quietly and meditated on the clear blue pool and felt the pain ease.

## What are the main steps of the Imagineering process?

Imagineering is a gentle approach to working with painless and/or invisible symptoms. I'll take you through the steps of using it and will illustrate with an example.

### STEP 1: IDENTIFY THE PARTS OF THE BODY THAT ARE (OR ARE NOT) AFFECTED

First, identify where in the body the symptom is located, and what parts of the body are not affected by the condition. Some conditions may be located in a specific area or organ, others may be pervasive and you will have to ask questions to identify where it is most concentrated, what is most affected and what is not.

> Ally comes to me in considerable distress. She has just discovered a lump in her breast and is waiting for a medical appointment to have tests. She can just about feel the lump if she presses but it has no pain or sensation. We establish that the lump is in her left breast and other areas of her body are OK.

### STEP 2: EXPLAIN CHAIN OF CONNECTIONS: WORDS-IMAGINATION-EMOTIONS-BODY

I then explain to her that our verbal awareness lives in the left side of our thinking brain and that the right side of our brain is the realm of pictures, metaphor and dreams (our imagination) and that the right side has more connection to her emotional brain which has connection to her body. We will be using her imagination to work with that chain of connections: words-imagination-emotions-body. Sometimes at this point a person will say: "*I don't have an imagination.*" Now, this may be a 'writing on your walls'. To clear that block you can ask some gentle questions and do some tapping. Or, you can point out that all their worries and anxieties are generated by the misuse of imagination and that you just can't get anxious without an imagination.

I also explain that everyone is unique in how they use their imagination. Each person will have their own experience—there is no right or wrong way to do this—it's a judgment-free space in which to play. Some experience imagination with colours, pictures and shapes, other people get sounds, music or voices, and some get a 'feeling sense' of being there. Whatever you get is fine.

*STEP 3: INTRODUCE IDEA OF A LIGHT ON END OF FINGER AND DO A 'TEST RUN'*

Our imaginations work best and we have better access to their output when we are calm and relaxed. So I ask the person to take three good breaths, each one a little slower and deeper than the previous one, and to let their exhale drift slowly out and away, and take any tension or worry with it. Then I ask them to imagine that they hold a bright light in their hand. It may be a flame or a flashlight or simply a ball of light. Once they have that light they shrink it down so that it gets smaller and brighter and fits on the tip of a finger. We are now ready to do an imagination test run. I like to use the inside of the head to do this, but you could choose another part of the body as long as it is NOT the part most affected by the condition.

> I hold my finger up with my bright light and Ally mirrors me as I put my finger in my ear and close my eyes. I ask her to take the light and her imagination inside her head and to shine the light around. I am quiet for a minute or so while she does this, then I suggest that she can come back out when she is ready to. She says there is nothing there, so I ask her to go back in, wait quietly, with curiosity and to let her imagination surprise her, to pretend. If there was something there what would it be? She says it's like she is in a woodland, it's quiet and still and there are little birds around. She likes doing this now.

Some people will report a very realistic visualisation like an anatomy book, others will have a metaphorical or dream like experience and a significant number will initially say *"nothing"* and may need some encouragement to *"pretend"* or *"guess"* or *"make it up"*. The important thing with the test run is that they have some sort of experience.

*STEP 4: APPROACH THE SYMPTOM WITH THE LIGHT*

Now that we have done a test run we approach the symptom. I generally ask the person how the light is going to get inside. Some chose to stick it in through the flesh and others will want to swallow it or insert their finger into their navel or back into the ear again.

> Ally puts her finger to her breast and shuts her eyes, I wait patiently. A minute later she withdraws her finger and says *"there's a round hard boulder of rock"*. So we tap with:
> **Even though there's this round hard boulder of rock in my breast . . . .**

*STEP 5: USE EFT ON WHATEVER COMES UP AND REPEAT STEPS 4 AND 5 AS REQUIRED*

Once you have the imagined metaphor—whether it is visual or a sound or a felt sense—simply put their description and their exact words into EFT, and tap for a round or two.

Then send them back in there with their imagination. Chances are that something will be different. Take their new description and put their words into the EFT setup and tapping phrases.

> Ally goes back inside and finds that the boulder now has an opening like a cave, so we tap with that:
>
> **Even though there is an opening and a cave in the boulder . . . .**
>
> Then as she goes back inside the cave becomes a womb and as she says the word 'womb' she gets overwhelmed with tears so we simply tap a few rounds with the one word "womb" until she calms down. Now the womb opens and she sees her adult son (who has mental health difficulties) curled up in there and sulking. Ally tells me that her son is now living independently and things are going well for him. However, that's not how it used to be, and there were years of intense and overwhelming difficulty.
>
> We use The Movie Technique to clear the emotion of several intense events dating from when he was a teenager. We address her guilt, her powerlessness at being unable to help him and her anger at his constant demands. When she returns inside she sees him smiling and then he picks up his bag and leaves the cave/womb and waves to her. We do some more tapping and when she eventually returns inside the boulder now appears to her as soft rubber like a child's ball. Ally is smiling and looks relaxed. A week later I hear the result of her tests, the lump is a benign cyst.

## Can Imagineering help us to find core issues?

Yes, Imagineering can often take us to the core issue that underlies the physical manifestation of dis-ease. It's a gentle approach that allows the specific core issue to come to consciousness once the person is ready to receive it and make the connections. Start with tapping for whatever they imagine. Then tap to clear the emotional intensity of any connected memories that come into awareness. You could use The Movie Technique or Tell the Story.

There is no set pattern to these cases—you simply start with the imagination, the images, sounds and feelings and let the body wisdom of the person take it where it needs to go. As the therapist you do not need to know the diagnosis or anything about the condition, you can trust that whatever is relevant will emerge.

One way to use imagination as a part of Imagineering is to guide the person's imagination into a healthy part of their body for comparison.

Susan has eczema so after a test run in her head we take her light into the broken and itchy skin. She is a musician and says that everything is an angry red in there and she can hear discordant and jarring Stockhausen. Then we take the light into a clear patch of skin on the other arm, the colour here is clear blue and she can hear Bach.

We use EFT choices:

**Even though it's angry red and jarring Stockhausen in this eczema skin I choose clear Blue Bach all over me!**

For both client and therapist, Imagineering is gentle and fun. The client's images and metaphors bring their own humour, and can fill therapy sessions with lightness that counters the serious nature both of the condition and the memories that may emerge. I hope you enjoy playing with it.

## Case Study 1: Painful Shoulder

Mary attended my EFT Level Three training. As part of the training I teach and demonstrate the EFT Imagineering technique. Mary did a 'test run' on herself, and reported the following:

"I saw an old fashioned university library with stained glass windows and shaded lights reflecting off polished wooden tables. But part of my skull, about one quarter in a mezzanine area, was full of small cartoon characters the "numbskulls" from a childhood comic book. The numbskulls were keeping everything working away efficiently. I liked this sense of the ridiculous juxtaposed against the sombre university library. I must put in here that I have never felt myself to be a very visual person and in fact never felt comfortable with visualisation exercises as I felt I always had to work too hard to try to get any mind pictures. However, this was not the case with the Imagineering."

Mary had a painful shoulder that had bothered her for about six months, and she had the tired and drained look of someone bearing the burden of pain. The pain was constant and seemed worse at night, to the extent that she found it difficult to get to sleep. She was often awakened from sleep with pain if she moved in the night. Mary is a generally optimistic and cheerful person but the pain was dragging her down, and painkillers had little effect. Having done a test run we now took the little light inside her shoulder which had an initial pain level of 9.

Mary says: *"My initial vision of my shoulder was that one half of it was made up of hard frosted white ice and the other half was made up of the burning fires of hell."*

We tapped with:

> ✣ **Even though there is hard frosted ice and the burning fires of hell in my shoulder, I truly and deeply accept myself and I really do accept myself whatever these images mean!**

*"I shone the light again and the ice was not so sharp or so frosted but clear and blunter as thought it had started to melt. The burning fires of hell were more like embers—I think I described the heat now as "granny" heat. Which repre-sented to me a more gentle, caring heat. This brought some tears to my eyes as I still miss my grandmother".*

We talked a little about her grandmother and then tapped again for the ice and heat and she shone the light again.

*"This time I just got an impression of Aladdin's genie. This genie was like a cartoon figure with an enormous upper body, and tiny legs coming into pointy feet. His feet danced from the cold ice to the hot embers and he danced as though he was jiggling from the cold ice to the hot embers and back again. His hot feet melted the ice and his cold feet then cooled the embers."*

It was obvious to all that Mary was now enjoying herself. She looked lighter, and we all laughed with the humour of the dancing genie jumping from the ice to the embers.

We tapped for the dancing genie. Each time Mary took her imagination inside with the light and then reported what she saw I simply reflected her exact words back to her with EFT.

> ✣ **Even though Aladdin's genie is dancing on the cold ice and the hot embers and I really don't know where that comes from I absolutely accept myself.**

Then we repeated the shining of the light once more. The image changed to an image of Cleopatra's needle stabbing into the centre of the front of her shoulder where it was most painful. We tapped for the needle and the feelings it provoked and shone the light again.

*"This time as I shone the light I got the image of a lizard wrapping itself around the needle and this lizard led to the blunting of the edges of the obelisk. We tapped and shone again and the needle disappeared and the lizard has draped itself over my shoulder to nurture it and protect it. "*

To some people a lizard would be threatening or unwelcome but to Mary this lizard was a healer and protector. She visibly smiled, relaxed and softened at this point so I asked about her pain levels which had reduced to about a 2.

Mary said *"Not only did my pain reduce significantly but the exercise left me with a tool to use when I felt the pain or when it was stopping me from sleeping. That tool was the lizard, I just got the feeling that if I imagined the lizard draped over my shoulder it would ease the pain."*

*"When I returned home from the workshop, I still had some remaining pain, but it would peak at a 5 or 6 rather than a 9 or 10. The big difference was that almost immediately I could sleep through the night without being awakened with the pain. Then after about 2 weeks or so the pain left completely for a period of about six months, I have some renewed pain now but when it comes back I imagine the lizard and it seems to ease it considerably."*

*"No one was more surprised than I was at the totally unexpected images that came to mind during this exercise. As I said before, I had never considered myself at all good at image work or visualisation and had no clue that my imagination could be so vivid and so diverse. The images also brought up lots of humour, and I think that for me humour is a great help to shift my energy and to get a new perspective on things.*

*I love the EFT Imagineering Technique because it offers a way of working with both acute and chronic physical symptoms that is:*

- *gentle and indirect*
- *respectful of a person's privacy*
- *fun and humorous*
- *fast and effective*
- *In fact all the best things about EFT!"*

## Case Study 2: A Pain in the Jaw

Liz came on my 'Art of Delivery' EFT workshop and shared her experience of
Imagineering:

*"Ten years ago I started to get pain in my jaw and face plus headaches that
my doctor said was migraine. It all got a lot worse when I started to work in a call
centre and sometimes I could hardly open my mouth wide enough to speak. I had
to take days off with dreadful migraines. Happily, my dentist fixed me up with
a plastic splint that looks like a boxer's gum-shield. I had to wear it every night
as the dentist explained that the problem was caused by my grinding or clamp-
ing my teeth when asleep. It did help, but I found that I had to also use a special
pillow or else my neck and shoulders would become painful. Whenever I went on
business trips or holidays I took this gum-shield thing and my pillow everywhere.
Still I would get the pain sometimes—after a long drive, a poor night's sleep or at
times of stress and worry."*

All of us experience stress in our lives and when it gets to a chronic level
our bodies have to find somewhere to put it. With some of us it is the lower
back or shoulders, with others it is in our breathing or gut. The jaw is another
common stress dumping ground.

*"I'd had a bad night and had driven a fair distance to get to Gwyneth's train-
ing group and my face was really sore so I gladly volunteered to be the guinea pig
for Imagineering. First Gwyneth told me to imagine there was a very bright light
on the end of my forefinger. I couldn't help thinking of E.T.! We took time to get it
really bright and then went exploring my knee, imagining the light on the end of
my finger entering the joint and shining around. It was a smooth walled pinkish
white cave and quite pleasant."*

I always like to do a test drive of the imagination before taking the little
light to the problem area. Usually I test by having the person put the little light
inside their ear and use it to take their imagination into the centre of their
head.

However Liz felt that the problem of her face and jaw and associated
migraines was too much in her head. We sought somewhere else to explore for
a test run, and Liz suggested her knee. The test run gives a person an experience of their imagination and lets the therapist know whether we are working
with visual imagination, or if the person experiences imagination in a more
auditory or feeling manner. Quite a proportion of people do not have a visual
imagination but we can still use Imagineering. For those who are highly auditory I might ask them to go inside with a tiny and sensitive microphone rather
than a light.

*"Then we went to my ear in order to get into the jaw area where the problem was. From my ear there was a dark chute down to the jaw and I didn't want to go down it so we came out of there and tapped on that fear."*

As the therapist at this stage I simply took Liz's description and reflected it back to her through EFT:

☞ **Even though it's a dark chute and I'm scared to go down there I really do accept myself whatever that means.**

Then I had Liz go back into her jaw with the light and her imagination.

*"When I went back in there was more light and a handrail and I went down the slope into the jaw area. It was dark and cold, rather claustrophobic. There was a shallow pool I had to cross and I didn't want to. The water was very cold and I didn't know how deep or what might be lurking in there. I felt lonely and scared."*

Again I simply reflected back the imagined experience using as many of the senses as possible:

☞ **Even though its dark and cold and scary and lonely and I don't want to cross that pool, I truly and deeply accept myself and all of this.**

*"A member of the group asked why Gwyneth had not come into the cave or the pool with me as I seemed to be needing that, as a child would. My perception was that it was important that Gwyneth did not come in because it was totally my place and I had to get comfortable in it by myself in my way."*

This is very important. The imagery and feelings change through the tapping. We do not need to interpret the meaning, or to get involved, or to try to change things consciously. As the therapist you simply reflect back through the EFT process whatever imagery or emotion arises.

At this stage a memory emerged for Liz from when she was about 11 years old. She had swum to the deep end of a public swimming pool, found herself out of her depth, got into a panic and felt that she was drowning. Liz had obviously been a stronger swimmer than she thought she was, as she had been able to struggle to the side on her own and had got her breath back. She survived but in that moment of panic she thought she was going to die. There were lifeguards and family members around the pool but none had seen Liz panic and struggle.

When a memory emerges during the use of the Imagineering technique, we simply switch to the Movie Technique and use EFT in the usual way by giving the Movie a name and then tapping bit by bit through the crescendos of the story. We did that with the Deep End movie for Liz and cleared the fear and panic so that Liz could experience it as more distant and tell it without intensity.

*"A surprise was that once the panic subsided I realized that I felt ashamed for having nearly drowned and I had never told anyone about it because I was embarrassed and just thought I was being stupid."*

That feeling of shame stopped Liz from getting the comfort, support and encouragement that could have prevented the trauma from getting stuck in her system. When we have to keep something secret and don't talk about it our brains cannot integrate the experience, and it gets buried with the full emotion ready to be triggered by innocuous triggers that match the pattern.

After doing a thorough job with the movie technique we returned to Imagineering and Liz went back to her jaw.

*"I went back in and into the pool. It was not deep at all—something like a Jacuzzi, the water was blue and just slightly warmer than it had been, and it was a pleasant place to be. There was also a crab in the water but just a tiny one and I was happy for it to be there."*

Very often in the imagery a creature appears when the shift has happened: the lizard that wrapped itself around Mary's shoulder and this tiny crab in Liz's jaw. At this point the whole group could see a change in Liz. Her face looked brighter and she was sitting up more in the chair. She still seemed sceptical though and did not report much change on that day. However six months later she said *"Since then I have not used the gum-shield or the special pillow and my jaw and face have been better than they have for years. I can still have a bad night occasionally and get some of the clunking back but it is rare now. I also feel my voice has changed and I have fewer problems with my sinuses."*

When I contacted Liz to ask her if she would like to write up her experience I made the guess that whenever in her life or work she felt out of her depth it was triggering that stuck memory. This included all of the panic and grim determination of survival, and the shame of being stupid, and not being able to tell anyone or ask for comfort. Liz was probably going through life with an equation of 'out of my depth'—'I am going to die'. I did not say anything at the time because that would have been intruding in her process but six months later I made that suggestion.

Liz said: *"That helped me make the connection that the jaw grinding was related to feeling 'out of my depth'. So now I can understand the meaning of the imagery. And isn't it amazing how the language and imagery of the subconscious wants to work to heal us? We really do know all we need to need to know in order to heal ourselves somewhere inside us. However, we need strange techniques like EFT and Imagineering to access those places and translate the messages. In fact, my experience with Imagineering proves that it did not matter whether I understood the imagery anyway. The cure happened before the understanding."*

Liz makes a really important point. Her imagination and the tapping did the work together and her thinking mind did not need to understand or create meaning. So when using EFT Imagineering let your thinking mind take a vacation. You don't need to interpret, or try to change, or get involved with significance. Simply use what the imagination provides and trust that your imaginative, creative mind and EFT together will do what needs to be done. And if memories emerge simply take them through the Movie technique and then return to the Imagineering process.

## Case Study 3: The Bones in the Cave

At the Denver Masters' Showcase in July 2007 I presented EFT Imagineering to an audience of over 200. I wanted to demonstrate just how this technique can be deep yet respectful, profound yet humorous and simple yet complex. For that I needed to find a demonstration subject who had both a chronic physical condition and openness to using their imagination. At the close of the day before I was due to present, I met Barbara Friedman who later agreed to work with me on stage.

She writes: *"For me the Showcase was a wonderful opportunity to learn from watching top-level practitioners use EFT, and my intention was to observe and absorb as much as possible. I'm not one to volunteer as a subject—ever— so it was odd to find myself sitting onstage opposite Gwyneth Moss on Friday morning.*

*I had seen Gwyneth on panels throughout the conference and she fostered a strong level of trust with her respectfulness of the client's privacy, her depth of knowledge and her confidence in her experience with EFT. The day before, Gwyneth noticed I walked with a cane and mentioned she needed someone for her demonstration of EFT Imagineering. Since imagery is both very private and familiar to me, I was receptive. When she told me not to tell her anything about myself or my problem, I was hooked. All she asked was: Are you visual?"*

The next morning Barbara struggled up the steps onto the stage, looking tired and worried and leaning heavily on her cane. I had purposely not asked her anything about her history as I wanted her imagination and EFT to do the work. All I knew was that she is a psychotherapist with many years experience who lives on her own and suffers pain and restricted movement in her hip.

Imagination blossoms when consciousness softens, so to prepare Barbara to use her imagination I asked her to slow and deepen her breathing and bring to mind a time of being in meditation or peaceful relaxation and then we did an imagination test run.

*"After some breathing to centre and relax, the first part of the Imagineering involved seeing a light on the tip of my finger, inserting the finger in my ear and lighting up the inside of my head. I shared with the audience the pleasant sense of what I saw and felt and the test run gave me confidence and also let me know that my highly analytical thinking mind could take a short vacation.*

*Next Gwyneth directed my attention to my left hip where I was having pain and difficulty, but left everything open for me to 'be there' and see what was there. I saw the interior of a fairly undefined, empty cave with a few bones in a pile and a lot of dust. No detail. Gwyneth then brought me out of the cave to describe my experience to the audience and we tapped with my exact words:*

> ✦ **Even though there's a pile of dusty bones in a cave I really do accept myself.**

*Asking me if I'd like to return, she gave me time to go back into the cave with the bright little light."*

When Barbara came out again she described the bones as no longer being dusty but like 'live' bones that had recently had flesh on them. So we tapped for that using her exact words. She returned to the cave again and this time told us that the bones were no longer visible and that she thought the bones were now inside her.

*"After several trips in and out, describing the experience and then tapping with what I saw, the cave became more and more defined. There was the sense and colour of firelight, a group of people sitting opposite me in a semicircle. They were mostly elder, male, Native American—and I could see drawings on the cave wall behind them."*

When Barbara first sensed the presence of others in the cave she really was not sure about them and we tapped with:

> ✦ **Even though I'm not sure and I don't like being not sure . . . I don't know what this means and I don't like not knowing . . .**

This seemed to shift something, because in her next trip inside she said:

*"I felt comfortable with these people, even though no one spoke. There was a sense of formality to it, as though something was going to be decided. I felt I*

*was inside the cave for the first time and I knew I was there because of my hip. (The pain there is bone on bone due to osteoarthritis.) By the last time I visited the cave and stayed there a while, I could see the group in more detail, feel the texture of buckskin in their clothing and sense the look of them as if we were all of the same tribe. But they remained at a distance and I still didn't have any specific information about the gathering, other than it was about this group of people being supportive and helpful to me and I felt supported and held in their stillness."*

At this moment Barbara smiled and her whole presence shifted from tired and worried to glowing and alive. Something profound was happening and I left Barbara in her cave for a while whilst I spoke to the audience. EFT is a very active technique, and I find that once a person experiences the shifts in energy that unblock whatever is blocked it is good to offer them a little silence and stillness to let the good work continue in privacy. A pearl of wisdom I learned from Ernest Rossi is that as therapists we need to know when to shut up and leave a person to work within themselves.

When Barbara opened her eyes and brought her attention back to the present moment she described a feeling of optimism and clarity. I asked her how could she find out and test whatever had changed in her hip. In response she pointed to the steps which she had climbed with such difficulty. As she walked across the stage we all saw how much more easily she moved and descended the steps. Coming back up was still painful but, she said, not as painful as it had been, and now she was using the cane for balance rather than support.

Seated again she marvelled at how she was feeling and moving and then expressed doubt that she could hold onto this feeling when she returned home. So I asked her *"Let your mind wander ahead through the coming days and is there anything that could bring the old feeling back?"* Barbara responded that carrying heavy groceries into her home could do that. So we tapped for:

> ⁂ ***Even though carrying heavy groceries on my own could bring that old feeling back I choose to find a surprisingly simple solution.***

*"Gwyneth talked to me a bit about what was going on in my present life situation, and then we began tapping on phrases she'd noticed in our conversation. Part of that tapping dealt with my present situation, not just the imagery but the true vulnerability of living on my own in a painful, impaired state, and 'having to do everything myself'. So we tapped on:*

✦ *Even though I'm on my own and have to do everything myself . . .*

*We tapped on other things that I can't recall exactly, except the phrase* **"Oops, silly me"** *which was really helpful in putting things in perspective. It instantly reminded me I often take my situation too seriously and make everything seem grim."*

I'd now like to conclude with Barbara's own view of her EFT Imagineering experience and the insights and understanding that she gained. Speaking to her a week after Denver she told me that she had kept the optimistic feeling and each day was walking a little further without her cane.

*"My understanding of what occurred is that I have extensive amounts of information about my physical condition but not enough information about the emotional and existential issues connected with it, (which is one reason I haven't scheduled surgery yet.) I believe that until I'm clear about the changes I need to make in my life and have the tools to make those changes, my body will not function optimally, even with a hip replacement. I feel that I don't want to move forward until I'm congruent in my heart and mind about where I want to go. EFT is the tool I believe will take me there.*

*But as I learned from the imagery, I haven't been in touch with my internal 'council' of support in choosing my next direction. Prior to the EFT Imagineering, the concept of my internal support system was about being strong enough to push through or overcome difficulties. This often left me exhausted and depressed, depleting my energy. In the imagery, I was struck by the compassion and caring of this group, who, in their silence, projected a healing energy through caring and concern. They were there, but they did not tell me what to do or what was going to happen. This was the type of inner strength I'd been missing in myself, though it's exactly the type I co-create with my clients.*

*It was mirrored in Gwyneth. She maintained a compassionate detachment that allowed me to own the experience free of her influence and free of my judgment and intellectualizing. It put me in touch with myself in a more spiritual way, and I could feel my energy shift to a different vibration.*

*I remember the exact moment in the cave when I no longer felt alone and I could feel myself come back into my body in the present. I remember smiling. At the same time I was aware of the pain and fear that had pushed me out of my body over a year ago, and how empty and alone I had been feeling since then. My pessimism transformed into optimism and I began to reconnect with my best self. I felt hopeful, even though I had no idea what was going to happen.*

*Throughout the rest of the conference, people came up to me to describe the changes they saw take place while I was 'in the cave', especially in my energy at the moment of the smile. Often they commented on the positive effect it had on them. Being approached by so many people anchored the good feeling of connection that had started in the imagery. Being supported by a group of people I didn't know, who shared their positive energy so openly, and who thanked me for the shared benefits, created a powerful, reciprocal feeling. It was the same experience I'd had in the imagery taken one step further."*

(This account was written by Barbara and Gwyneth from memory and without having seen the DVD of the session. In viewing you may see some inaccuracies in detail.)

## AUTHOR'S BIOGRAPHY AND CONTACT DETAILS

Gwyneth Moss teaches EFT and runs EFT events and conferences in Yorkshire, UK. She has a Cambridge University physics degree and an MBA and brings an enquiring mind and a Quaker's spiritual common sense to the teaching of EFT. Featured on Gary Craig's Mastering EFT DVD set, she is known for practical innovations and clear presentations.

Websites: www.emotional-health.co.uk and www.EFTevents.com for conferences and further learning. Email: hello@emotional-health.co.uk

# Surrogate Tapping for Animals

## GWYNETH MOSS, EFT MASTER, EFTCERT-HONORS

### What do you mean by 'surrogate tapping for animals'?

It still surprises and shocks me that I am writing under the above title. Though I had read reports of EFT surrogate and remote healing, I stuck close to the boundaries of rational science and left such work to the intuitives.

For some of us, especially those who are Reiki trained, the concept of healing at a distance is nothing new. And those with a homeopathy background are accustomed to treating animals. For me with my scientific upbringing and Cambridge Physics degree, it always seemed a step too far to use EFT at a distance for an animal.

But students were always asking me if they could use EFT for animals. And at the same time, I wanted to teach how to manage group work and to demonstrate that in 'borrowing benefits' there need be no link or common issue between the borrower and borrowee. So I combined these requirements, and it was with more than a little uncertainty that I built into my EFT Practitioner workshops a group exercise designed to teach:

- Working with groups
- Setting up Borrowing Benefits
- EFT for Animals
- Surrogate work

I need not have worried as the results have been little short of astounding and have led me to explore surrogate work further.

I'd like to share three very special and moving EFT experiences. These were the results of the first three times I ran the exercise which has been repeated a dozen times since and ALWAYS with immediate and dramatic outcomes for the animal.

In each of these three amazing cases, a group of 12 tapped together for a pet known only to one of them. The one who knew the animal role-played the animal, and I acted as therapist, leading the 'pet' through EFT. The others in the group tapped along with us, repeating the words we used and borrowed benefits for themselves as well.

For the set up phrases, we used whatever words came to the person speaking for the pet, or to me as therapist and then added something about the pet being loved, safe and cared for. Each of these cases took about 15-20 minutes of tapping and there was a great deal of humour as well as strong emotion experienced by the whole group.

## Case Study 1: Oscar's shaking tail

Sue, a participant at one of my workshops, was offering a temporary home to Oscar, the cat of a friend of hers. The friend, whose name was Dawn, could not look after Oscar due to changing circumstances (leaving her boyfriend).

Sue was worried about Oscar. His tail and whole rear quivered and shook, and he stumbled as he walked and sometimes fell. Her three other cats would not eat with him and he was generally in poor condition. The vet had told her that it was a neurological condition and nothing could be done for him.

Having gone through the usual preparatory discussions for Borrowing Benefits, we tapped as a group with Sue leading us and speaking as Oscar:

> ✣ *Even though my tail shakes, I'm a good cat and Sue and Dawn love me.*

> ✣ *Even though I don't know where I live, I'm a good cat and these people care about me.*

Sue was guessing at Oscar's emotional state and the events that had happened to him in relation to his owner and his owner's ex boyfriend who did not treat Oscar well.

> ✣ *Even though that man wanted to get rid of me . . .*

✤ *Even though that man was bad to my owner and I couldn't protect her . . .*

The words *"came from nowhere"* Sue said with surprise. After about 15 minutes of tapping, Sue felt a deep sense of calm and we tapped a round of *"I am Sue"* to separate her energy connection with Oscar.

When Sue got home from the workshop she found that Oscar's tail was no longer shaking, he was walking better, still stumbling slightly but not falling, the other cats were much more relaxed with him and he with them, and they were all eating together. Three months later Sue confirmed that the improvements were sustained.

## Case Study 2: Kitten the 'Scaredy-Cat'

In another workshop, a group of 12 tapped for a middle aged cat who goes by the name of 'Kitten'. Kitten's owner is a friend of Moira who role-played Kitten, and once again I acted as therapist and the group tapped with us.

Kitten was a 'scaredy-cat', very nervous, startled at any movement and spent most of her time hiding upstairs. We started tapping with:

✤ *Even though I'm scared of footsteps, I'm a good cat and Moira loves me.*

Then I asked Moira if she knew what had happened to Kitten when she was a kitten. Moira didn't know and so she made up imaginary events:

✤ *Even though that man hurt me and I bit him and I couldn't escape, that was then, this is now, I'm with good people now, I'm safe now.*

✤ *Even though footsteps remind me of that man and I'm terrified, there are good people around me now and they love me.*

We tapped together as a group for about 15 minutes until Moira felt a sense of deep calm. I asked her to picture Kitten and she pictured her snuggled up all relaxed. When she got home Kitten's owner said: *"I don't know what's got into the cat, she's so much calmer"*.

Weeks later Moira confirms that Kitten is still much calmer, doesn't startle at footsteps and now spends most of her time downstairs instead of hiding under beds. It is interesting that when she enquired of Kitten's owner as to Kitten's early experiences she found out that Kitten had been the runt of the litter and was raised in a chaotic household and her experiences had probably been more of neglect than of cruelty. So even if Moira's imaginings were off track, the tapping did the trick.

## Case Study 3: Poppy—Destruction and Disruption

The third case is the most moving. Sue, a participant at another of my workshops told us of a tragedy. Her brother and his wife have four young children. They also have four cats and until recently a vibrant and intelligent Border Collie named Shadow who was like a fifth child. One morning in the summer, Shadow was hit by a car and was so badly injured that she had to be put to sleep. The raw and painful grief of the family was such that they believed that no dog could ever replace Shadow.

Then they heard from a neighbour that a 6 month old Jack Russell terrier called Poppy was to be returned to the rescue centre because his new owners could not handle him. The family felt sorry for Poppy and agreed to take him. Well Poppy proved to be more than a handful and chewed the carpet, terrorized the cats, jumped and barked and was constantly on red alert. Sue told us that this was a turning point for the family. Poppy's young life had brought hope, and if Poppy had to be returned to the rescue centre, the children would be inconsolable. However, Poppy's behaviour was causing havoc.

So Sue role-played Poppy and I led the group in tapping. We started with Poppy's behaviour and then went on to address his insecurity:

> ✦ *Even though I bark and jump, I'm a good dog and they want to love me.*

> ✦ *Even though I've been in three homes and I don't know where I belong and nobody wants me and I have to be noticed, the children love me and want me to stay.*

> ✦ *Even though I'm scared I'm not good enough, it's ok, this family loves me.*

EDITOR'S NOTE:
Here is yet another option to use when a client finds it hard to say 'I deeply and completely accept myself'.

As we tapped, Sue was feeling Poppy's emotions and feeling some shift, but it wasn't until it came through me to offer:

⤋ *Even though I can't be Shadow, I can be Poppy, and Poppy is Poppy.*

At this point it was like an electric shock went through Sue and as we tapped that subsided to a deep calm and she tapped a round of **"I am Sue"** to de-role herself.

Sue visited her brother a week later. The front door was opened and left open (previously Poppy would have rushed out barking and jumping), and as Sue walked into the kitchen she found Poppy curled up in a basket, a quiet little 'angel'.

A month after the workshop, Sue reported to me that Poppy has all the natural enthusiasm of any puppy of 6 months old, and there is no more destruction and disruption. The cats are now friends with Poppy who in her young fun way is helping the whole family to heal.

## What is meant by 'First Position Surrogate' tapping?

Since these first three cases we have completed a dozen group tapping exercises for animals (usually cats, dogs or horses) and generally with dramatic and immediate results. The role play helps the person to tune into the animal as I refer to them as the animal name and ask them questions like *"and what makes you need to bark like that Poppy?"*

My experience as the therapist leading the tapping group is that:

- Anyone can do this. Those who have role played animals are not gifted psychics or spiritual healers, they are ordinary people learning EFT

- The person role-playing the animal does not have to be the owner of the animal; some of the most dramatic cases have been through a friend or neighbour of the owner

- Through role playing and tapping, the person goes into a 'stream of consciousness' state in which memory and emotion are experienced in a manner which is unlike acting or guessing

- Once the major emotions or events are cleared with tapping, the role player experiences a deep sense of calm

- Given the strong emotions experienced, we have always de-roled the role player with a round of *"I am Me"* tapping

Role play is what I have termed 'First Position Surrogate' as the person speaks as *"I"* and feels the emotions of the animal.

## Can I do this alone or does it help to work with others?

If you want to use EFT to help an animal or pet this way, I would suggest that you find at least one other person to tap with you. The one of you that knows the pet can then tune into the feeling of the pet, or simply speak from the pet's perspective of what you know happened or imagine could have happened. If in doubt, guess. The other then acts as EFT therapist, asking questions and leading/guiding through the EFT process. Having one of you manage the process frees the other to manage the content and to be open to what comes to you without having to think about the words.

If you can collect a group of three or more to tap together, so much the better. Though there is no proof, my gut feel is that the above three cases were turbo charged by the action of the group. Once you sense the work is done, the person speaking as the animal needs to de-role themselves by repeating and tapping with **"I am me"** and saying their own name.

First position surrogate tapping requires the tapper to step into the subject's consciousness. Many would say that for human subjects this would be unethical, however that is the scope of another article and one of the reasons I have limited my exploration of surrogate tapping to animals.

## What is meant by 'Second Position Surrogate' tapping?

We have also investigated 'Second Position Surrogate' where the tapper has a dialogue with the animal whilst tapping. This can be done by tapping on a 'Magic Buttons Bear' or a soft toy or even a photo or drawing of the animal.

For example, while tapping on a soft toy, you might say:

- ✦ **Even though you get really scared, Maggie, and you pee on the kitchen floor, you are a good dog, Maggie, and we love you.**

- ✦ **Even though something nasty happened, Maggie, and you were punished and couldn't defend yourself then, you are a good dog, Maggie, and we will be kind to you.**

When we used this in one of my workshops, after several rounds of tapping for what was known or guessed of Maggie's experiences before being rescued and re-homed, the tapper pictured Maggie as calm and relaxed, in marked contrast to her normal anxious and edgy state.

'Second Position Surrogate' tapping makes use of the connection between tapper and subject, and builds in an imagined dialogue. It is easiest when tapping ON something such as a tapping bear or some representation of the subject, however the tapper should take care not to lead the dialogue too soon towards a desired outcome. This could happen, for example, if the tapper is overly attached to the outcome {see *The Pursuit of Excellence*}, and perhaps feels tempted to use words such as: *"Snow, you can go outside again now and be a happy cat."* Resistance or underlying issues need to be given the chance to emerge and be recognized then tapped through.

## What is meant by 'Third Position Surrogate' tapping?

In 'Third Position Surrogate' tapping, the tapper simply tells the story of all he knows or imagines about the animal, whilst tapping on himself as the members of the group tap along. For example:

- ✢ **Even though Snow is such a sad cat without Blackey and just sits and stares out of the window, Snow is a good cat and Mrs Jones loves Snow.**

- ✢ **Even though Blackey was taken away and never came back and Snow couldn't say goodbye, Snow is a beautiful cat and Mrs Jones loves Snow very much.**

Again, in Third Position Surrogate the tapper will come to a point where he imagines the animal looking calmer, brighter or changed in some way.

This is the least intrusive of the three surrogate positions as the tapper is talking about the subject and not getting into the subject's consciousness. Using surrogate tapping in this way side steps issues of permission as the tapper is simply telling a story of what he knows. It may be that this position is also working more on the tapper's emotions, beliefs and feelings about the subject. Cases where surrogate work has had no or limited effect often involve the tapper being over invested in or attached to the outcome for the subject.

## Why does this work so well with Borrowing Benefits?

In all the above cases, the members of the group were given Borrowing Benefits instructions to choose a specific event, ache or pain, or specific situation in which they anticipated difficulty (such as an interview). That was then put to one side while they tapped with the animal tapper. Animal stories contain universal emotional themes:

- Separation from mother and siblings
- Knowing who you belong to
- Confusion about what is wanted of you
- Rejection of your best efforts
- Bullying by bigger or older animals
- Loss of an owner or companion animal
- Humiliation and cruelty
- Being trapped or powerless in the face of threat
- Abandonment

These themes resonate strongly with the tapping group and tears are not uncommon. The stories are highly emotional, especially as we do not judge or blame an animal as we would a human in a similar situation, and it is moving how easily and quickly the animal comes to forgiveness.

In the case of a highly aggressive Alsatian dog that had been subjected to cruelty and humiliation, through the role player we witnessed intense hatred of mankind turn within a few tapping rounds to compassion and a willingness to serve. (The rescuers of the dog in question were later told by recruiters for the police dog service that he was *"too good natured for police work"*)

*EDITOR'S NOTE:*
This feels like a crucially important point, reminiscent of Patricia Carrington's article on the borrowing of personal resources. In this case, when at least partially in the role of an animal, one borrows its innocence and integrity; qualities at the heart of all humans, if sometimes deeply buried.

Emotion is thus strongly tuned in whilst tapping, so it does not surprise me that after the exercise each group member usually reports a significant change in whatever he selected to work on. THIS WORK IS HIGHLY BENEFICIAL FOR THE HUMANS DOING THE TAPPING AS WELL AS THE ANIMALS BEING TAPPED FOR.

## Some concluding remarks

From this work with animals, my conclusion is that there is a real and powerful effect in surrogate tapping which is worthy of further investigation. In tapping for animals we can be humbled by their stories and how completely they forgive.

Animals do not lie, neither do they judge or criticize. Nor can we attribute results to placebo. Change is real change and not simply compliance. In exploring surrogate work with animals we are exploring the energetic connections between all things and who knows where this will take us.

## AUTHOR'S BIOGRAPHY AND CONTACT DETAILS

See 'The Imagineering Technique' by Gwyneth Moss for biography and contact details.

# Deep State Re-patterning (DSR)

TANIA PRINCE, EFT MASTER, EFTCERT-HONORS

## Introduction to Deep State Re-patterning (DSR)

Deep State Re-patterning (DSR) has been described as a 'deep and profound method of healing'. It is an advanced approach to using EFT that combines ideas from NLP, Hypnotic language, Inner Child work and Soul Retrieval.

Most methods of using EFT focus on working with current life issues, generally from early childhood and upwards, to create health and well-being. In many cases this can be of great benefit to people, however not everyone gains the resolution they seek.

Finding and working with the root causes of issues can be a powerful way of using EFT. DSR provides a method of finding the deepest roots of issues; for example, roots such as those that occur during the birth process, in the womb, and even before this lifetime (i.e. 'past lives' and ancestral issues). These roots are often very challenging to access using traditional EFT methods.

---

DSR has also been described as a process of: *'recreating the past to rewrite our future'*

---

A lack of belief in the existence of 'past lives' does not preclude a person from using this approach as it can equally be seen as a powerful metaphorical way of working.

## What are the key features of DSR?

- DSR can be an extremely fast process for finding what needs to be worked on to clear the client's problem. It can often find the root of a problem within minutes.

- DSR is a relatively gentle process. People can have a lot of fun using this method of working.

*EDITOR'S NOTE:*
This method of dissociation is similar to the concept of the ECHO referred to in Matrix Reimprinting, with the scope for further dissociation by moving the screen further away, etc (as discussed below).

- DSR can identify issues that are not easy to find. This is because of the very direct questioning techniques, and also because the events are seen on a screen, and therefore dissociate the client from the experience being worked upon.

- DSR can create deep and profound whole-life transformational healing. Often during the process of DSR, the client begins to realise why she has done certain things in her life. She begins to notice the patterns of behaviour that run through her life, and as a consequence achieves greater self understanding.

## How does DSR relate to NLP?

DSR is an advanced EFT technique, and as such requires proficiency in basic EFT approaches. It uses ideas from NLP, however no prior knowledge is required as this is naturally incorporated into the process.

NLP can be described as 'the art of communication'. The words used in DSR often have a hypnotic quality. Communication isn't just about the words we speak; tonality and body language also come into the equation. This aspect of DSR is more difficult to represent in a book. In order to fully experience the way language can be used, it is advisable to listen to a live recording of DSR[1] or attend a training course.

## Can I use DSR to deal with the root cause of a problem?

Absolutely; this is the very essence of the approach. DSR works by dealing with the deepest roots of the client's problem, often locating them within minutes. Why is it important to deal with deep roots? One of the major reasons is that if you clear the roots, you stop the problem recurring.

Imagine a problem like a dandelion. {See *The Colour of Pain* for a similar metaphor.} If you pull it out of the ground by dealing with the surface leaves and flowers, the deep roots break off. It looks like you have dealt with the problem of the dandelion issue. However, within time the root grows and a new dandelion pops up. This can be the same with personal problems. You need to fully clear it.

Another important reason is that clearing the problem at the deepest root level requires less tapping and can be quicker. Why? An easy way to understand this is if you envisage the problem as a triangle, one in which the pointed end faces down. The point represents the beginning point of the problem, the root cause. The volume of issues that need to be dealt with to clear the problem at this stage is small. Go up the triangle and it widens out. This widening out represents the increased number of events occurring as a result of the root cause. That increased number of events related to the problem (as you progress up the triangle) usually leads to it becoming more complex, and thus requiring more work to eradicate it.

---

Tapping our issues at root cause should be EASY. If it feels like hard work it may indicate that there is a deeper root.

---

In this case you simply need to find out when that earlier event occurred and tap it through

## Can I use DSR to 're-write' personal history?

Our perception of life events (whether 'good' or 'bad' or in between) has a profound effect on our quality of life. It can even affect who we think we are—our identity {see *Who Do You Think You Are?*}. If you have many events in your life in which you have run away from challenges or stressful situations, when you think about who you are, you might say: *"I am a weak person"*. I have worked with many people who have experienced endless panic/ anxiety attacks. They have felt an intense need to flee situations. As a consequence of this they have built a low self-esteem based on their behaviour in these events.

---

Imagine, however, if you could rewrite these events so that instead of running away, you see yourself behaving in a much more resourceful way.

---

Imagine how this would change how you perceive yourself to be. Instead of seeing yourself as weak, you might now perceive yourself as strong! Imagine the difference this would make in your life!

DSR naturally changes history. As you tap through the events using DSR, they begin to look different. You can gain a totally new perspective. In fact history can change completely. I have also seen many violent scenes transform, so that the person at the receiving end of that violence becomes strong and resilient and somehow the sense of violence fades from the event.

## Can this change in history generalise to other memories?

Another interesting phenomenon I have observed is that, as a consequence of clearing very deep underlying events, events that occurred after the originating point can change without directly tapping on them.

For example, after tapping on a past life experience, June (please see Case History 4 below) revisited an event that took place in her current lifetime. However, she now saw the event differently. Instead of seeing what had really happened, that she was in a fraught situation, she now saw herself leave the situation (this was not as the event had occurred in her memory/reality prior to doing DSR). We tapped this through until she was comfortable with the new memory that had occurred in her personal history.

Perhaps you may fear that changing how your mind thinks about these events will leave you vulnerable to violence. It has been my experience that you will keep with you whatever you have learned that keeps you safe, and this will keep you safe in the future.

## When should I stop tapping?

One of the most interesting effects that I have discovered using this approach is that there can be many points during the process that seem to indicate that no more tapping is required. These are often false endings. If on the other hand you continue to identify and clear belief after belief, you will find that you reach a far more profound place of healing, one in which joy and bliss are present. DSR isn't just about clearing the problem state; it is about transforming life, clearing beliefs that don't work, embedding beliefs that do. DSR is about learning from past experiences to heal and experience joy now.

EFT can be used either in a very superficial way or a very deep and profound way. Many people who use it in a superficial way may still experience results; however those results are not to the same

EDITOR'S NOTE:
Brandon Bays, the author of The Journey, speaks of similar false endings and she too stresses the importance of persistence in order to reach the bliss that inevitably awaits the persistent traveller.

degree that you can achieve by working at a very deep level. By deep level, I mean one which deals with the roots, and in doing so, takes out more than just the emotions; it takes out the beliefs as well. With DSR you should continue to tap and clear until you reach a deep and profound resolution of the issue.

## How can DSR help with integrating disconnected parts?

Sometimes when we experience trauma we 'lose a part of ourselves'. In some cases it may just be a small sense of loss, but in others it can seem as if a part of us breaks away completely and seems locked in time (at the moment the trauma occurred). Tapping through and clearing the emotions from that point in time unlocks the moment.

However, unlocking the moment and gaining a new perspective on the event does not mean that we have reconnected with all parts. We may now need to reconnect with any part that we lost contact with as a consequence of the trauma or high emotional state.

DSR factors this into the process. It does this by healing the trauma and going well beyond the

EDITOR'S NOTE:
It is interesting that re-integration of parts is not normally specified in the Matrix Reimprinting process, although the concept of a part being 'locked in time' is strongly reminiscent of the ECHO.

point of healing until the part, or Inner Child/adult is vibrant and healthy. Once this stage is reached, the healed person on the screen is asked if she is OK about reconnecting with the client to create wholeness. If there is agreement, the EFT reintegration protocol is used. The wording of this can vary depending on whether you are dealing with a past life, different generation, or present life event (see the example script in Case History 1).

If working with the ancestors or past life events you may reword this to ask whether the past life person or ancestor would like to pass a gift (or whatever needs to be passed on) to your client, stating the intention that it will be for the client's higher good. When agreement is reached, tap this in.

*EDITOR'S NOTE:*
The person on the screen is treated as a 'client' rather than 'self', just as in Matrix Reimprinting.

## How can I use DSR to create a 'safe place' for my client?

Clients often attend therapy for issues that have a great amount of emotion attached to them. EFT is one of those therapies where techniques can be used to minimise the client's distress whilst working on these potentially highly emotional issues. Going into past lives and to different generations of the family line has the potential to touch upon highly traumatic material. Thus DSR uses approaches to minimise the potential for distress. These involve dissociating the client from the experience or event.

This is done by getting the client to see whatever event is the root cause on a screen, as opposed to reliving it.

To help maintain the dissociation, third person language is also used.

## How can I make the 'safe place' even safer?

Creating a greater distance between the client and the screen will generally minimise the distress levels. If necessary, the screen can even be put so far away that it becomes the size of a pin head. If during the session the client becomes distressed, ask her to move the screen further away, or turn the colour to black and white. There is no need for the client to experience emotions during the DSR process. Visual language is also used to help keep the client comfortable. Visual language such as: *"What can you see?"* as opposed to: *"What can you feel?"* is used throughout the process. *"What can you see?"* is much more

*EDITOR'S NOTE:*
Interestingly, Gwyneth Moss speaks of allowing the client to decide on the sense to be used in Imagineering, where there is perhaps less likelihood of abreaction.

likely to allow the client to remain comfortable, whilst: *"What can you feel?"* may well plunge the client directly into her emotions.

## Can you give me some examples of third person language?

In standard EFT we often use phrases that put us in an associated perspective, such as:

> ✢ *So even though I have this butterfly feeling in my stomach when I think of spiders . . .*

Using this type of language can lead to the person feeling the emotions very easily. In DSR we would rephrase it as follows:

> ✢ *So even though she felt butterflies in her stomach when she thought of a spider . . .*

Using third person language helps keep the person from fully connecting with the emotions. It puts the person 'outside' the experience and therefore much less likely to experience intense emotions. The affirmation, however, is phrased in more normal EFT language as follows: *"I love and approve of her anyway"*.

Other examples of third person language are:

> ✢ *So even though she didn't have enough . . .*
>
> ✢ *So even though she felt betrayed . . .*

## What if the picture on the screen is difficult to accept?

Sometimes what occurs on screen may go beyond the client's values, making it unacceptable. For example, using the term: *"I love and approve of her"* may not be accepted by the client if, for example, the 'her' in question has just committed a murder on the screen (this can happen in both past life and ancestral issues).

One of the presuppositions of NLP is that the person is not her behaviour and that ALL behaviour is driven by underlying emotions. It may therefore be helpful to explain to the client that what you are asking her to say (i.e. *"I love and approve of her anyway"*) is not justifying the behaviour. It is accepting that person at a deep core level, without the issues she obviously has.

Another way to get around this is just to modify the affirmation to: *"I want to love and approve of her, she was doing her best with the resources she had"*. {See *How to Get Yourself Out of the Way* for more ideas on how to deal with difficulty in acceptance.}

## How can I use DSR with highly emotional clients?

Although DSR is set up to help keep the client comfortable, some clients will associate with the issues and begin to feel intense emotions anyway. However, these are generally not as strong as the emotions that she would have experienced if you had not used this dissociative approach. To deal with this you need to ask:

---

*"Are these the emotions she over there was feeling?"*

---

(When you say 'over there', you are referring to the person on the screen.)

EDITOR'S NOTE:
Although the wording 'she over there' may feel initially awkward, it does have the effect of helping to separate a client from potentially upsetting events on the screen.

Generally the answer to this is 'yes'. Once you have established this, ask your client to look at her over there on the screen and just re-establish the dissociative language. It is important to have good rapport with the client if you do this. Also re-establish that you want to take the problem out from the roots. However, because the issue that 'she over there on the screen' has is connected to the current problem, it is quite natural that your client will have flipped back to the current time.

I have seen this happen many times. However, getting the person to focus on the event on the screen and fully clearing the issues at this root level is important. When you clear these, you generally notice the current life emotions are cleared as well.

If your client is still associated with her current issues and you have established that 'she over there' (the person on the screen) felt these feelings, ask the client to erect a wall between herself and the screen so she cannot see it. You can then tap on what is over there. The client does not need to be seeing the events at this point. It is OK just to have quick views of what is happening on that screen, and put it away and tap.

# The 15 Stages of Deep State Re-patterning

## Stage 1: Establish rapport

This is a pre-requisite for effective therapy. There are many excellent NLP books on this subject so I will not go into it here. I would however recommend mastering the art of rapport.

## Stage 2: Identify the problem

One of the easiest ways to identify the client's problem (or your own if you are working on yourself) is to ask:

*"Tell me a little bit about your problem"* (or think about your problem)

*"How do you know that you have this problem?"*

It is important to establish this at the beginning before doing any work on the problem. Firstly, it clearly shows what evidence the person is using to identify this as a problem and secondly, it also provides the information necessary to test the result.

## Stage 3: Open your client's mind to the timing of the root cause

The first thing that you need to do is identify the client's belief structure. It is always advisable to work within this structure, otherwise you may find resistance occurring and you can lose rapport. If this happens it is difficult to get results in therapy. The easiest way to find out about your client's beliefs is to ask: *"Do you believe in past lives?"* If she does, then you can set the scene for going through the DSR process by opening her mind to all the different options as to when the root cause occurred.

People normally find it relatively easy to access events from early childhood to adulthood, whereas birth and pre-birth experiences do not always come to light as easily during normal EFT sessions. It is important to open the client's mind to the possibility that the roots of the problem may well have occurred at these points in time, or in a past life, or have been passed onto him or her from ancestors.

It is important that you do not use your language to emphasise one idea over the other possibilities when presenting this idea to the client. This keeps the client from being influenced by any bias you may have, and she is then free to come up with the answers that come from her own subconscious mind.

---

It is important to work within your client's belief system.

---

If the client is not open to the idea of past lives, then it is important to reframe this idea so that you can still use this approach. The way that you can do this is by explaining that this process can equally be seen as a metaphorical way of working with the mind. Explain also that the mind likes to work in metaphors and stories. I also like to add that I personally have had great results working in this way with clients.

*EDITOR'S NOTE:*
This is a close parallel to the principle from elsewhere in this book that tapping can work perfectly well on made up stories.

If the client is OK and agrees to this, proceed to the next stage in the process. I have never come across a client who hasn't agreed to work using this approach when the idea has been presented in this way. You need to focus her mind on the true purpose of therapy: to gain a result or outcome. The method of gaining that outcome should pale into insignificance in comparison.

## Stage 4: Identify the root cause and when it occurred

DSR uses questioning techniques to pinpoint moments or periods in time when the problem first occurred, the root cause.

This process can be likened to going through a set of doors that lead to the memory or metaphor. At the beginning of the questioning process, your client does not need to know what the event was, although some people instantly have the memory pop into their mind. Others only access the memory after they have been led step by step through the doors.

---

The first thought that pops into mind is key. If necessary, guess!

---

It is important to establish with the client that you want her to go with the first thought that pops into mind as you ask the questions. If you don't establish this she will often censor the information and her rational mind might try to make sense of it. The first thought is often the subconscious material.

FIRST QUESTION: The first question I ask is to establish whether the root cause was in this lifetime or before this lifetime? If the client answers: *"Before this lifetime"* and this seems to resonate, I then establish whether it was:

a. in a 'past life', or
b. from the ancestors.

Using a combination of conversational hypnotic language (Milton model language patterns from NLP) and questions, I then say: *"And as you gain that level of awareness of that, I want you to look at that screen, and I want you to guess what occurred, then that sets the scene for your current problem. Now I don't know if you may SEE THE EVENT ON THAT SCREEN or whether you might just sense what it was, but when you have done that, I want you to tell me WHAT CAN YOU SEE?"*

At this point I give the client time to process what is going on for them. Please note that the words in CAPITALS are given more emphasis and are effectively 'commands' to the unconscious mind. These commands often pass unnoticed by the conscious mind. You need good rapport to use language that is as direct as this. Although the wording used does not have to be the same, there are reasons why language is phrased in this way. The whole process above generally only takes up to a minute.

On the other hand, if the client says that the event occurred: *"In this life-time"*, I then open her mind up to the three possibilities:

1. in the womb,
2. during birth, or
3. after birth.

The reason to distinguish between these three possibilities is that birth and pre-birth experiences do not always immediately pop into people's mind unless you have opened the client up to the possibility that events at this point in time may well be relevant.

Sometimes doubt can creep into the client's mind. You can often tell this has happened if the client says: *"I am not sure if I am making this up"* or looks hesitant. It is important to deal with this before it causes a problem. To do that you can say:

---

*"It really doesn't matter whether this is real or not, because in EFT we can make up an event and tap on it, and still get results. So I want you to go with that first thought."*

---

When you have opened the client's mind to the three possible times when the roots in this lifetime may have occurred, ask her to guess which one resonates or pops into mind.

If she says the root cause occurred after birth, you need to establish at what age. The reason to ask this question is that sometimes she will go to more accessible memories. If you get an age for the event it may well open the client's mind up to an event that occurred that is not in her conscious mind.

A great example of this occurred when I worked with a client called June (Case History 4). During part of the work she did, the age she identified as the root cause and the immediate event that she saw on the screen differed. As she realised this, the image on the screen quickly changed to an earlier event in her life that she had not been aware of, one which was the deepest root of that problem.

## Stage 5: Create a level of dissociation to keep the client safe

At this point we are close to identifying what the event was that caused the client's problem. Ask the client to imagine a screen in front of her, one which she has full control over. She can move that screen back and forward, and/or dim the picture. The reason to establish that she is in control over the screen is because it is important, if necessary, to adjust the screen to minimise any discomfort the client may experience. Factors such as the distance at which the client sees the screen can have an impact on the emotional intensity the client may feel. Moving the screen further away can often lessen the intensity of any emotions. Dimming the screen for some clients can also lessen the intensity.

## Stage 6: Identify the event or significant past other

Now that the screen has been established, ask the client to guess what the event was and put it on the screen *"over there"*. Pause and give the client time to process this. Then let her begin to describe what she sees on the screen. If she pinpoints a moment in history and the description does not coincide with historical events or costumes, just continue with what she said and make no comment about it.

---

It is of no importance whether this is historically accurate.

---

You may need to ask a few questions to clarify what she is seeing. An important question to ask, if she does not make this obvious in the description, is whether the person that she sees is male or female. The reason to identify the gender of 'her over there' is so that you can use appropriate third person language.

## Stage 7: Identify the emotions

This is the point where you need to begin to tap. However you first need to identify what to tap on. This can be done by asking the client to *"guess"* what emotionally is going on for her over there.

By encouraging guess work you make it more likely that the client will bypass the conscious mind and gain access to subconscious material. It can be useful for tapping purposes to ask: *"What is happening that is causing her over there to feel that way?"* If the client does not know, simply take her first answer as your starting point, the emotion that she guessed was there.

## Stage 8: Tap on the guessed emotions until they are clear

Tap through the emotions. The tapping at this point can be very simple such as:

+ *So even though she feels really sad because she was all alone, I completely and totally love and approve of her anyway*

After each round of tapping ask: *"What do you see now, what is emotionally going on for her over there, now?"* And in the above example you might ask: *"Is there still sadness there?"*

## Stage 9: Continue to track the process, repeating earlier steps if necessary

At this point it can be very interesting as the image often begins to shift. The client can begin to notice that things are changing for her over there on the screen. Continue with this process, identifying the emotions until the person on the screen seems at peace. The imagery on the screen should change as you continue to tap. Sometimes the person on the screen fades after a few rounds of EFT; you need at this point to bring them back. You can just do this by asking them to do so. This can be a false end point.

## Stage 10: Deal with beliefs and life lessons

*EDITOR'S NOTE:*
Research shows that we generally won't let ourselves want what we don't believe we can do or pull off. We don't generally express it that way, though, saying instead things like: 'Who cares?' or 'I never wanted that anyway', or 'That's not like me!'

Beliefs can have a powerful controlling effect over our lives; generally we can only do what we believe we can do. Changing beliefs can be a powerful way to transform a person. There are two main beliefs we target with DSR:

- identity level beliefs, and
- generalised beliefs about the world and life.

Identity level beliefs are those that refer to 'who we are', such as: *"I am a strong person"*, or *"I am a resilient person"* or *"I am a bad person"* etc. The other type of beliefs targeted by DSR are beliefs about life and the world. These include beliefs such as: *"The world is a dangerous place"*, or *"People can't be trusted"*.

The natural way that beliefs change in life is that we begin to experience things that create doubt in our old belief. Given enough doubt, we then take on board a new belief. We can use this natural phenomenon in EFT by setting up the original belief such as *"I am not good enough"* as the problem.

Then as we begin to tap on this belief we start to use transitional language such as:

1. *"What if I was wrong?"*, *"What if that doesn't mean that, just because that _____ event happened?"*
2. *Then . . . "What if I am (new belief)?"*
3. *And then finally . . . "I am (new belief)!".*

So, applying this to the belief *"I am not good enough"*:

1. *"What if I am good enough?"*, *"What if I have always been good enough?"* and *"What if I just didn't know it?"*
2. *Then . . . "I am good enough!", "I have always been good enough!".*

I always find it is useful to use my voice to put across conviction in the new belief.

## How can I use questions to discover beliefs?

Ask the client to tap on the karate point and go inside her own mind and ask the person on the screen the following questions:

- *"Because that happened, what did it mean about who you are?"*
- *"Because that happened, what did it mean about life?"*

A typical answer to the 'about life' question might be: *"It means life isn't safe"*. You would then need to tap this through using EFT and break the decision about life not being 'safe'.

Even if you are dealing with a pre-birth person on the screen, it makes no difference—you still ask the questions.

---

I often add: *"They can communicate telepathically"*.

---

This is more to lighten the mood and is not always necessary. Tap through each of these answers until the person on the screen no longer has the limiting belief.

## Can I use lack of meaningful evidence to collapse beliefs?

One of the simplest ways to collapse a belief is to identify the evidence the person used to form that belief. For example, one of my clients formed the

EDITOR'S NOTE:
This is one of the mainstays of cognitive re-structuring, a key component of cognitive behavioural therapy (CBT).

beliefs: *"I don't get my needs met"*, *"There isn't enough"*, *"I always fail"* because she was unable to feed properly when she was born.

Tapping through as follows usually collapses the belief really quickly:

> ⚡ *So even though I could never get enough milk and I decided that MUST MEAN I always fail, I completely and totally love and approve of myself anyway*

Tap this through in the normal EFT way emphasising the 'MUST MEAN'. Of course looking at this as an adult, not being able to get enough milk as a baby does not necessarily mean that the person 'always fails'. The problem here is that they connected not getting enough milk to 'always failing', when they are not really connected.

## How can I build 'life lessons' into the process?

Ask the client to tap on the karate point and go inside her own mind and ask the person on the screen the following question:

*"What did you need to learn from this experience to heal from it?"*

A typical answer might be: *"I needed to accept myself for who I am"*. Assume the person on the screen didn't take these learnings at the time and set this up in EFT as the problem:

> ⚡ *So even though she couldn't accept herself, I completely and totally love and approve of her anyway.*

> ⚡ *So even though she felt who she was, was unacceptable, I completely and totally love and approve of her anyway.*

> ⚡ *So even though she just couldn't accept who she was, I completely and totally love and approve of her.*

| EYEBROW: | *She didn't feel acceptable* |
| SIDE OF EYE: | *Who she was just didn't feel acceptable, she couldn't accept herself* |
| UNDER EYE: | *She just couldn't accept who she was* |
| UNDER NOSE: | *She couldn't accept who she was* |
| CHIN POINT: | *But what if it is OK to let that go now* |
| COLLAR BONE: | *What if she can begin to do that* |
| UNDER ARM: | *Because what if who she is, is good enough, and what if she can begin to accept herself for who she is* |
| TOP OF HEAD: | *She couldn't then, but what if she can now? What if it is OK to do that now?* |

I have come across the concept many times where people have something to learn in life and if they don't learn that, they have to repeat the same lessons so they have another opportunity to learn. This pattern can keep repeating.

We address this in DSR by asking the client to ask the person on the screen:

*"What is the learning that you needed to take from that lifetime that would set you free now?"*

Then assume that the person on the screen didn't learn it and set it up as the problem. Tap from the problem state through to opening her mind to the learnings she needed to take, with phrasing such as:

&#10070; *. . . what if it is OK to learn from that experience now, what if I can do that?*

&#10070; *. . . I can take the learnings that _____ (whatever she needed to learn)*

This type of phrasing in EFT goes from focusing on the problem to creating a transition state, such as: *". . . what if I can let that go now?"*, and then going to the solution, i.e. the learnings.

For example, if the client says she needed to learn to forgive herself, then you can set the EFT up as follows:

&#10070; *So even though she couldn't forgive herself, I completely and totally love and approve of her anyway.*

Good phrasing to create a transition to what she needed to learn is:

*"That was then, this is NOW."*

*"That was then, this is now, what if she can do that now? She couldn't then, but what if she can now? What if it is ok to DO THAT NOW?"*

*"What if it is OK to learn from that experience?".*

*"What she did wasn't right, but what if it is OK TO LEARN FROM IT?"*

*"She can accept she was wrong"*

*"What if learning from the experience and forgiving herself will help her in a very positive way to become a better person? I think it will, what if it will?"*

Another good question to ask the person on the screen is:

*"What does she need to learn from the experience to help you here now?"*

I have put some of the tapping sequence in capitals to highlight the use of Hypnotic language; embedded commands that can speed up how long it takes to tap through issues. Embedded commands, when presented well, will bypass the client's conscious mind and quite often be automatically accepted by her subconscious mind.

## Stage 11: Verify that all the unhelpful emotions are gone

When all the emotions have been cleared, there is an optional stage of checking from an associated perspective. Ask the client to get inside the person on that screen and check whether there are any other emotions that need to be cleared. If there are, tap on what is revealed by this stage.

## Stage 12: Re-integration

Once the person on the screen is fully healed and has a sense of vibrancy you can then re-unite the part back into the mind/body system and create wholeness (see the Case Studies below for the full script). DSR uses different wording dependent on whether it is a current lifetime experience you are dealing with, or one from a past life.

Re-integration is done in order to create wholeness and inner harmony.

This is the protocol I use when dealing with events from the client's lifetime. I use this process whether dealing with a child or adult. The reason for this is that when we experience trauma we can lose parts of ourselves, and this can occur both in childhood or when we reach adulthood.

1. Completely clear the Inner Child's emotions using EFT, until a place of peace is reached. This stage is very important. If you only partially heal you may not achieve re-integration.

2. Tap on the karate point and ask the healed Inner Child if it is OK to re-integrate back with the adult.

3. Listen to the answer, reassuring the Inner Child that what it wants is important and that you are listening.

4. If the answer is *"No"*, ask: *"What needs to be healed to allow re-integration?"* This will often provide a tappable issue, if so, tap it through until it is clear and then re-ask the question. Continue until the Inner Child is OK with re-integrating with the adult.

It is important to gain permission. If you ask and do not gain permission you need to find out why and deal with the objection. One example that I had of an objection was that the child felt the adult needed to do some work on themselves before it would come on board and re-connect. In this case we tapped and dealt with the issues the child raised. Continue until you have cleared all the tappable issues brought up by objections to re-integrating.

Another lady when asked the re-integration question, got a sense/image of fog, like a cloudy sky and a feeling of choking. This was tapped through just using normal EFT language. Instantly the fog lifted and the lady had a sense of the sky being cleared. When asked again about re-integration there was no objection.

Asking for permission is also being respectful and not forcing. This is important to establish.

Once you have agreement for re-integration, tap on the karate point and have that sense of bringing that part back on board. Many people have the sense of bringing it into their heart. The following is a typical example of the language used whilst tapping and re-integrating the Inner Child:

KARATE POINT: ***Having that sense of re-connecting with that part***
EYE BROW:      ***Beginning to connect with all those wonderful resources***

SIDE OF EYE:  *Feeling and sensing that connection and communication in a wonderful way*

UNDER EYE:  *That wonderful . . . . . . . . (name a quality that that child now has—an example that I have come across has been wisdom. Other examples might be innocence, strength, determination), . . . . . . FEELING THAT NOW.*

UNDER NOSE:  *Connecting with that . . . (name another quality that that child now has, such as determination)*

CHIN:  *Feeling all that strength now as all parts begin to re-connect as one*

COLLARBONE:  *Feeling all those wonderful feelings and experiencing that sense of oneness, now*

UNDERARM:  *Allowing that integration to complete and feeling those wonderful feelings of connection and wholeness.*

After completing the re-integration process, some people have felt a strengthening of their 'inner core', the central part of their body.

## Stage 13: Fast forward to other significant points

Sometimes when dealing with issues, you need to clear more than just the root cause. In this case ask the mind to pop onto that screen any other events that need to be dealt with to allow the client to heal fully.

Clear all the emotions, beliefs etc from each event until there is nothing more that pops onto the screen (Stages 6—12).

## Stage 14: Testing the Outcome

Using the information from Stage 2, test the client's current life issue to see whether there is any more work that needs to be done or whether the issue is gone.

This is an important step because you now need to provide the client with the evidence that their issue is no longer there (if that is the case). If there is still something there, you as the therapist need to acknowledge that, and set up a way to work on what now needs to be dealt with.

## Case Study 1: Abundance and 'not being able to achieve it'

*BACKGROUND TO THE CASE*

Elaine described her problem as 'not believing at a core level that she was going to succeed with her business'; this realisation was accompanied by a really intense feeling in her chest; a feeling of unknown origin. Elaine had tapped on this issue previously but gained little or no progress, although immediately after tapping she often felt really good and very positive. The change did not last, however.

*THE SESSION*

When asked when she felt this first started, she said two generations ago. She was asked to guess what had happened two generations ago and put it onto a screen in front of her. Immediately she saw a still picture of a young woman dressed in a black and white waitress' outfit similar to those worn in old Victorian tea rooms. The woman was serving people but was very unhappy doing it. Looking at the image she sensed that she was her grandmother as a young woman.

When asked to guess what was emotionally going on for this woman, she came up with the words, 'know your place' and 'don't get above your station'. Each of these was tapped on, as well as all the other aspects that surfaced. Elaine also sensed that the woman on the screen felt she should be 'grateful' that she was even allowed to be a serving girl, as that was all she was meant to be in life.

As the tapping progressed, the still image became a movie. The woman seemed much more contented, happy and at peace with her life, although she was still serving in the tea room. The scene then jumped to an image of her grandmother as Elaine knew her. She looked warm, soft, loving with a "*smiley face*". Elaine also felt at this point that the warm, loving grandmother was sending a feeling of "*love and approval*" to her.

Asked to go to any further events from then to now that needed to be cleared, she immediately saw an event that occurred at the age of eight. This again was represented as a still image. She looked very unhappy. This related to a period in her life where her family had decided to move to a different part of the country, (to Wales). She had been made to leave all her school friends.

The issues experienced by the child were heightened by the fact that Welsh was the predominant language of the area they moved to, and Elaine spoke only English.

As a small child she felt that her *"feelings were not being taken into consideration"*, and she felt powerless, amongst many other emotions. Asked to guess what was emotionally going on for the child, we identified and tapped through all the emotional aspects until the child felt at peace and happy. The visual image changed in line with the clearing of negative emotions. As before the imagery changed from a still image to a movie, one in which the child was now happy.

## RE-INTEGRATION OF THE INNER CHILD–SOUL RETRIEVAL

When the emotions of the child were fully resolved we asked the child if it would like to re-connect with the adult and bring all its wonderful resources back so that it would feel whole, connected and loved. The answer was an immediate *"Yes!"* We then went through the re-integration steps of DSR. As the process completed, the client said that she felt whole as if something had returned to her. She said the feeling ran down the centre of her torso, her *"core"*. Asked a few days later whether that feeling of wholeness had remained, she said it had. She felt a sense of difference within herself.

## FOLLOW-UP NOTES

Elaine noted that she had no previous knowledge of her grandmother working in the type of establishment she had seen on the screen. As to whether this was 'real' or not we will never know. What is more important is that it got the therapeutic result.

Another important point to note is that the emotions and themes explored by working on the 'grandmother' from two generations ago were also emotions and themes in Elaine's life.

The work done re-integrating the eight year old child was successfully achieved in this session. Previously this had been attempted by a hypnotherapist, however because the uncomfortable emotions were not cleared, the adult (client) felt she *"did not want to let the child go"*. With the emotions unresolved, the attempted re-integration made the client feel *"really sad"*. When the emotions were resolved she experienced re-integration

*EDITOR'S NOTE:*
This shows the immense potential of integrating tapping with other techniques such as hypnotherapy.

as a *"joyous"* experience. Describing it in more detail she said: *"It felt like a piece of my soul returned"*. She said that she felt a fragment of her soul *"had been floating around where it shouldn't have been"*, and that she had been able to retrieve that fragment and put it back.

Asked about succeeding in her business she said: *"I certainly do not feel now at any core level that I am not going to succeed in my business"*. She went on to say: *"I have no doubt that we will (succeed), I know things are changing"*.

## Case Study 2: Not deserving abundance

### BACKGROUND TO THE CASE

Sue was working on abundance issues. She was doing an exercise looking at the things that meant abundance for her. Looking at a speed boat and thinking about the idea of her owning one she suddenly felt an overwhelming anger rise within her. She was shocked by the experience and especially the intensity of the emotions that had consumed her at that moment.

What this event revealed to her was that at a deep level there was a sense that she didn't deserve to have or ride that speed boat. Sue had actually tapped on deservedness using standard EFT methods on current life experiences before. It obviously had not cleared the issue at any deep level. I worked with her a few days after this experience.

Going through the DSR process she identified the root cause as a past life. She also sensed that it was ten past lives ago.

Asked to guess what happened and put it onto a screen she was able to clearly visualise a thin man with a big long beard and wearing clothes she described as Elizabethan. Guessing what was going on for this man, she said he was bad. She sensed that he had done many bad things both to animals and humans. He was from a family that had high expectations of him but he was not able to live up to those expectations so he had had to lie and cheat. He had a lot of resentment and did bad thing just to *"show them"*.

We tapped on each of the issues such as:

> ✢ **So even though he felt angry that he was never good enough, I completely and totally love and approve of him anyway**

As we tapped through the emotions, when asked to describe what she saw on the screen, Sue smiled and said that the man was no longer thin, he had put weight on and was more open (emotionally open). She sensed he was happier. We continued to tap until complete emotional resolution occurred. At the point we finished tapping on the emotions, she saw the image change. She laughed out loud as she saw him looking vibrant, jumping on the speed boat and riding around.

When this point was reached we re-integrated her with whatever needed to be passed on to her for her greater good, bringing it into her heart.

### FOLLOW UP INTERVIEW

In an interview a few weeks following the session, Sue said that she had not been aware that she had the problem with deservedness until that moment looking at the speed boat. She also said that if she had been asked 'did she deserve financial success' she probably would have answered yes to the question. However, now that the work had been done using the DSR she could sense that it was very different. She sensed that there was far greater conviction and certainty at a very deep level that she did deserve abundance.

## Case Study 3: Extreme distress at seeing her aging mother in a home for the elderly

### BACKGROUND TO THE CASE

M had been brought up in a family where the father had extreme anger issues. At the drop of a hat he could turn from calm to abusive. Her mother had also been very manipulative and controlling.

M's mother had gone into a residential home. Due to her mental state the mother only had moments of lucidity. M was very distressed by the state she found her mother in when she visited. This was not a one–time reaction from M. She had extreme feelings of responsibility for her mother and had experienced these feelings many times in her life. This was a lifelong issue that was causing M extreme distress.

I asked M how she knew she had the problem and she noted that she had *"a wound"* between her heart and stomach. Just using this piece of information, we identified that the root cause of this feeling had occurred when she was 7 years old. She did not immediately see anything on the screen; however after asking a few open questions it became clearer to her what was happening, questions such as: *"What is happening to her?"*

The seven-year-old child was fearful because of the violence and arguing taking place between her mother and father. We tapped through emotions. I asked the client to ask the child what she needed to learn from the experience to heal from it, she answered: *"To trust people"*.

- ✛ *So even though she couldn't trust people . . .*

- ✛ *So even though it didn't feel safe to trust people . . .*

As we were tapping through we began to shift it around with: *"It wasn't safe then, but what if it is safe now . . . what if it is safe to trust now . . ."*

As we began to clear this, the words: *"responsibility"* came up, together with: *"I have to be the grown up"*. The emotion linked to this was fear.

At this point a memory with her husband popped up and she mentioned that *"responsibility"* even happened with her husband. She would carefully put a few Christmas decorations up, while he half flung up the rest. She would then tell him how to do it. She thought of her behaviour as silly but couldn't stop it.

I then pulled her back to the seven-year-old child and asked what would happen if she let go of this decision. She said the child was fearful because if she didn't take responsibility then she was frightened she was going to lose them. They might die.

We tapped through the whole of this, connecting it together in the tapping sequence. As we did this, many events popped through her mind as she realised what a powerful influence this had had over her lifetime.

After clearing this she realised that fear of loss had run her life, making her feel the need to take responsibility. I asked her if she would still feel the need to correct how her husband did the Christmas decorations? She replied: *"If he makes a mess of it, so what!"*

We then asked: *"Because those events happened, what did it mean about life?"*

She said: *"It means life is a scary place"*.

Using the same type of process as above we tapped this out, linking in the behaviour that she had adopted because of the worrying belief.

- ✛ *So even though I have to worry, I have to think about problems . . . .*

- ✛ *So even though life is a scary place . . . I have to worry to keep me safe . . .*

After the session which took about an hour she felt a profound sense of peace and commented: *"I was very surprised. I had no idea that was there. I would never have thought it. But when we hit on it, it sparked all those examples in my mind".*

## Case Studies 4: Creating profound change

June's case shows how DSR can be used just as easily on current life events to create profound change in a person's life.

The initial session concentrated on what June described as relationship issues where she felt *"let down by people"*. Throughout the session June remembered points in time where she had witnessed traumatic events. When invited to find the root cause, June went to an event that she identified as being a past life. The past life experience was of an eight year old girl who witnessed abuse.

After we had cleared the emotions associated with this, June found herself drawn to revisit an event that had occurred quite recently in her current life (in which she witnessed abuse) and was shocked to find that the memory had changed. Instead of staying to witness the abuse, she now 'saw' herself leaving. We had not tapped on this specific event, but we did however tap to enable her to be able to accept the new memory. After this first session, June experienced tremendous shifts in how she felt.

In our second session, we dealt with: *"I am responsible for the happiness of others"*, dealing directly with current life events. During the course of this session we dealt with an event that had occurred at the age of seven. In this event, having been confronted by her mother, June the child had lied. Tapping through and clearing the emotions, June now described a very different scene. The child no longer lied, she was holding her head up and accepting that what she had done was wrong. June then said: *"Oddly enough, the lie has gone! But she did lie, I know she did! I don't know how I can see it differently when I know what I did! This is bizarre!"*

The actual time spent using the DSR process with June was 85 minutes, spread over two telephone sessions.

## Follow-up notes

It is now several months since the sessions and June confirms that the shifts experienced have remained with her. *"The changes have been phenomenal! Where do I begin? My confidence has increased ten fold. My ability to move forward with my life has definitely increased . . . (I feel) greater clarity and more connected with myself . . . I am able to tap at a deeper level now. My purpose in life is clear, I didn't have that before".*—June

## AUTHOR'S BIOGRAPHY AND CONTACT DETAILS

Tania Prince is an EFT Master. She is also a UKCP registered Hypno-Psychotherapist as well as being a TAT Professional Trainer, a Master Practitioner and Trainer of NLP and a counsellor. She has over 16 years of experience working in this field. She is a regular speaker at major international EFT Conferences as well as having been a presenter at the TAT Conference in Dublin. Tania's work has been featured on both TV and radio in the UK and abroad. She has a background that stems from the sciences which include chemistry and microbiology as well as having been in show business for ten years.

Tania practices from two clinics in Cheshire (UK), as well as working over the phone with clients. Her main specialities are social phobia, public speaking and health issues. She also runs training courses in EFT at all levels, as well as Deep State Re-patterning Energy Practitioner Courses. She is an AAMET recognised trainer in Meridian Energy Therapies.

Further Information on Tania can be found at www.eft-courses.co.uk and www.nlp-hypnotherapy.com Email tania@eft-courses.co.uk

REFERENCES:

1. The live recordings can be found at: www.eft-courses.co.uk

# Integrated Energy Techniques

## Emma Roberts, EFT Master, EFTCert-Honors

Integrated Energy Techniques (IET) are a way of utilising advanced language patterns and visualisation techniques to enhance the practice of EFT. Language is our primary means of conscious communication with clients, and the use of carefully designed questions powerfully assists us to access core issues even more quickly than before.

### How can I use language to make the memory more distant?

IET skills are extremely useful in managing the client's state whilst tapping, as per this example of a remembered birth trauma, where I use a similar dissociation method to the Movie Technique, but using language to distance the memory, gently sneaking up until it is safe to identify with it fully:

- *Even though baby Cara nearly died . . .*

- *Even though she was trapped . . .*

- *Even though it was so dark . . .*

- *Even though she was frightened . . .*

- *Even though she didn't understand . . .*

GRADUALLY PROGRESSING TO:

- ✦ *Even though I nearly died . . .*

- ✦ *Even though I was trapped . . .*

- ✦ *Even though it was so dark . . .*

- ✦ *Even though I was frightened . . .*

- ✦ *Even though I didn't understand . . .*


TO REFRAMES:

- ✦ *. . . I was so brave.*

- ✦ *. . . I did survive.*

- ✦ *. . . I was amazing.*

- ✦ *. . . I was strong.*

- ✦ *. . . I am alive.*


TO CHOICES:

- ✦ *. . . I choose to remember I was a beautiful baby.*

- ✦ *. . . I choose to remember Mum loved me.*

- ✦ *. . . I choose to know I am OK.*


Notice the gradual progression from 3rd person, to 1st person, to reframes, to Choices.

IET are also invaluable in assisting the practitioner to really step into their client's experiences, whilst knowing they have the tools with which to guide the client to a new, more useful place. We all experience the world through our senses, primarily those of sight, sound and touch. In NLP terms these are known as Visual, Auditory and Kinaesthetic (VAK). Kinaesthetic includes the senses of taste and smell. By being able to recognise the senses through which the client has encoded an experience in their memory bank, we are able to use advanced language skills to change these 'files' and re-encode the memory. Use of the VAK systems is also an extremely valuable way of testing our work as all aspects will be challenged. Any remaining piece that may have been hiding outside our awareness will then present itself ready for tapping.

## What questions can I use to access core issues?

Questions that test each sensory component of a memory are vital to check complete freedom:

- *How does it look?*
- *How do you feel as you look at it?*
- *What are you hearing?*
- *How do you feel now?*
- *Are there any smells associated with the memory?*
- *Tastes?*

Smells and tastes are particularly powerful as they have a direct and unfiltered neurological route to the amygdala, the seat of trauma. Think of a selection of familiar smells and how they make you feel . . . it's instant, isn't it! Baking bread, coffee, freshly mown grass. These lead us into powerful positive states very quickly. The same can be said for negative states, and often by collapsing the associated smells from a memory, a client will experience total release. Tap on the smell itself, sometimes even without the words to begin with as they can interrupt the process.

## Integrated Energy Techniques—Case Study

Louise is a young woman with a history of anorexia and bulimia. Her history included parental divorce and an incident of sexual abuse, both of which happened within two months of each other when she was eight. She had been in and out of therapy all her teenage years and whilst she could get temporary respite from her eating disorders the relief never lasted and the bulimia would return.

Louise was now married with two small children and was concerned not to pass her eating anxieties on to her daughters.

She was aware, from her years in psychotherapy that the eating problems started around her tenth birthday when she was sent away from home to boarding school. She was the youngest in the school, and the only one from a split home.

We tapped through various memories from that time when Louise had felt abandoned and very alone. She would take refuge in her Tuck Box (a lockable food hamper used by British boarding school children) and gain temporary comfort. But nothing seemed to take away her pain. No amount of food could clear the feelings.

Gradually she began to put on weight, which resulted in her being teased by her peers at school. At home her mother was critical of her weight and put her on a strict diet regime. She hated the food she was being given, she said it felt 'cold'. She began to throw it back up as she couldn't bear the coldness in her body. As she put it: *"the food wasn't nurturing or loving"*. Bulimia soon became her way of feeling in control.

We tapped through all the aspects above:

✢ *Even though I was abandoned . . .*

✢ *Even though they sent me away . . .*

✢ *Even though I was all alone . . .*

✢ *Even though the food felt cold . . .*

✢ *Even though I felt unloved . . .*

✢ *Even though I had to get it out of my body . . .*


As is so wonderful always with EFT and IET, the next piece to work with presented itself. It was the sexual abuse. Louise had done much work with this before we met so was able to tell the story easily and did not seem to have any high emotional response to it. She had obviously told it many times before and it seemed almost boring to her. Still, I took the precaution of tapping on her whilst she spoke.

As I was quite close to her I was able to carefully monitor the details of her physiology whilst she spoke and what I noticed was that she seemed to be rolling her tongue in her mouth between sentences. I asked her what was going on in her mouth and she said her tongue felt very big and furry, like there was no room in her mouth for anything else. We tapped on that and it seemed to reduce a little, but not completely. I asked Louise whether this was a familiar feeling and she said yes, it happened before every binge eat. Was there any taste with it? Yes—Louise started to cry and retch. What was happening? She said she had a taste and smell in her mouth she couldn't bear, and it was the smell of her abuser. She was desperate for some chocolate, something sweet, to get it to go, to escape it.

This was the perfect opportunity to tap, and we started tapping simply with: *this smell* and *this taste*.

We did not do very many rounds on either, which surprised me, before the smell and taste faded.

Louise said she had always been very sensitive to smells in particular, but also tastes. There were particular smells which she knew she overreacted to, particularly those of dirty or old musty clothes, and bad breath.

She then had the insight that her boarding school was full of old musty clothes and blankets etc. No wonder she had needed to eat! Perhaps there had been more to it than the surface abandonment.

I suggested that Louise tap on the first sign of any feeling in her tongue or unpleasant smell and see what happened with the bulimia. I wasn't sure we had completely cleared it, and I wanted to see whether any more aspects would arise. The session was over. The other important factor I suggested was that if tapping didn't reduce the feelings then she was free to binge anyway, because there may be another layer to it, I didn't know. I think there was something important about giving her 'permission' to eat as she liked whilst doing the work. Perhaps that in itself gave her some comfort.

I didn't see Louise again for a couple of weeks although we exchanged emails. There had been a couple of times when she had noticed the feeling coming back in her tongue, but had managed to tap through it and keep on track. She had noted the times and we tapped through them when she came back. They were both to do with people wearing dirty clothes.

But the bulimia didn't return, nor has it done again, and that was over two years ago.

We did need to do further work as Louise needed to learn how to eat properly and enjoy a healthy relationship around food, but the old behaviours were gone in that first session.

I think that Louise had encoded the memory of the abuse in her senses of smell and taste, both of which are extremely powerful. By tapping with those senses, continually testing as we went, Louise was able to change a core behaviour that she had been battling with for years.

I am sure that the many hours of psychotherapy and counselling she had done to that point made our work quicker and easier, but nonetheless without getting to those primary senses I doubt she would have been so very successful in the end.

## AUTHOR'S BIOGRAPHY AND CONTACT DETAILS

Emma Roberts is an EFT Master and co-founder of The EFT Centre in London where she offers a variety of EFT and IET professional trainings and self development workshops. She specializes in working in serious disease, sexual abuse and trauma, as well as fertility issues and support. She has a private practice in SW London.

    website:   www.theeftcentre.com
    email:     info@theeftcentre.com
    phone:     +44 (208) 704 4704

# The EFT Movie Maker

EMMA ROBERTS, EFT MASTER, EFTCERT-HONORS

What are the main components in a movie? What do you need to make it a success? Well, firstly, you need a storyline, with leading characters and an ending, then you need a cast, then the script and finally the background music.

But even if you have all these elements, what ultimately needs to happen to make it come alive for the viewer? IT NEEDS TO CONNECT WITH THEM in the same way a good therapist connects with their client. We need to step into the movie experience in the same way as we do our clients' experience.

## How do I help my client to 'step into the movie experience'?

In some ways, being a successful therapist is much like being a film director! It is the energy the viewer gives to the film that gives it its power. And in the same way, the energy the client gives to his negative memory is what keeps it stuck.

So what can we do? Our role is to help our clients create a whole new movie of their future possibilities. This will only truly succeed if the forerunners have been allocated to history.

Have you had the experience of seeing a sequel to a favourite film and being disappointed because you were still strongly attached to the original movie?

The new movie needs to be different and compelling in order to be credible. This is all the more so with clients, who may have a string of original movies they are still attached to.

## What are the key steps?

Firstly, after a couple of sessions (maybe longer if the client is severely traumatised) set your client homework based on the Personal Peace Procedure. However, unlike the PPP where we list every negative memory, this list will be very specific, connected to every time your client felt X. For example, get your client to list every time he remembers feeling 'not good enough'.

By keeping it to one issue it will be easier for the client to focus, and the homework will get done.

In the next session, ask your client:

- *If you were to stack all these movies in a pile on top of each other, how tall would they be?*
- *Are they films, DVDs or even those old strips of tape stored in tins?*

Now get your client to imagine taking the movies to a museum (for example the British Museum) and have them stored in a secure unit so that they are safe, but a long way away, alongside other important historical references. Then ask:

- *How do they look?*
- *How do you feel now?*

Then ask your client to select one movie from the archives to work on today. It must be a movie that best represents all the others; the one that if it were to be cleared, would change all the others, like a piece of a hologram.

Begin with the Movie Technique or Tearless Trauma Technique {see *Glossary*} and work until you reach a point of indifference, where there is no remaining charge.

Then ask your client to imagine how this change might affect the other movies in his emotional library. Just ask the question, do not expect or anticipate a reply, he may well not have one yet, but the unconscious will be working on it behind the scenes.

Then help your client to begin to create a new movie, a blockbuster in which he has the starring role, while at the same time being both producer and director.

Begin with the storyline (what does your client want now?). Create a movie/scenario that represents him in that place. Build it up with colours, sounds, smells and a cast. What music does your client want? Remember that your client is in charge, this is his movie, his responsibility, and he has the perfect tools to create it perfectly.

Your role as therapist is to build it up so that it becomes not only 100% compelling, but also possible and achievable for your client. Tap on any tail-enders as and when they arise.

When you have the finished product, ask your client to run it several times, each time allowing the screen to become a little larger, a little closer.

Then, when it is completely perfect, get your client to step into the production in the leading role and fully experience this future now.

Finally, when this is fully congruent, ask your client to design the title shot, colours, words etc and tap on your client (if that is how you work) as he does this. Write the title on a small card for your client to carry in his wallet, and have coloured pens in your office for your client to decorate it with.

What you will find is that this new 'movie' becomes automatically accepted by the unconscious mind, and your client's instructions as director/producer to himself as star will allow your client to move forward towards the changes he is looking for with even more ease and enthusiasm.

## EFT Movie Maker—Case Study

Jim had a core belief: 'I'm bad and everyone knows it'. Rather than challenge that belief and get into conflict with Jim, despite it being very clear that he was a lovely human being, I started with:

   ✢ ***Even though I am bad and everyone knows it . . . .***

Whilst tapping continually I asked Jim:

1. How do they know it?
2. How do you know they know it?
3. What tells you you are so bad?
4. Where did you learn that?

I find that feeding questions into the tapping rounds, rather than stopping to ask them, often produces 'truer' answers, I think it allows a bridge to the unconscious mind to release the core information faster.

Jim was able to answer all the above easily:

*EDITOR'S NOTE:*
Although Emma always physically taps on her clients, there seems no reason why this technique of feeding questions into the tapping rounds should not work just as well with the client doing his own tapping.

1. They can just see it.
2. The look on their faces.
3. I just look at me and I know . . .

Here, Jim began to give me a series of experiences which for him supported his belief. So I stopped him there and asked him to imagine making all these memories into mini movies.

- If you were to stack all these movies in a pile on top of each other, how tall would they be?
- Are they films, DVDs or even those old strips of tape stored in tins?

Then I asked him, which one, if released, would clear all the others in the pile? (NLPers and IETers will notice the presupposition in this question) Jim selected one which he named 'The Geek'. We tapped on this using the Movie Technique:

✢ *Even though I have these 'The Geek' emotions . . .*

The SUDS went from a 10 to a 4 in a couple of rounds.

Further questioning revealed that Jim felt he had let everyone down, he had failed his friends. We tapped on these aspects and then he felt able to tell the story.

He had been about 7 years old and been selected to be the goalie in the A team in football. He was small for his age and some of his team mates had not been happy with choosing him because of his size. They had their first match and it had started off well, but had started to pour with rain. Jim had saved three goals and the score was even. Just before time the ball headed back in Jim's direction again, in his words:

*"All I could hear was everybody shouting at me, but I couldn't see anything, it was raining so hard. I threw myself in the direction I thought the ball was coming*

*in, slipped in the mud, and slid headfirst into the goal post where I knocked myself out. Apparently just before I hit the post the ball winged over my head and we lost the match. I remember coming round and crying for my mother. Some of my team mates were around me, as well as the referee, and they started to mimic me and taunt me for losing them the match. I just wanted to die, it was so pain-ful. They were chanting 'Geek, geek' at me as I was carried off the pitch. I can still hear their voices."*

We continued to tap on some of the above aspects until Jim could see the memory in a new light, as just one of those things. He said: *"Boys will be boys!"*

Then I began to help Jim create a new movie to replace the old one. This new movie needed to represent how he wanted to feel now, instead of I am bad, what would he like to feel? What would be more useful?

EDITOR'S NOTE:
This is a theme that many of the articles in this book draw on, especially Matrix Reimprinting and Deep State Re-patterning.

He wanted to feel 'I am OK', 'I am a good person'. So I asked him, when he is OK, and a good person, how will that look? What would he be wearing? Where will he be? Who might be with him?

He said he would be standing tall, wearing jeans and a T shirt, walking on cliff tops with his dog. So we began to create that movie:

First Jim created the background, the cliffs, the sea below, the grass, sun-shine, and a small path. Then he imagined putting himself and his dog into the picture, walking along the path. I asked him whether the picture was in black and white or colour, and how sharp the focus was. It was a colour movie and the focus was very crisp and clear. Was there any music playing as he watched the movie? Yes, Tubular Bells (Mike Oldfield), but not too loud.

What did he feel as he looked at that movie, did it need anything else? He decided it needed a gentle breeze so he added that.

Having checked out for any incongruencies, any tail-enders, such as 'Even though this is not real ...' I asked Jim to become the leading man in this movie, which he called 'Life is good, I am good'.

He stepped into the movie, and as he did so his physiology in the chair noticeably changed, he became more upright, his breathing seemed deeper and this skin tone altered. He said he could actually feel the wind on his face and smell the sea! I asked if there was anything more he needed but he seemed very happy.

I then asked him what happened to that old thought of 'I am bad' when he was in this place? He said it was hard to bring it to mind, he felt invigorated and energized and very positive.

I asked him then to step out of his movie for a moment as we needed to design the credits etc, and particularly the title shot. I gave Jim a small card and some coloured pens and he quickly created the title 'Life is good, I am good'. I asked him to step back into the movie now, taking the card with him. How easy was it to re-experience those new feelings now? Very easy!

We completed the session by imagining himself in a number of different situations in the future with these new feelings available to him at any time. How did that change that old belief of 'I'm bad'? Jim said it just seemed untrue to him now, it wasn't him.

So I asked him to return to the pile of other movies that we started with and asked him how, by making these changes, did it alter his feelings about these other movies? . . . Just guess . . . and he said he thought that he would see them from a different perspective and that they would no longer have such a hold on him. We would check that out in a further session, but in the meantime he could leave the movies where they were and enjoy experiencing life in his new role, 'I am good'.

We did return to the pile of movies a week later and as I suspected, there was little to no charge on any of them and we managed to work through them all very quickly.

## AUTHOR'S BIOGRAPHY AND CONTACT DETAILS

See 'Integrated Energy Techniques' by Emma Roberts for biography and contact details.

# The Tsunami Technique

EMMA ROBERTS, EFT MASTER, EFTCERT-HONORS

In these days of mass disasters, natural or otherwise, I thought you might be interested in an EFT phenomenon which came to the fore during a trauma workshop that Sue Beer and I organised at The EFT Centre, London.

The workshop was for a small group of Level 2 and 3 EFT practitioners and focused more on working with clients than self application. However, we wanted to give them an experience of Tearless Trauma so they would know how it would be for a client.

Thinking that the most contained way of doing this as a teaching example would be to go for a group experience, we asked them to each pick a specific memory/image/photograph from the Tsunami that still 'got' them now. We knew that no one had had any direct experience of the Tsunami. Most of them had a problem even finding this memory.

We did a group tap on these 'Tsunami emotions' and it quickly became apparent that each and every one of them had associated into something completely unrelated to the Tsunami. It seemed that when the slight Tsunami emotion had cleared, other more powerful and seemingly unconnected emotions and past events surfaced.

Whilst this in itself is not particularly unusual with EFT, it did come as a surprise in this environment. It revealed new aspects of earlier specific traumas that they thought they had cleared, and in a couple of cases specific events were recalled that had hitherto been repressed.

Obviously we then had to take a detour from the course content and help them clear these issues—swiftly achieved.

Again, none of the above may be a surprise, and although unexpected, all the responses were easy to clear and some important work was done. However, these were an unusual group in that they were all dedicated EFT practitioners who had worked consistently through their own issues and who were using EFT on an ongoing daily basis and considered they had cleared the big trees from their emotional forests.

Sue and I now use the 'Tsunami technique' with some clients who seem stuck, or who have no specific memories to work with. We use it as a way of facilitating the unearthing of underlying trauma where there doesn't seem to be an obvious door to go through, and it ALWAYS gets results. In a seemingly roundabout way, something good and positive has emerged from the appalling events of that Boxing Day in 2007.

## What are the key steps of The Tsunami Technique?

- Check no direct emotional involvement with Tsunami
- Pick a Tsunami memory/image/photograph
- Put it on a screen, behind a curtain (as in Tearless Trauma)
- Tap on this 'Tsunami emotion'
- Keep tuned into your client and monitor her emotional response
- Ask: *"What does it remind you of?"*
- Tap on whatever comes up, following the chain until emotions are fully resolved
- Test results with both the emergent specific event and also the original memory

### The Tsunami Technique—Case Study

Very occasionally someone comes to see me and there seems to be no way of getting near any core issues, no obvious memories, no way to get a foot in the door.

This was the case with Pam. Pam just didn't feel good. She felt exhausted and down (although she didn't think she was actually depressed), and had no energy. She said she was dragging herself through life. She wanted to get her *joie de vivre* back; her enthusiasm for life; her energy.

I asked her all the obvious questions:

- When did this start?
- What was happening in her life at that point?
- Is it all the time?
- Is it worse in some situations than others?

The answer to every question was: *"I don't know"*. So I asked her for some information about her background, her childhood etc.

Everything was *"ok"* and *"nothing happened"*.

By this point I was beginning to feel like I was interrogating Pam, although she seemed fine with it, but I felt we were getting nowhere and that we needed to start tapping.

So I began tapping on the information she had given me:

EDITOR'S NOTE:
The reader/practitioner may well be quite familiar with this feeling! This seems like an excellent idea for when nothing seems to be working.

✤ ***Even though I don't feel good***

✤ ***Even though I'm exhausted***

✤ ***Even though I feel down***

I tried sneaking up on it with tapping phrases such as

✤ ***Even though I don't know, I do know***

✤ ***Even though I don't know, part of me does***

✤ ***Even though I can't remember***

✤ ***Even though I don't know, I am safe***

✤ ***Even though I don't know why I feel like this, and maybe I don't need to***

EDITOR'S NOTE:
Emma's cautionary note is important, as subconscious defenses are generally in place for a good reason, however dysfunctional they may seem. She goes on to explain the vital role of rapport in working in this area.

I am always cautious about using these sorts of phrases as I don't want to re-access old trauma that has been repressed for a reason, but I was watching Pam very carefully, communicating mainly with her unconscious mind, trusting it to work with me and keep her safe. The unconscious mind is our security guard and when we gain rapport with a client both consciously and unconsciously experience shows we can trust it to keep the client safe.

Anyway, I was still getting nowhere very fast, and whilst we could have continued like that and probably got results in the end it would have probably taken a long time. In my mind we needed to get a foot in the door with a memory to really begin to facilitate change.

So conversationally I asked Pam whether she had had any traumas in her life I should know about (knowing the answer would be no!) and then led into asking whether she had been affected by 9/11 or any other similar disaster, had she known anyone involved etc. Again, the answer was no, which allowed me to feel safe introducing the Tsunami Technique.

So I asked her whether any of the media images or reports from these disasters had stuck with her in any way, and was she able to bring up an image from the media about any of these?

Yes, she was, she would never forget the second plane hitting the Twin Towers. Whilst I doubt any of us will forget that awful image, I could tell by observing Pam that this had a particular meaning for her, her colour changed, she looked a little distant, and she was tapping her foot very quickly. Immediately I asked her to put that image behind the blinds in my practice room and began tapping on her.

- ✦ *Even though there is something about that image*

- ✦ *Even though I don't like that image*

- ✦ *Even though I have this 9/11 image*

When she seemed a little calmer I asked her what thoughts she noticed, and what did that image remind her of?

She said it didn't remind her of anything as such, but that she couldn't stop thinking about the man who was on his mobile to his wife as the plane crashed, and about how he could do nothing to stop it. She was beginning to get a little upset so we continued tapping:

- ✦ *Even though he couldn't do anything..*

- ✦ *Even though he was powerless . . .*

- ✦ *Even though she couldn't do anything*

- ✦ *Even though she was powerless*

I asked Pam whether these feelings resonated with her in any way, had she ever felt like this?

She said yes, she felt it all the time when she was growing up. Her father had been an alcoholic and had been violent to her mother. He had never touched the children but used to fly into rages and knock her mother about in front of them. Pam was the eldest and felt that she should have been able to stop him but had been paralysed with fear every time. She felt very guilty. She had kept this pretence of a happy childhood up to the world, and part of her still believed it. *"I thought it was normal"*, she said.

Recently, however, her mother had died of a brain haemorrhage and Pam was convinced this was because she had been hit around the head so many times. In Pam's mind this had led to believing that she had killed her mother because she hadn't been able to stop him. She and her siblings had made a pact never to talk about what had happened.

I asked her to go to the first time this had happened and make it into a mini movie, giving it a title and putting it behind the blind with the 9/11 movie, guessing at the intensity.

We quickly tapped on **this 'Dad hit her' emotions, 'Dad hit her' movie**, clearing various aspects such as the fear, the sadness, the helplessness and the shame she felt.

Eventually Pam was able to bring both movies out from behind the blind and run them without feeling overwhelmed. It is important to note that she was able to feel some emotion about them now; she could recognize that her Dad's behaviour was not OK and she felt sad for her mother but this was not intense and felt appropriate. I point this out as before we began the work she didn't seem to be able to access any emotional response at all to any of my questions. She seemed to be totally shut down.

I continue to work with Pam regularly and she is already much happier and more energized. She has made changes in her life which previously she had felt powerless to do, such as a change of job. She has remembered more specific events and we are working through them systematically, both together and Pam on her own. It is no longer dangerous to remember.

Without excellent rapport and The Tsunami Technique, I think it would have taken a very long time to get anywhere important with Pam. I would not have used it if I had not felt it was safe for the client. It is not my role to bring repressed memories to the surface. However, we had made an agreement to work together, and I believe our unconscious minds were in agreement too.

## AUTHOR'S BIOGRAPHY AND CONTACT DETAILS

See 'Integrated Energy Techniques' by Emma Roberts for biography and contact details.

# EFT and Being True to Yourself

## Ann Ross, EFT Master, EFTCert-Honors

*'Knowing others is intelligence; knowing yourself is true wisdom.*
*Mastering others is strength; mastering yourself is true power.*
*If you realize that you have enough, you are truly rich.'*

From the Tao Te Ching by Lao Tzu

### What do you mean by 'being true to yourself?

Very often, we are putting a lot of energy into living up to the expectations of others and this can obscure and inhibit the greater presence and power within us. When we are congruent inside, we project congruence to the outside and people respond naturally to those who are congruent. When we meet someone, our sensory system makes a rapid, non-conscious calibration of everything in their physical appearance, hair, facial feature, posture, proximity. All of those physical indicators communicate non-verbally the thinking and feeling states of a person. Even when we speak, the tone, timbre and quality of our voice, along with the rhythm of our speech is instantly measured and judged.

When we are congruent (i.e. being true to ourselves), our physiology changes and people and events respond to help us create the life we want. We live in an exciting time, as we move into co-creating and designing our own destiny. If our thoughts and feelings are creating our reality, it is time to become aware of what those thoughts and feelings ARE in order to release and integrate them and to love and accept ourselves no matter what.

## What stops 'me' from being true to myself?

As you give some thought to this question, you may like to consider the following:

- Are you afraid of the consequences of being true to yourself?
- What bad thing would happen to you if you were?
  Very often, you may hear a dialogue like:
- *I can't be true to myself because . . .*
- *I may hurt someone.*
- *What would 'they' say?*
- *What would "they" think?*
- *I might rock the boat.*
- *I am afraid to be different.*

The bottom line is: we are afraid of being true to ourselves because we will lose love. We fear that if we are true to ourselves we may incur judgment or criticism, and then we will not be loved.

So in a sense we learn to 'toe the line' or avoid 'rocking the boat' or avoid 'standing out' in order to get the unconditional love that we may remember from when we were very young, or that we have a deep knowing is there for us.

> EDITOR'S NOTE:
> We fear losing love, or perhaps feel inadequate, or unsafe, or not in control.

## How can I consciously notice when I'm 'lost' in negative feelings?

A way of noticing may be when you feel worried, down, bad, struggling, unhappy or depressed. We tend to blame others in our desire to be right rather than happy. It is really difficult to take full responsibility for every moment of the day and the way we have created it. The first step may be to notice—without judgment—the feelings you have, and then locate them in your body. It is your judgment of yourself and others that takes you away from being who you really are. Your body has an innate wisdom of its own and you can trust it. All you have to do is ask and it will tell you everything you need to know. It is the seat of your unconscious mind, or what is sometimes called your Inner Child. Whatever you choose to call it, the miracle of your body has more inner resources and knowledge than you ever dreamed possible. Learning to trust that knowledge may be the best thing you ever do. If you cannot trust what your body tells you, what can you trust in your life?

I have created a dialogue for your Lost Self which may be helpful. Please bear in mind that you could well be in psychological reversal and to help counteract this I recommend that you do some deep breathing before you start your tapping procedures. {See *Identifying and Neutralizing Reversals*.}

## Dialogue of the Lost Self

- *I am such a bad person nobody likes/loves me.*
- *I can't love or accept myself because . . . (fill in the blanks)*
- *I feel so awful, worried, depressed . . .*
- *Nobody listens to me or understands how bad I feel.*
- *Nobody recognizes or respects me.*
- *I feel like I am paddling upstream—really struggling.*
- *I feel heavy hearted.*
- *This feeling of being at rock bottom.*
- *It is 'their' fault that I am like this.*
- *I can't forgive 'them' or myself for what happened.*
- *I hurt (for whatever reason).*
- *I can't cope.*
- *I am so overwhelmed with it all.*
- *Life is so exhausting I can't stand it anymore.*

Take time to notice where these feelings are in your body. Do they have a colour, a sound, a shape or a size? They may even have a voice. You have the opportunity to be really creative with this dialogue. Use your imagination to bring the feeling out of you and have it sitting in a chair (or in the palm of your hand) so that you can create an image of what it looks like and what it wants to tell you {see *The Inner Committee*}. You may like to measure the level of the intensity using SUDS. Most importantly, get talking to it and find out what its purpose is. It then gives you an opportunity to find it a new role in your life—a role that may be more helpful to you than what you are experiencing currently.

- *Even though I am such a bad person, and nobody likes or loves me, I am doing the best I can.*

- *Even though I can't accept myself because (fill in the blank), I am doing the very best that I can given the knowledge and information I have right now.*

- *Even though I feel so awful, worried and depressed, I am open to the possibility of miracles.*

| | |
|---|---|
| EYEBROW: | *I am such a bad person nobody likes me or loves me* |
| SIDE OF EYE: | *I can't accept or love myself* |
| UNDER EYE: | *I feel so awful, worried and depressed; I am so focused on all of these negative feelings* |
| UNDER NOSE: | *I feel so bad* |
| CHIN: | *I am so afraid I am never going to come out of this* |
| COLLARBONE: | *Part of me just wants to stay here—it's just so much easier* |
| UNDERARM: | *I feel so awful* |
| TOP OF HEAD: | *And I am open to the possibility that I am creating dialogue with all those parts of me and maybe that would be more helpful* |

- *Even though no-one listens to me or understands how bad I feel, I am open to the possibility that I am listening to myself and maybe that's what's really important.*

- *Even though no-one recognises or respects me and that makes me feel. . . . I deeply and completely love and accept myself anyway.*

- *Even though I feel like I am paddling up stream, really struggling, feeling so exhausted I just want to give up, I am open to the possibility that I am listening to all those parts of me now.*

| | |
|---|---|
| EYEBROW: | *No-one listens to me or understands how bad I feel* |
| SIDE OF EYE: | *They just don't respect how I feel* |
| UNDER EYE: | *I am really struggling* |
| UNDER NOSE: | *Really struggling* |
| CHIN: | *And I am listening to myself now* |
| COLLARBONE: | *Maybe it's really important to listen to myself* |
| UNDERARM: | *I can respect how I feel* |
| TOP OF HEAD: | *And maybe it's ok to feel these feelings* |

☩ *I feel so heavy hearted and I deeply and completely love and accept that part of me.*

☩ *I accept this feeling of being at rock bottom even though it feels . . .*

☩ *Even though it's their fault that I am like this, I am open to the possibility I can take responsibility for my own feelings.*

| | |
|---|---|
| EYEBROW: | *I feel so heavy hearted* |
| SIDE OF EYE: | *This feeling of being at rock bottom* |
| UNDER EYE: | *It's serving me in some strange way* |
| UNDER NOSE: | *I am so exhausted* |
| CHIN: | *It's their fault* |
| COLLARBONE: | *Maybe, maybe not, maybe, maybe not* |
| UNDERARM: | *Maybe I can take responsibility for how I feel* |
| TOP OF HEAD: | *And I would like to let those parts of me know that they don't need to work quite so hard to let me know how I feel* |

☩ *Even though I can't forgive them or god or myself for what happened and I can hold on to this for as long as I like, I love and accept myself anyway.*

☩ *Even though I hurt so badly, I am open to the possibility my body is just letting me know how I feel and that's ok because I am listening to my body now.*

☩ *Even though I can't cope, I am open to the possibility I am a survivor and I have always coped before.*

| | |
|---|---|
| EYEBROW: | *I can't forgive* |
| SIDE OF EYE: | *I am so hurt* |
| UNDER EYE: | *I can't cope with all these feelings* |
| UNDER NOSE: | *I don't want to cope with all these feelings* |
| CHIN: | *I hate these feelings* |
| COLLAR BONE: | *I hate myself* |
| UNDERARM: | *Perhaps I could be more gentle on myself* |
| TOP OF HEAD: | *And maybe I am in the process of releasing these feelings now* |

☩ *Even though I am so overwhelmed with it all, I am ok and I can let go and relax.*

✦ *Even though life is so exhausting I can't stand it anymore, I love and accept all those parts of me no matter what.*

✦ *Even though I am never going to come out of this and that feels me with despair, I choose to be open to miracles.*

EYEBROW: ***I am so overwhelmed by it all***

SIDE OF EYE: ***I just can't cope***

UNDER EYE: ***I am so exhausted***

UNDER NOSE: ***I can't stand it anymore***

CHIN: ***Yes I can***

COLLARBONE: ***No I can't***

UNDERARM: ***Whether I can or whether I can't, I deeply and completely love and accept myself anyway!***

## Step 1: Developing your awareness is the key.

Begin to notice or become aware when you are continually focused on negative feelings. Thoughts become things, and you will be living up to all your expectations and creating your own self-fulfilling prophecies. You will probably realize you are doing this, so the quicker you can connect to your body and work with it the better, otherwise you can be locked in your 'story' for the rest of your life.

Notice (without judgment) what is NOT working for you in your life, your work or relationships.

If you see your life as a waking dream, what is it telling you? What is happening for you that is causing you pain, worry or fear? You may even notice a pattern that may have been around for a long time. Think of the first time that ever happened to you. Find your core belief and any specific events. What is your life mirroring back to you?

> *EDITOR'S NOTE:*
> Finding core beliefs can be challenging. Since working with EFT on specific events is so effective, using the Personal Peace Procedure can help uncover those core beliefs over time, and neutralize the disempowering beliefs.

## Step 2: Regular tapping

Tap half an hour twice a day, or a full hour as regularly as you can during the day. Do this on a daily basis until you feel less judgmental and more accepting of yourself and others.

You may choose to use Pat Carrington's 'Choices Method' if that resonates with you.

Remember that you are working with parts of yourself or your Inner Committee and it's important to listen to them all.

> ⸎ *Even though this is only a part of me, I am open to the possibility that I am clearing these feelings one baby step at a time.*

> ⸎ *Even though I am so overwhelmed with all these negative feelings, I choose to know I am safe and I can let go and relax.*

> ⸎ *Even though it's all so painful and I am not sure how much longer I can cope, I am open to the possibility I only need to do one baby step at a time and that's enough.*

| | |
|---|---|
| EYEBROW: | *It's only part of me* |
| SIDE OF EYE: | *Baby steps* |
| UNDER EYE: | *It's so hard* |
| UNDER NOSE: | *It's so hard* |
| CHIN: | *What if I could have it easier?* |
| COLLARBONE: | *No I can't* |
| UNDERARM: | *Yes I can* |
| TOP OF HEAD: | *And whether it is or whether it isn't, I deeply and completely love and accept myself* |

You may like to consider your Personal Peace Procedure and take time out for yourself to tap away negative beliefs and feelings {see *How to Get Yourself Out of the Way*}. In this day and age we are incredibly busy. Time is running out. It is important to remember the things that are really important and give them priority.

This may be a crucial stage for you to reach out for help. You do not need to do this on your own. It is NOT a sign of weakness. Let go of your ideas of having to be strong {see *Tapping for the Highly Sensitive Person*}— that's part of the problem. So tap on being afraid to express your feelings. Your body is letting you know it is time to let go. Nothing will fall apart if you let go.

> ⸎ *Even though I have to be strong because that is what they said, and I was just a child, I thought it was the truth. Maybe it was their truth and they learnt it from the writing on their walls and they did a*

*great job of teaching me. Maybe I can let them have their beliefs and I can create new ones in a surprisingly easy way.*

🔹 *Even though I am so afraid to express my feelings, I am so afraid I will fall apart and then I will never get back together again, I am open to the possibility I am in the process of releasing all these fears right now.*

🔹 *Even though I am so afraid that I will fall apart if I let go, I am open to the possibility I am creating inner strength which may be more helpful for me.*

| | |
|---|---|
| EYEBROW: | *I have to be strong* |
| SIDE OF EYE: | *Otherwise I am weak* |
| UNDER EYE: | *That's what they said* |
| UNDER NOSE: | *And I believed it* |
| CHIN: | *I was just a child* |
| COLLARBONE: | *I believed what the grownups said* |
| UNDERARM: | *Maybe that was their belief, it doesn't have to be mine* |

## Step 3: Pay attention to your physiology.

Are you in radiant health? Or do you wake up in the morning feeling low or in pain. Remember that your body is simply reflecting back to you your inner process. Your body is also the source of your Inner Child and will very quickly let you know when you are not being congruent. Of course the more clear you become, the more sensitive and intuitive you will be, so you become practiced at discovering what your body is telling you. It is a cry from your body and your Inner Child for some kind of attention.

Generally it may be at this stage in the negative dialogue of the lost Self that you make an unconscious decision or a choice. The unconscious decision may be to give up on life in some way and believe all the diagnosis and psychological reasons why you are in pain or ill, because it explains why you feel like you do. However, the diagnosis gives you permission to make the diagnosis even more real and act that out in whatever way works for you.

I have personally watched someone over a 2 year period be incredibly stressed—offered EFT assistance which was ignored and pooh poohed (I had to tap away my own frustration) and I could see this person getting lower and lower until she was diagnosed with a serious illness. When I commiserated with her, the relief on her face was palpable. She now had a reason for feeling bad and unfortunately the prognosis was not good. Her condition will become worse unless there is a drug in the next 10 years which will cure her. She knew she was stressed but was unable to see the link between mind, body and spirit.

I had a similar experience when working with another client with very painful rheumatoid arthritis:

A part of her Inner Committee that was resistant to changing or giving up the disease told us that all the years of feeling unloved, unseen, unheard and depressed made her want to *"give up and just be in a wheel chair"*. There was no joy or happiness in her life. At a conscious level of course there was, but she was unable to really 'feel' it and when she did it was only for brief moments, and then she would once again be overwhelmed with the emotions and beliefs that made her unhappy. This is a slow process and we are now working with that part of her Inner Committee that believes that only a miracle can keep her from a wheelchair.

My feeling is, if you develop your body awareness, you can more quickly and easily discover when something is not quite right and begin to apply EFT or any of the other energy psychology modalities. In terms of primary health care in my experience there is nothing quite as powerful as EFT to clear blocked energy in the body and create health and well being.

A student experienced something similar, having a very stressful job and not listening to his body (or in his language—ignoring all the physical symptoms) ended up in a wheel chair until he came across EFT and downloaded the manual from Gary's site and gave himself a goal to tap every day. He walked into my level 1 EFT class—albeit it wobbly, after being told he would not be able to come out of his wheelchair. He went from strength to strength and needless to say is passionate about EFT and the energy psychologies now. If you watch the video on Gary's website you will see the gentleman in the wheelchair finally doing exercises jumping up and down after many months of intensive EFT.

More evidence that if you are aware of physical symptoms and listen to your body's cries for help, you can make a choice to use EFT and give yourself an improved chance of being well.

## Can you recommend some tapping scripts for this?

Locate the problem (or the feeling of it) in your body, then put your hand on it and allow the healing warmth of your hand to go through to that place. Now make yourself small and go down to that place under your hand and use a magnifying glass to explore the pain, the discomfort or the bad feeling or whatever it is in your body {see *The Imagineering Technique*}. This exercise works even for those who cannot easily visualise. If you are one of these people, don't despair, but use your imagination and know that 'sensing' is even more powerful. Notice whether this area under your hand is hard or soft. Is it rough or smooth? Is it bigger or smaller than your fist? Does it have a colour? If it had a sound what would that be? If it had a voice what would it say?

- ⸬ *Even though I have this . . .* (fill in the blank), *I am open to the possibility that my body is just letting me know how I feel.*

- ⸬ *Even though it's (describe what you see or feel), I am open to the possibility I am ok and my body is just letting me know how I feel.*

- ⸬ *Even though I have this . . . , I would like to thank my body for doing such a great job in letting me know how I feel and I am in the process of releasing what no longer serves me.*

EYEBROW:        *This . . .* (fill in the blank)
SIDE OF EYE:    *This . . .*
UNDER EYE:      *This . . .*
UNDER NOSE:     *This . . .*
CHIN:           *This . . .*
COLLARBONE:     *This . . .*
UNDERARM:       *This . . .*
TOP OF HEAD:    *Maybe it's safe to release this now*

## Step 4: Consider how you want life to be

As soon as you think about what you really want and who you want to BE, your mind begins to consider it. New neural pathways are fired up in the brain and your attention is diverted (albeit briefly) from negativity.

What feels good for you? Maybe in some strange way you did not get permission to act or feel good when you were young and now it feels difficult to play and have fun. Maybe you were brought up to believe there was only one way to do things and anything else outside of those 'rules' was judged and 'made wrong'.

There are many techniques and tools to use which I have taken from various powerful coaching programmes and some of my favorites are:

*SCRIPTING:*

- Wouldn't it be wonderful if I could feel peaceful and free?
- Wouldn't it be wonderful if I could feel calm and relaxed?
- Wouldn't it be wonderful if I could be radiantly healthy?
- Wouldn't it be wonderful if I could feel happier than I ever dreamed was possible?
- Wouldn't it be wonderful if I felt fulfilled and loving?
- Wouldn't it be wonderful if I could just love and accept myself?

Notice how your energy vibration lifts as you play this game.

*REFRAMING:*

This tool gives hope, it lifts the spirits, and it helps a new perspective to be born. It creates a more flexible point of view which gives new meaning in life.

*WALT DISNEY MOVIES:*

I had a client who found it very difficult to connect with good feelings and I invited her to watch Bambi, Snow White, Sleeping Beauty, Beauty and the Beast. It helped her to remember and connect with the deeper feelings of joy and sadness and fun and playfulness.

*WHAT IF UP GAME:*

Instead of playing the 'What if game' negatively, how about playing it positively?

- What if it works?
- What if it is fun and lighthearted
- What if I can do this
- What if I can be successful
- What if I can be vibrantly healthy etc.
- What if I could have more loving relationships?
- What if life could be easy?

Notice as soon as you try this that your feelings lift?

How about music—notice how particular pieces of music are uplifting for you?

## THE FIVE MINUTE HOLIDAY:

So close your eyes for a moment and imagine yourself in a beautiful place and notice—what can you smell, what can you touch, what beauty can you see, what can you feel, what can you hear; for example the sound of birds or the ocean. Use all your senses. Now notice what is happening in your body. The brain cannot tell the difference between imagination and reality. When you imagine in glorious Technicolor and Dolby sound you will notice a reaction in your physiology. You will feel more relaxed.

## GOING FOR A WALK IN NATURE:

You can connect with the bigger picture in a way that is right and natural for you. Walking is a good way of getting the neural pathways in the brain fired up which creates physiological changes leading to more energy and a more vibrant state of being.

It is all about shifting your state of being which is reflected in your physiology.

## THE CRAZY GRATITUDE DANCE:

How about dancing the crazy gratitude dance[1] you can find on YouTube? The more fun you can have the more you realize that your beliefs are based on shifting sand . . . and you have the power to clear them permanently? How exciting is that?

*THE LAW OF ATTRACTION:*

This is not just about being positive and vibrating at a higher rate of love, joy and fulfilment. It is about being congruent with yourself, having your mind, body and heart in alignment. When you are truly in alignment, the world is a much more peaceful, loving, supportive place and your relationships dramatically change for the better. You also become more successful and well and emotionally stable. You begin to respond to circumstances rather than react. You are no longer attached to the outcome. You begin to trust yourself!

## Step 5: Work on trusting and believing in YOU

Many people are striving unconsciously to be perfect in an attempt to get the love they want. It is important to remember in this context that perfection is an imaginary standard. {This is similar to Judy Byrne's metaphor of 'just another hill'.} Despite the non-existence of the perfect mother and the perfect child, the Lost Self seeks perfection in order to win the love it longs for intuitively. It tries harder and harder to please a parent, even when there isn't a parent around. This takes a lot of energy, leading ultimately to exhaustion and a feeling of not being good enough. The perfectionist loses himself in an endless round; a lifetime of 'unselfishness' and pleasing others in an attempt to receive love, leading to resentment and disillusionment.

There is nothing wrong with doing the best you can or excelling at whatever you put your mind to. But when it tips over into self criticism and blame if you lose or do not achieve, it causes you to be afraid of doing something wrong in case it may have consequences (there may be remembered trauma and punishment). These feelings and outer strategies to get love may not be helpful; they are certainly not working and simply add another layer to clear with EFT.

## What if I am afraid of losing control?

If you are afraid of losing control, paradoxically you become even more out of control as a result of all the negative worries, fears and doubts. It is said that when you resist something it persists, and it is certainly my experience that this is so. In my opinion and experience the most powerful work at this stage of the Lost Self is Inner Child work, which has been around in a therapeutic sense for many, many years. Unless we connect to that Inner Child state in a safe setting, the child within is emotionally underdeveloped, and will remain isolated and alone. Unless we reclaim our Inner Child feelings of wonderment and innocence, our Inner Child remains wounded. The pathway of the Inner Child leads to a feeling of wholeness; to a sense of coming home to yourself.

## What do you mean by the Inner Child?

Millions of people all over the world have an Inner Child. Carl Jung called it the 'divine child', or it could be called the True Self. It is the emotional self; it is where our feelings live. When we experience joy, sadness, anger or fear, the Inner Child is coming out. When we are being intuitive, playful, creative, and surrendering to the spiritual self that we recognise deep within us, we can welcome our authentic self. We all have an Inner Child, and the wounds our Inner Child received, continue to manifest and to be acted out in our adult lives.

The Inner Child in a spiritual sense can be a wonderful and positive resource for reframing. For example: *"I wonder what your inner clown would say, or think, or do?"*

When we re-parent our Inner Child, we create all the love and support we never had as children and we grow up again.

## Step 6: Decide who are you being true to

In your sadness, pain and hurt, you don't know who you are any more. You just go along with everyone else. Generally, you do not have the energy to be different. You try hard to conform—to fit in. Heaven forbid that you are different in any way. You do not rock the boat or speak up when you need to.

It takes courage to speak up for yourself; however if you can summon this courage, the reward is greater respect for who you are becoming and the realization that other people are wanting the same thing but are as yet, unable to do it. They are resonating with you and applauding and admiring your courage. Having courage is part of the journey home to your Self. Taking a stand for what you believe in, but without attachment to what others believe, is a great step towards self-fulfilment. A healthy respect for difference becomes easy when you fully understand that the 'writing on someone else's wall' is not the same as yours. This can happen when you can allow that to be OK in your physiology, in other words when there is no longer a 'trigger' for you, just a feeling of peace, no matter what!

Being true to yourself is about doing what you love. It is about living a life of choice rather than circumstance. Although it may seem out of our reach right now it's something to aspire to. We have a 'knowing' about how that feels because we have probably already experienced it. It feels free, it feels easy and effortless.

We have choice every moment of every day. It's time to stand in your loving power and choose what feels right for you and respect and honour that. No need for explanations or justifications any longer. When there is peace within you, you are in your point of power and it's from this space that miracles become possible.

## What do you mean by the 'Self'?

The Self signifies the coherent whole; the unified consciousness and unconsciousness of a person. The Self, according to Jung[2], is realized as the product of individuation, which in Jungian view is the process of integrating one's personality.

Or the Self can be described as Infinite Being or radiant Love and Light, or it can be called a state of being, beyond expression. You can claim your own language. It is whatever works for you.

You may experience a sense and feeling of deep connectedness with everything and everybody, a 'oneness' with everything. Think of times when you have felt deeply connected. Time stands still and there is a feeling of deep peace and loving acceptance within. We sometimes call it being in the flow, in the zone, relaxed and flowing, perhaps a sense of letting go and letting God. Perhaps letting go is the most important feeling of all. This is when we are in peak performance and everything just flows; when there is no longer any resistance to our flow. When our dreams come true, seemingly effortlessly.

It is important to remember that we need to take action during these times, as it is inspired action such as this that moves us to where or who we want to be.

# Dialogue of the True Self

- *I love life.*
- *I see the beauty around me.*
- *I am so grateful.*
- *I feel really happy and at ease with myself and those around me.*
- *I feel joy more often.*
- *I feel fulfilled and loving.*
- *I love and accept myself.*
- *I experience ease and calm.*

What if you could take a stand for what really works for you without fear? What if you could feel clear and light and filled with fun; when you really know who you are and you can recognize that you are a unit of energy having a physical experience?

EFT brings you back home to your values and trusting in your Self. By releasing pain, fear, anger and any limiting beliefs about yourself you can deeply and completely love and accept yourself despite what appears to be going on in the world. EFT and TAT open the way for the Self that you are already to flow through you. Then you can deeply and completely love and accept yourself despite what appears to be going on in the world. If we have no control over our emotional wellbeing, we lose ourselves.

## Can I use painful feelings as emotional guidance to know when I am not being true to myself?

Yes! We can learn to use our will and inner power to hold our course with the flow instead of allowing it to overcome us. We can use our inner strength and inner truth to allow us to go with the flow. We can be within the flow with truth and awareness, having the ability to see the difference with loving power, and move from a state of exhaustion and good intentions to ease and fluidity. We can allow tenderness towards ourselves and others, and open to trust.

Precisely when we are yearning for something different, it is time to hold and allow something new to grow and bloom in a safe space.

⚡ *Even though I am feeling all these little boy or little girl feelings, I am open to the possibility that I see the beauty around me and I am so grateful.*

⚡ *Even though I have been lost, I am open to feeling more joy, more often.*

⚡ *Even though I have these painful feelings, I love and accept myself and I am in the process of experiencing more ease and calm.*

| | |
|---|---|
| EYEBROW: | *Little boy , little girl feelings* |
| SIDE OF EYE: | *I have been so lost* |
| UNDER EYE: | *It's been so painful* |
| UNDER NOSE: | *Maybe I am in the process of coming home to myself now* |
| CHIN: | *I wonder what that would be like* |
| COLLARBONE: | *Maybe I could trust myself* |
| UNDERARM: | *I wonder what that would be like* |

⚡ *Even though I haven't been able to love and accept myself for whatever reason, I love and accept myself anyway.*

⚡ *Even though it's been really hard to love and accept myself and I have been beating up my Inner Child big time, I love and accept that child inside of me and I would like to let it know it's safe now.*

⚡ *Even though I've been judging myself big time and that made my Inner Child even more afraid, I would like to let it know that I love and accept it no matter what.*

| | |
|---|---|
| EYEBROW: | *I can't accept myself* |
| SIDE OF EYE: | *Been judging myself big time* |
| UNDER EYE: | *I am good at that* |
| UNDER NOSE: | *I took up where my parents left off* |
| CHIN: | *I learned from them* |
| COLLARBONE: | *Maybe I have punished myself enough now* |
| UNDERARM: | *Maybe I can feel peaceful no matter what* |
| TOP OF HEAD: | *Maybe I can feel peaceful because that is my divine birthright* |

Being true to your Self has nothing to do with having to deserve it or being good enough or indeed being good! The old paradigm of 'no pain, no gain' no longer resonates with you. You look for easier, more enjoyable and inspirational ways of living your life. What other people think no longer impacts upon you.

Why would you not? What if you could make your emotional well being a matter of curiosity and adventure instead of being 'lost' in the pain and hurt?

Keep coming home to your Self. Close your eyes—fall in love—and stay there!

## Some final quotations

'Is it easy? Is it fun? Am I getting results?'—Deepak Chopra

'Don't listen to those who say: *"It's not done that way."* Maybe it's not, but maybe it is! Don't listen to those who say: *"You're taking too big a chance."* Michelangelo would have painted the Sistine floor, and it would surely be rubbed out by today. Most importantly, don't listen when the little voice of fear inside you rears its ugly head and says: *"They're all smarter than you out there. They're more talented. They're taller, blonder, prettier, and luckier and have connections . . ."* I firmly believe that if you follow a path that interests you, not to the exclusion of love, sensitivity, and cooperation with others, but with the strength of conviction that you can move others by your own efforts, and do not make success or failure the criteria by which you live, the chances are you'll be a person worthy of your own respect.'—Neil Simon

'I know this now. Every man gives his life for what he believes. Every woman gives her life for what she believes. Sometimes people believe in little or nothing yet they give their lives to that little or nothing. One life is all we have and we live it as we believe in living it. And then it is gone. But to sacrifice what you are and live without belief, that's more terrible than dying.'—Joan of Arc.

## AUTHOR'S BIOGRAPHY AND CONTACT DETAILS

Ann is a talented and creative therapist, coach and facilitator. She is recognised world wide as an inspirational teacher and presenter, with a highly developed intuition and a heart and mind attuned to a more expansive view of the world. Ann is well known for walking her talk and inviting students and clients to do the same. She is the creator of 'EFT for Being True to your Self' and has been featured on radio, and in magazines many times. She trains level 1/2/3 EFT and is a TAT Trainer. She has also developed many workshops and courses such as 'Millionaire Mindset', 'Who do you think you Are' and 'Designing Your Own Destiny'. Ann also trains people to be EFT coaches and leads interactive teleclasses to accelerate learning and develop emotional intelligence.

She finds joy in leading retreats all over the world and in helping people to transform their lives and discover who they really are!

Website:   www.eftuk.net

Email:       www.taptothetop.com

Phone:    +44 (0)1395445617

### REFERENCES:

1. Crazy Gratitude Dance on YouTube: http://www.youtube.com/watch?v=1NeMC1Fl3J0
2. Reference to Jung's view of the self

# The Inner Committee

## Ann Ross, EFT Master, EFTCert-Honors

### What do you mean by the Inner Committee?

I am on a diet, I'm walking past the baker and I smell the delightful smell of bread baking. I look in the window and notice the cream doughnuts. I love cream doughnuts! The smell of baking bread is making my mouth water.

I hear a voice in my head that says *"Wouldn't you just love a doughnut? Just one!"* Then, I hear another voice or thought: *"You can't do that, you will never lose the weight that you really want to lose this week! You will never be able to fit in to that new dress or suit!"*

I pause, consider (sometimes not) and I make a choice whether to go into the baker's shop or not. So, I choose to go into the baker shop and purchase the doughnut. I find a nice park bench and happily munch my doughnut, and while I am doing that I hear:

1st Voice:  *"You are a bad girl/boy! You will never lose weight if you carry on like this!"*

2nd Voice:  *"But I hate depriving myself. When I deprive myself I feel as if I am losing out on life."*

1st Voice:  *"You have no discipline, you are weak, and you will never lose this excess weight!"*

3rd Voice:    *"I am feeling guilty."*

1st Voice:    *"So you should!"*


Get the picture?

We have a constant dialogue going on in our heads during our waking hours. *"Shall I, shan't I?"* So, unless we are doing what we really want to do we are constantly in conflict, constantly arguing with ourselves. Can you imagine the amount of wasted energy that this inner dialogue takes up in our lives?

Look around you, what do you notice about the body language of those around you? What do you notice about the language, the words they use? Now, notice your own language. What is your Inner Committee saying?

Notice also what your body is telling you. Your body will not lie to you, but your intelligence will tell you all kinds of stories and you can get 'lost' in your stories.


## How can I tune in to and talk to my Inner Committee?


What if there were a simple, fun way of discovering your stories and having dialogue with your Inner Committee? Instead of trying to push those members of your committee away or ignore them, or deny them, how much more healthy would it be to use EFT and lovingly integrate your committee as part of who you really are?

1. Sit quietly and drop into stillness. Have a large blank piece of paper and a pen ready to work with. You might like to use coloured pens to make the identification easier.

2. Draw a small circle in the middle of your paper. Give the circle two eyes, a nose and a mouth. Is it a smiley mouth or a sad mouth? Just do it without thinking too much. Write 'ME' in the middle of the circle. You might want to give 'ME' hair, a nose, eyes and a pair of ears just for fun! We are creating a mind map. Yours!

3. Now, begin to listen to those inner thoughts that arise as soon as you allow yourself to become quiet.

4. *"This is ridiculous; I haven't got time for this!"* Draw a line from the circle to the outside of the paper as close or as far as you wish. At the end of the

line think of a name you would like to call this thought: *"Ah! So, this is Mr/ Mrs/Miss/Master Ridiculous?"*

Write 'Mr. Ridiculous' at the end of the line. You might want to draw what he might look like. Use your imagination to see what expression he has on his face. What is he wearing? What kind of clothes might he wear? How might he walk? (Write it down) What feelings does he generate in you? Where are they in your body?

ME:          *"Well, Mr. Ridiculous, why are you bringing yourself to my attention?"* (our Inner Committee wants our attention). *"What do you wish to tell me?"*

Ridiculous:  *"Well, this is so stupid, this is time wasting, we should just be getting on with our work".*

ME:          *"What work"?*

Ridiculous:  *"The work we have always done. I don't want to try anything new. Something might happen. I don't want to change. I am afraid of change. It is not safe to change".*

Another thought enters: *"Now, now, don't panic. We don't have to do this all at the same time".*

Draw a line from the face of ME, outwards and you might like to name the thought 'Mrs./Mr./Grandpa Reassuring'.

ME:          *"So, Mrs. Reassuring, what are you bringing to my attention?"*

Reassuring: *"Well, Mr. Ridiculous is only being argumentative because he is very nervous of change. I can re-assure him."*

ME:          *"Good. Do you want to give it a try?"*

Reassuring: *"Well, Mr. Ridiculous, if you just stop all your negative chatter for a moment and take a look at the possible benefits of doing work that ME really likes, how do you think it might feel? How do you think it would feel if ME could earn good money, enough to help us feel secure for the rest of our lives without having to struggle all the time, because ME loves the work so much?"*

Ridiculous:   *"Bah! You have all gone mad! It is totally ridiculous to think that anyone can have their cake and eat it! Besides, we can't afford it!"*

Enter Mr. Inspiration:  *"Hmmm I have been listening patiently to you all and I have a suggestion. Why don't you invite all the members of the committee to the outside of ME and have a proper meeting? Rather like a board meeting, you know?"*

Draw another line from the face of ME out as far as you wish. Name the thought 'Mr. Inspiration'. What does his face look like? What is he wearing? How does he walk?

If you are following this exercise, you should now have 3 members of your Inner Committee on the outside and you are getting to know them and what they have to say to you quite well!

Just listen quietly to the dialogue and notice what is being said at the committee meeting which you have called; which you are a witness to.

## Are you suggesting I bring my Inner Committee out into the open?

Yes! You might end up with 7 or 8 members all wanting to say something to you. Name them all. Get to know them intimately. Be aware of the purpose behind each thought. These are the negative thoughts that we all carry with us throughout our lives. How much better would it serve you to acknowledge your Inner Committee rather than ignore it?

What might it be like to be able to talk about our Inner Committee openly rather than pretending these thoughts do not exist. WHEN WE CAN BRING THESE THOUGHTS INTO REALITY AND NAME THEM AS PART OF WHO WE ARE, WE CAN LEARN SO MUCH MORE AND HAVE FUN WITH IT AT THE SAME TIME!

My Mr. Ridiculous is telling me *"People who read this will think it is all "ridiculous!"*.

However . . . I have another member of my Inner Committee who is called Miss Outrageous and she just loves to say her piece. She has pink hair, with a matching pink rose, which she wears, cockily on the side of her head above her ear. She has a cheeky face with a ring in her nose and excitement in her voice and she says *"just do it!"*

So, here we are! My committee is exposed! What fun!

Somehow though, it doesn't feel like an exposure, but more a sharing of part of me which may well also reside in you. Do you recognise yourself?

What might it be like for you to bring your Inner Committee out into the open? Maybe just for yourself, until you are more used to the idea?

## How do I use EFT with my Inner Committee?

The best thing about your Inner Committee is that all the parts of YOU now have a voice, and it is here that the deepest work and your tapping statements begin!

Gary Craig says over and over again *"My consistent thoughts become my reality!"*

As we become attentive to the personalities and conversations in our head, we can begin easily to recognize the limiting or negative thoughts and feelings that cause us pain or keep us blocked!

It does require practice; but it is worth the effort.

When you have a picture or visual and have written down the details, you can identify the uncomfortable feeling words and begin to tap on each specific personality on your committee.

As the personality emerges, and you see the role they are playing in your life it becomes easier to tap away the bothersome feeling and beliefs that they generate.

Become aware of how those members of your committee are affecting your physiology.

Let's look at the tapping phrases you might use:

You could start as soon as you get a reaction. It is important to learn to develop your awareness about how you are feeling during the day and in your interactions with people.

A reaction may be sight, sound, touch or smell, as in the smell of baking bread, which would make your mouth water (thoughts create a physiological response).

- ⚕ **Even though the smell of bread is making my mouth water, I love and accept myself.**
- ⚕ **Even though I would love a doughnut, but it's bad for me, I choose to know it may not be helpful to have one.**
- ⚕ **Even though I want to satisfy this craving I choose to know that I am in charge, not the craving.**

REMINDER PHRASES: *I want that doughnut! It's bad for me. I will put on weight. I can't have it. Doughnuts have consequences. My mouth is watering.*

- ☩ Even though I will feel deprived if I didn't have a doughnut I love and accept the part of me that feels deprived

- ☩ Even though I just wanted a treat, that good feeling of filling my empty space, I choose to know I can treat myself in more healthy ways

- ☩ Even though I will feel empty and I just want some comfort, I love and accept myself anyway

REMINDER PHRASES: *I will feel deprived. I want to fill my empty spaces. I want some comfort. I can't have a treat. This feeling of deprivation. This disappointment. I can't have a doughnut.*

- ☩ Even though a part of me does not want change, I love and accept Mr. Ridiculous.

- ☩ Even though part of me is afraid of change, I choose to know that Mr. Ridiculous is doing the best he can and so am I!

- ☩ Even though change takes me out of my comfort zone and I feel afraid, I choose to see the learning in the change instead.

REMINDER PHRASES: *He's afraid of changing. Afraid of changing. Doesn't want to come out of his comfort zone. Too scared. Don't want to change. Afraid of it.*

- ☩ Even though it's totally ridiculous to think I can have my cake and eat it, I love and accept myself, no matter what!

- ☩ Even though I can't have it all, Mr. Ridiculous said so, I'm open to the possibility this may be an old belief that I inherited from Mum.

- ☩ Even though Mr. Ridiculous is keeping me stuck, I love and accept him; I thank him for keeping me safe from putting myself out there and I'd like to invite him not to work quite so hard. Maybe he could even work with me instead.

REMINDER PHRASES: *I can't have my cake and eat it. No I can't. I can't have it all. That's for other people, not me. I'm not allowed to.*

- ♦ **Even though I'm not allowed to have it all, I choose to know I'm in the process of learning how to do it.**

- ♦ **Even though Mum said I couldn't have it all I choose to know that it was Mum's writing on her wall; she was doing the best she could at the time and so am I.**

- ♦ **Even though I hold myself back because I don't believe I can do it, I choose to invite Miss Outrageous to the party!**

## Any final advice?

It is important to create some really strong, positive members of your committee so that you can draw on their individual strengths to support you on your journey to wholeness.

You may know that you have inner strength during a crisis, or that you are able to be very supportive with your friends when they are having problems. You may know that you have a unique talent or skill that is always there for you no matter what. Make sure those strong parts of you form a part of your committee and invite them to assist you and all the other members that make up your Inner Committee.

The most important thing with this technique is to play with it and have fun. You will be amazed at what you can clear!

# AUTHOR'S BIOGRAPHY AND CONTACT DETAILS

See 'EFT and Being True to Yourself' by Ann Ross for biography and contact details.

# Who Do You Think You Are?

ANN ROSS, EFT MASTER, EFTCERT-HONORS

*"Your mind transcends limitations, your consciousness expands in every direction and you find yourself in a new, great and wonderful world. Dormant forces, faculties and talents become alive and you discover yourself to be a greater person than you ever dreamed yourself to be"*

PATANJALI, INDIAN PHILOSOPHER

## I don't understand the title. Surely I already know who I am?

It can seem that way, but the reality is often very different. We can be so identified in our stories, that we get 'stuck' in judgement and criticism of ourselves. Then we get stuck in 'acting out' from the identity which has been created for us from the 'writing on our walls'.

I use Gary Craig's analogy over and over again to help students and clients: *"EFT is a powerful tool for transformation and can shift us from 'who we are not' to an identity where just about anything can become possible for us"*. Using EFT we can move gracefully and with ease into Gary's 'Palace of Possibilities'. This does not mean to say that there will be no discomfort. As change happens we are stepping right out of our comfort zones into a new way of being in the world. The good thing about that is: we know we are changing when we feel uncomfortable. Very often chaos comes before peace.

If we can see the whole experience of change within us as a learning experience, rather than a trauma, the process can be more easily understood and released. EFT is far gentler than any other technique I have come across. If we can ask questions in a spirit of inquiry rather than judgment, it can be a golden opportunity for deep clearing.

## Where does my identity come from?

Our identity is mostly learned from childhood, parents, teachers and siblings (i.e. from OTHER people). In our adult lives, our identity is coloured by TV, magazines and the media telling us in glorious Technicolor and 'surround sound' that in order to be loved and acceptable we have to be a particular size, smoke a particular brand of cigar or wear designer labels. Our identity becomes invested in how much we earn, whether we are successful (or not), how many holidays we have or how many cars there are in the garage.

So our identity can, for example, crystallise into:

- I am a person who has to be perfect, or
- I am a person who is a therapist, or
- I am a person who is afraid of failing.

It is from identifying ourselves in this way that we can become trapped in a reflected sense of self that may bear little resemblance to our 'true' self. And as a result we may act out our lives from the perspective of 'who we are not'. In fact we can become LOST in the identity of 'who we are not'.

*EDITOR'S NOTE:*
This is a close parallel to one of the key themes in Chapter 2 of Eckhart Tolle's 'A New Earth'.

## How can I let go of *'who I am not'*?

We can do this by tapping away anything that we do not like or cannot accept about ourselves or others (it's important to include 'others' because we can often project onto others what we don't accept in ourselves, as discussed below). When these issues are tapped away we give ourselves permission to act out our new and more authentic identity. And when we do this, life becomes easier and starts to flow.

Start by making a list. It's easiest to start with other people, so think of the things you dislike/hate the most about other people.

For example:
- I hate it when people tell lies.
- I hate it when people let me down.
- I hate it when people judge or criticise me.
- I hate it when people hurt me.

1. I hate/dislike it when . . . . . . . . . . . . . . . . . . . . . . . . . . . . . . . . .
2. I hate/dislike it when . . . . . . . . . . . . . . . . . . . . . . . . . . . . . . . . .
3. I hate/dislike it when . . . . . . . . . . . . . . . . . . . . . . . . . . . . . . . . .
4. I hate/dislike it when . . . . . . . . . . . . . . . . . . . . . . . . . . . . . . . . .
5. I hate/dislike it when . . . . . . . . . . . . . . . . . . . . . . . . . . . . . . . . .

As we are thinking and feeling these beliefs, they are our reality. We are creating our futures through these thoughts and beliefs. After all, it is the truth for us. The truth then becomes real and we act it out. Quantum mechanics tells us that we are somehow picturing these thoughts and feelings, and if we believe them to be real we simply act them out. If we have thoughts and feelings of not being good enough for example, they can become a self-fulfilling prophecy, and we give ourselves the evidence, vehemently and eloquently: *"You see? This shows you how I try but nothing works! I can't be good enough!"*

## Are you saying that my thoughts, and not other people, create my problems?

Yes! When we look at others and find them lacking in some way, we are simply looking at the differences in the 'writing on our (respective) walls'. We are all so different. Each of us has unique writing on our walls, which is peculiar to us and nobody else. There may be some similarities but there will always be differences.

We tend to complain when life does not go our way, and may even insist that the blame is definitely 'outside' us, or in some way make it 'outside' of us. We blame the husband, the wife, the boss and the politicians. And in the UK we even blame the weather!

But the problem is inside. When we judge and criticise others, we are doing it from a place inside of ourselves; a place that we do not like about ourselves. Guess what? There is no outside—it is all happening inside of you, right now . . .

It is called projection. We think we know what other people are thinking. And when we judge and criticise them for it, it makes us feel better; for in those moments, other people become WORSE or LESS than we are.

On my courses I often give the example of the boardroom table and the Directors sitting around a beautiful bowl of flowers. There may be 10 or 20 people sitting around the table all looking at the same flowers. One person will see a rose, the other a daffodil, the next a piece of fern or ribbon. They may argue and get upset and hotly defend their point of view. However, they are all arguing about the same bunch of flowers! Each will be experiencing and seeing something totally different—it will be a different angle, a different perspective.

And, they are all getting it right! What if we are all getting it 'right' and we just have a different perspective on life? What if we could respect our differences? What if we could find common ground without being stuck in judgment?

## How can I track down the origins of my false ideas?

Instead of being tied up in the identity of who somebody else thinks we *should* be, or we *ought* to be, or we learned to be, how much more healthy to *choose* who we want to be in the world and begin to act that out!

FOR EXAMPLE:
- I am a person who feels guilty when I don't call my Mother.
  (Feelings—guilty, sad, procrastinating, heavy, frustrated)
- I am a person who cannot be true to myself because . . .
  (Feelings—confusion, unhappiness, sadness, trapped)
- I am a person who cannot say "no" because . . .
  (Feelings—angry, frustrated, trapped, overwhelmed,
  giving away power leading to helplessness)

Find five statements starting

1. I am a person who . . . . . . . . . . . . . . . . . . . . . . . . . . . . . . . . . . . . .
2. I am a person who . . . . . . . . . . . . . . . . . . . . . . . . . . . . . . . . . . . . .

3. I am a person who . . . . . . . . . . . . . . . . . . . . . . . . . . . . . . . . . .
4. I am a person who . . . . . . . . . . . . . . . . . . . . . . . . . . . . . . . . .
5. I am a person who . . . . . . . . . . . . . . . . . . . . . . . . . . . . . . . . .

Then ask yourself:
- Where did I learn this belief?
- Who taught me that?
- How do I know that about myself?
- What specific events occurred in my life to have me believe it? For instance, the time my father slapped me when I told him no. My mother screaming at me to *"do as you're told!"* The time my neighbour threatened me. The bully in my classroom taking my lunch money.

You may be surprised that you may end up with a list of information about yourself that displeases you.

## How can I use this information to help me decide who I really am or who I really want to be?

On another piece of paper draw a line down the centre of the page. On the left hand side, write down the statements that most upset you or give you the most emotional discomfort out of the ones that you have written.

Notice your feelings about the statement and write your feelings underneath your statement.

In the right hand column write down the complete opposite. You are clear now about your beliefs about yourself. You have a starting point. The right hand column is how you want to BE in the world.

EXAMPLE:

| WHO I THINK I AM: | WHO I REALLY AM: |
|---|---|
| I am a person who cannot say *"no"*. | I can say *"yes"* to ME. |
| FEELINGS: | FEELINGS: |
| Trapped, frightened, sad, pressurised | Strong, self empowered. |

The idea is to clarify how you feel when you identify yourself in this way. It is going on in your mind anyway and it might be helpful to bring it to the surface so it no longer remains hidden from you (for whatever reason).

## OK, so how can I use EFT to make these changes?

I have devised some EFT statements for you to try on, just like a new shirt or a new dress. These should give you ideas to create your own setup phrases:

- ✛ *Even though I am a person who cannot say "no", I love and accept that part of me anyway.*

- ✛ *Even though I am a person who cannot say "no" because I might not be loved or liked if I say "no", I love and accept all those parts of me no matter what!*

- ✛ *Even though it is hard for me to say "no", I choose to say "yes" to ME and honour myself.*

REMINDER PHRASES: *It is really hard to say "no". Not acceptable to say "no". They will reject me. I can't do it. It is too scary.*

- ✛ *Even though I can't say no because they will not love/like me anymore I choose to say YES to me, maybe I could love myself enough to say "no".*

- ✛ *Even though I'm not important enough to say "yes" to, I choose to say "yes" to me, anyway because I am worth it!*

- ✛ *Even though they won't love me any more I choose to know that maybe I can love ME even more!*

REMINDER PHRASES: *They won't love me any more. Definitely not! I can't do it. I'll be letting them down. This is too scary. Maybe, maybe not. What if I could?*

- ✛ *Even though saying "yes" to me is selfish, I choose to know that unselfishness breeds resentment and I don't want to be resentful.*

- ✛ *Even though I can't say "no"- what will people think? I choose to know that they might respect me a lot more.*

- ✛ *Even though it's really hard to say "no" I choose to know I can say it from a loving strength inside of me.*

REMINDER PHRASE: *I love the feeling of being strong enough to say "no". I feel good. Strong. Free. Loved. I love ME. Saying no feels good.*

Become creative and tap as much as you need to until you are in alignment with your right hand column! Tap away any 'tail-enders' to being who YOU really are despite what others may think! And, remember those SPECIFIC events in your life that gave rise to these feelings and beliefs. It is important to clear them as they come up for you. Tap for each one.

When we change ourselves at identity level, the whole world begins to change around us, and people, events, and circumstances are perceived differently. We can live a life of fulfilment and happiness, loving and accepting ourselves and others, no matter what!

## AUTHOR'S BIOGRAPHY AND CONTACT DETAILS

See 'EFT and Being True to Yourself' by Ann Ross for biography and contact details.

# EFT and Continuous Tapping

BARBARA SMITH, EFT MASTER, EFTCERT-HONORS

Anyone who already uses the basic EFT recipe on themselves has probably also created some form of Continuous Tapping to meet a particular need. In this article, I will present several applications where Continuous Tapping proved really useful. Some you can use instantly, to move effortlessly through everyday life. Other applications are for experienced EFT practitioners who will find it highly useful for addressing some of their clients' biggest challenges.

## What is Continuous Tapping?

Continuous Tapping is the simple process of tapping a range of points in a continuous loop, while you hold in your mind, or name an issue that you would like to address. There is no formal protocol. Some people like to name the issue at every point, and others do not. The body points that I most commonly use for myself are the eight points that start at the top of the head, and move downwards, ending at the underarm. There are no absolute rules about this. One set of substitute points that I find useful is to continuously tap on the point of the thumb and finger points shown in the full version of the EFT protocol. Do what works for you.

Once you have mastered the basic EFT protocol, it is easy to incorporate Continuous Tapping, and integrate it into almost any form of helping and healing.

In this article we will explore several applications using the Continuous Tapping process

- Introduction to doing it yourself.
- How Continuous Tapping can keep children calm and focused.
- Using Continuous Tapping in daily life.
- Continuous Tapping for trauma resolution for EFT practitioners (with exercises).
- Emergency EFT at work—for everyone.
- How Sandy healed himself after a traumatic event with many aspects.
- Do-it-yourself EFT for everyone, with Continuous Tapping.

## How can I use Continuous Tapping for myself?

If you have no trauma healing experience, reading about traumatic events can activate your own old history, so tap along as you read the first sections, and gain some practice in applying Continuous Tapping for yourself before reading the later trauma applications.

CONTINUOUS TAPPING OPENS THE DOOR
TO A LIFE CHANGE—A PERSONAL ACCOUNT:

For most of my life, I thought exercise was getting up in the morning. I believed I that I was useless at sport. I still remember the leader of my netball team calling me *"butterfingers"* when I missed a pass. That was probably more than fifty years ago, so while there is not much charge in it now, the effects are still there in my attitude to physical sports. And I still remember. I gave up, and never really seemed to get the message that if you did it more, you would probably improve. I did know this in many areas of my life, but somehow I never transferred that message to my attitude to exercise. Hence it has been a huge challenge for me, as an adult, to imagine that any physical activity might actually be enjoyable.

When I was in my forties I started to accompany my partner on his daily jog. I did not enjoy it. I did not feel better after some practise.

Three years later I was still lacing myself into my sports shoes, thinking *"is this really me?"* but over time I developed enough determination to walk for at least half an hour, most days.

I purchased an exercise bicycle; I did not use it. I had good intentions, but I never did like riding a bike.

The breakthrough came unexpectedly. After learning about Continuous Tapping, I decided to try it out using Gary Craig's Personal Peace Plan. One of the issues that popped up was the realisation that, now that I was getting older, it would be wise to give my heart a bit more of a workout than it was getting from a gentle stroll around the river each morning. So I began the continuous finger tapping whilst thinking about the need to give my heart more of a workout. Nothing else: just tapping on all the finger points, and holding the thought. I DID THIS NEARLY EVERY DAY.

Several times over the next weeks, the notion that I could just run a little bit, popped into my mind, until one day I thought *"I'll run to the corner"* And I did; without another thought. While I was running the few paces, I was thinking *"Is this really me?"* YES!! Of course I ran out of breath very quickly, so when I was back to the walking phase, I continuously tapped on my fingers.

I continued with this process over several weeks, gradually increasing in strength. No effort. I did not suddenly become a marathon runner. But I did start to enjoy the feeling, and some new comfort in my body. I now tap continuously on the finger points when I find myself becoming breathless, or slowing down, and after a couple of minutes my breathing is back to normal. The amazing thing is that it was NO STRUGGLE AT ALL. I still get surprised at how much 'second wind' is available when I apply this simple continuous tap. Now, I usually run for about 20 minutes of our 'walk'. Not all at once. This is a work in progress, but even if I never do more than I am doing at this moment, it will be enough. My blood pressure has improved, and I have even lost some weight, without trying.

Imagine that!

What is even more surprising is the way in which other, quite unrelated difficulties or life blocks have unravelled themselves during this process. Try it and see.

## Can you give me an example of how I might use Continuous Tapping with children?

Certainly. Have you ever been behind the scenes with a group of 8 to 10 year olds preparing for their end-of-year gym display? Do you remember the potent mix of anxiety, excitement, tension and tears?

The children are dressed, primed, ready . . . and waiting. Mothers and helpers are giving last minute instructions. The previous class is performing, and in fifteen minutes our children's turn will come. There is nothing to do but wait, and the tension is high. This is the time that anxiety and nervousness set in. All eyes will be on them. Hands are clammy, mouths are dry, tummies squirm, anxiety builds, tension rises . . . and they wait.

I call the kids to attention, and ask first who feels excited. They all do, but their excitement is mixed with anxiety, and a litany of woes comes out. Someone has lost her ribbons; another is afraid she will forget her moves; another is scared she will need to go to the bathroom yet again. And so on.

I offer them a little game. *"Do this"*, I say, and I start tapping on the top of my head. This class is used to following instructions, so there is no need for complicated explanations. I just say *"do what I do"*, and we all begin tapping together, starting at the top of the head and moving down to the underarm and back to the top of the head, in a continuous loop. As we proceed, I repeat some of the worries they have expressed, together with some of the ones I have heard before, using a different statement at each tapping point; just tapping and feeling, tapping and feeling . . .

*". . . I hate waiting . . . my tummy is squirming . . . I'm just clumsy . . . I'm the fattest . . . I know I will forget to count . . . my legs feel wobbly . . . my shoes aren't right . . . what if I need to go to the bathroom? . . . they'll laugh at us . . . I can't see my Dad . . . we won't win an award . . . it will be my fault . . . the coach will be disappointed . . ."*

After a couple of rounds some children are giggling and hamming it up, adding new possibilities. They are becoming more relaxed, starting to enjoy the process.

I ask them to think of the absolutely best part of belonging to gym club. Now they are open to remembering the good parts, and they shift their attention to telling me how much they love gym, what fun they have at prac-tise, and how they are looking forward to the party afterwards.

We begin the final process. Everyone taps around the seven points again, while I repeat back their positive statements.

*". . . I love gym . . . it is such fun . . . she (the coach) likes us . . . she is so proud of us for trying . . . I'm already better than last year . . . it's OK to be still learning . . . perhaps this feeling in my tummy is really excitement . . . I can do perfect forward rolls now . . . maybe I can have much more fun than I think . . ."*

And everyone has a great day.

## What about using Continuous Tapping to resolve historical trauma?

Every year, new research continues to expand our understanding of the mind-body connection, so it is important to keep learning. This article therefore is a work-in-progress.

EFT is the perfect modality for trauma resolution, because traumatic events are embedded so completely in body and mind. So Continuous Tapping can be very useful to facilitate healing. I always use EFT when it appears that trauma may have been involved.

*EDITOR'S NOTE:*
In other articles, it is mentioned that we respond to present-day triggers with the resources that we had at the original age of the trauma. This is why an adult reacting to a trigger that activates childhood trauma will often respond in helpless, confused ways—only the resources (knowledge, coping skills) that the client had as a child are available when the trauma reaction is triggered.

Peter Levine, in his book 'Trauma Through a Child's Eyes'[1] describes how MRI scans show that electrical activity in the body sends messages from our brain's 'early warning centre' directly to our body's fight/flight/freeze mechanisms, bypassing the thinking/planning/reasoning parts of the brain altogether. When we recall or are reminded of an old terrifying event, something in our autonomic nervous system acts as if the traumatic incident were happening now. Our bodies respond as if this were a current threat to life or integrity. We are instantly aroused, and prepared for danger. Once we understand that, it is not surprising that we can't think ourselves out of what seems to be an over-reaction to an everyday event. Our bodies are fired up for fight or flight.

You can see from this, how easy it is for some people to re-traumatise themselves when something is happening in the present that reminds their system of a long forgotten terror. Often they may not even be conscious of what has triggered the reaction, or know why, but what they do experience is how they are 'over-reacting' to something that is happening now.[2]

I have found Continuous Tapping to be invaluable when such situations arise. It enables people to stay calm, present, and able to both feel and think. I suspect, after a few more years' of research, we will fully understand how this happens. But right now, it is enough to know that it really works. And that is why Continuous Tapping has become the most used technique in my emergency tool bag.

## When would you NOT use Continuous Tapping?

While I teach both the basic recipe and Continuous Tapping to trauma clients to ensure that they can change easily from one to the other, I do have a caveat for people who want to resolve traumatic memories at home. Why? Because one of the common problems with people who have terrifying memories of some past event is that they have usually coped by deliberately or unconsciously avoiding anything that reminds them of what happened. As continuous tapping involves allowing ourselves to remember while we tap, these previously avoided or forgotten memories may be re-experienced as if they were happening now. Not only can this be very distressing and frightening, but the re-experienced event may feel so overwhelming that it is very difficult for us to stay present, or to think clearly.

If you have unresolved trauma issues that you cannot think about without becoming upset, the safest route is to work first with an experienced EFT practitioner who will ensure that you can keep tapping and stay present while you revisit the old event in your mind. I like to teach my new trauma clients to use the short EFT protocol, as well as continuous tapping. I help them choose specific issues for homework, based on what has been shared in the therapy session. Together we choose and write down trigger words for events and aspects that they might bring to mind while continuously tapping. This simple process allows people with tendencies to dissociate or abreact to use continuous tapping at home to resolve old traumatic experiences safely and easily without undue distress.

## How do I calm a distressed client in a therapy session?

In the actual therapy session, people need to talk about their experience and it is the therapists' role to notice when a client starts to get distressed, and to keep the therapy safe. EFT can be very effective in helping people avoid escalations of terror and panic. Here are my three usual interventions.

1. Tell the client to stop, and continuously tap until she feels calm again, and to continue this process every time she starts to feel overwhelmed.

2. Stop the client, and say that since this story is upsetting, it would be good to be really comfortable with a calming down procedure first. Then I teach clients to use the short protocol using words, like *"even though this is really upsetting . . ."*

3. Suggest that the issue is too big for now and that we choose a small part to begin. Something with a SUDS level of no more than 5, to get the client really confident in their capacity to calm themselves down.

Small steps are always safer than giant strides, but occasionally a person will escalate instantly into deep distress. Extreme distress calls for an extreme interruption. In such cases, I look right at the client and say: *"Look at me. Do what I do. Keep looking at me."* I demonstrate on myself and say: *"Tap here . . . now here."* I'll make little coaching type remarks like: *"That's right . . . good . . . feeling yourself coming back."* I keep going, and keep up eye contact, and say things like: *"Feel your feet on the floor."*

Trauma work is the only situation in my work when I am really assertive and insistent. At this moment, the practitioner is the lifeline that keeps the client safe, so I do take charge.

Try the following exercises. Their purpose is to give you a taste of what it is like to be involved in someone else's horror story. And to give you an opportunity to practise the process of continuously tapping while you read. These stories are based on a combination of various real events:

EXERCISE 1: AFTERMATH OF A SIEGE

You have been invited by a victim support group, who know that you practice EFT, to help a family who have been involved in a siege situation where a policeman and a young male civilian were killed. It is now two days since the incident and you are visiting the family of six (three adults and three teenagers), who have been sequestered in a safe house as their home is now a crime scene. Each member of the family knew the dead civilian; each had a different relationship with him, and each was exposed to a different aspect of the siege. Each person has different events in the past that remind them of what happened. Some of their previous life experiences impact on the current crisis. The family members are well supported, but need someone to help with trauma resolution. The situation is still dangerous, and the death of a young person triggers guilt (what could we have done?), sadness (my friend is dead), fear (what will happen next?), helplessness, shock and horror.

If this account touches on any old upsetting memory of our own, this is the moment to do a little Continuous Tapping. Stop here and tap continuously as you re-read the previous paragraph. If the old experience is still bothering you, tap for that as well. Tap until you are ready to go on.

## Exercise 2: Shooting In The Street

In the following example the shooting has just happened, so fear and shock reactions will be uppermost. In addition, everyone is anxious, as the perpetrator is still at large. Imagine that you are an eye witness when someone is shot and critically injured in the street. The perpetrator is holed up nearby. Along with several bystanders, you are shocked and horrified, and probably scared as well. The police have arrived, and are securing the scene. The medics are on their way. There is noise:—sirens, screams, traffic. You, along with others are herded together, and you wait. The police are seeking information from the witnesses.

If you have ever been involved in any kind of hold-up you may well have an instant re-play going on for you. Tap continuously until you are free of arousal, and read on.

Imagine what a difference it would make to these people if you could sit with them and offer to help them calm themselves down. It is extremely difficult for people to be clear and coherent when they are in shock, and the tapping could make a significant difference. I am sure you can see how much easier it would be to just start tapping, than it is to use the complete EFT algorithm. No set up is needed. The issue is already up in each person's thought field so all you need to do is to start tapping, and talking about what happened.

### EXERCISE 3: THE TRAFFIC ACCIDENT

You may like to imagine what it would mean to be holding an injured victim's hand at a traffic accident. She was the driver of a motor vehicle and had been involved in accident. Now she is in danger of sliding into deep shock. You ask if you can hold her hand, and she gives a shudder and a little nod. Imagine tapping on her finger points, looking at her, and helping her talk about how it feels. You could coach her along with little statements such as: *". . . you're safe . . . it's all right . . . look at me . . . tell me where it hurts . . ."* Comment on each little sigh, as you follow the nod of her head. All you need to do is to follow and name what is going on for her, and acknowledge the awfulness and give reassurance. And keep tapping.

1. Did you find it easy to imagine what to say to her? If not, learn from the many EFT experts in this book, and create your own list from their words.

2. Did you know that human contact will help to keep her from dissociating?

## How can I use Continuous Tapping for post-traumatic stress?

Have you ever experienced a terrifying event, where your life has been at risk, and someone or something reminds you of it? Within a blink of an eye you will very likely be feeling, hearing, re-experiencing the full catastrophe all over again.

How does this happen? Current research on the mind-body interface shows clearly that when we are reminded of a past trauma, the human brain causes the release of a cocktail of chemicals into the body that are designed to prepare us for fight or flight, just as if the original trauma were happening right now. After a few seconds the cognitive mind can reason that there is no danger now, but unfortunately we do not yet know how to say to the autonomic nervous system *"pull back all those chemicals, we don't need them now."* This body response is the trigger for what we know as Post-Traumatic Stress. However, when we tap continuously, something seems to shift in the body that frees us from this constant traumatic replay.

You can get a feel for Continuous Tapping as you read the following account of Sandy. While some people find it easy to stay grounded whilst reading true life horror stories {see *The Tsunami Technique*}, others may not. So this is a good opportunity for you to try out the Continuous Tapping process. Tap as you read, and if your arousal goes up, stop reading and tap several rounds before continuing.

SANDY USES CONTINUOUS TAPPING
TO OVERCOME A TERRIFYING EVENT:

When I first met Sandy, he had been on sick leave for four months. He had been burned in an explosion at work. Sandy sustained serious burns, but his body was now healing, and he had been cleared as being ready for light work. He reported that whenever he thought about returning to work, all he could see was a picture in his head of his mate running away from the explosion in a ball of fire. What he described was not just sadness and pain and survivor's guilt. Nor was it related to the trauma and stress he suffered during the burns treatment. He was frozen in the moment when he saw his now dead mate, as a ball of fire. He experienced the event as if it were still happening, with all of the aspects of horror, shock, and high nervous system arousal replaying in a continuous loop in his body and mind. He told me he couldn't sleep; he was jittery in the day time, and having adverse reactions to the high doses of medication that were supposed to cope with the sleep problem. Things were getting worse, rather than better. He was berating himself because he thought he should have been over this already.

Does this account trigger any kind of trauma experience in you? If so, please stop reading now and tap continuously on the eight EFT points from top of head to under arm. Keep going until your body feels calm and relaxed. Test, by re-reading from the beginning. If necessary, keep tapping until you can stay relaxed while reading. When you are calm, begin reading again. Keep noticing what is happening in your body and tap whenever you feel any arousal.

BACK TO SANDY:

Sandy responded well to my suggestion that he try this very new idea about tapping on the body's main calming down points. *"I'll do anything*", he said. We started with the short EFT protocol, addressing the possibility of going back to work. He talked about having this terrifying internal picture of his mate as a ball of fire.

I could have set this up as a regular EFT protocol, but because of how quickly trauma arousal can take over, I chose the Continuous Tapping model, which is very easy to start whenever the activation comes back. We tapped together as he thought about the idea of going back to work. He moved spontaneously through other memories as they came up, keeping the tapping going for several minutes. After about ten minutes, I asked Sandy if he was ready to take one small peek at the inner picture, and see what happened now. He closed his eyes, shook his head, blinked a couple of times, and then looked directly at me and said in a totally normal voice: *"It's not there any more. I know it happened, but it has faded somehow, and I feel kind of free."*

I now heard how Sandy had been struggling to cope with another terrifying re-play of his experience in the burns unit, whenever he relaxed or closed his eyes. He remembered coming out of anaesthetic. Shaking and tapping as he talked, he explained that this had woken him in terror several times a night. He tried to avoid it by making himself really tired before going to bed, but nothing seemed to work. He was now sleep deprived and at his wits' end. We used Continuous Tapping with random reminders at each tapping point and after a couple more rounds, Sandy felt free. We spent the rest of the session on a little integrating discussion about his life, tapping together as we talked. He shared some of the horrors of the previous weeks. I was surprised he was still alive.

On his next visit, Sandy looked clear eyed, and full of confidence. He had made three trips past his workplace without incident and he felt ready to get back to work. He reported that he had not needed to tap any more, but he felt reassured knowing that he had a new technique he could use any time.

I am so grateful for this new technique. In my early days as a trauma specialist, it was difficult to let go of some of the horror images. Continuous Tapping works for me, too, and I stay calm and relaxed without effort.

Not all trauma situations resolve themselves that fast, but one-off specific incidents are more likely to be resolved quickly. And Continuous Tapping added into the EFT mix offers us a tool that we can take with us, wherever we go.

As you might expect, there are many other issues involved here. Sandy still has trauma issues related to his time in hospital. He has burn scars that have changed his appearance and that limit his movement. But for people like Sandy, resolving the traumatic activation is the step that will make it possible for him to rebuild life.

## How can I use Continuous Tapping as a self-help tool?

The wonderful thing about EFT is how much we can deepen our lives, and enhance our experience using Continuous Tapping.

You don't need a lot of EFT experience to apply Continuous Tapping, but you will get the best out of Continuous Tapping if you have already done some basic work on your most troublesome core issues with an EFT therapist. At the very least you need to make yourself familiar with the basic recipe and underlying principles of EFT. Then you will be ready to deepen your experience and enhance your life—anytime, anywhere.

When using EFT on myself I rarely use any kind of setup process, but I do keep a notebook. I like to write down ideas, thoughts and new issues the moment they appear. For instance, if I find it difficult to hold a particular issue in mind, I write in my notebook: *"I don't want to think about X"* and that is where I begin. I concentrate on my reluctance as I tap around the eight points from the top of head point to the under arm point. I stay focused on what I have written, while I continuously tap. Mostly I have no words, but I am open to anything that comes up as I tap. If and when the words come, I write them down, too. They may not be significant, but they often become the focus for a future tapping session.

## This all seems just too simple. Isn't there more to it than that?

Continuous Tapping does indeed seem like a simple process, but its effects can be profound. The words, ideas and messages that arise as you tap are often outside of everyday consciousness. So I wait for these words and memories to surface, just softly following where instinct takes me. And I add them to my notebook. Are you tapping already? If not, see what happens if you keep up a continuous tap as you read. You may surprise yourself.

You may already have a 'hot list' of topics you would like to address—*"one day"*. If so, keep yourself within your comfort zone at first, choosing an issue with a SUDS level of up to six or seven.

Recently I set myself a ten week plan to resolve a physical limitation in my own life. As I settled down to some focused tapping, I realised again how often it is that some little memory or insight pops into my mind right in the middle of a round of EFT. Sometimes it has absolutely nothing to do with the subject at hand. I don't like interrupting myself once I am in the flow, so I can easily forget these memories, insights and ideas that arise. They hover in consciousness for a moment or two, and then they are gone. These days I try to capture the newly surfacing thought or feeling, as soon as it appears, and I have discovered that they often come from my deeper self. I have found it is much easier to recall them and write them down when I am using Continuous Tapping. It is easier to stop at any moment because I don't have to remember where I am up to; hence my attention is available to catch new issues as they surface.

## Ok, so how do I do this? What process do I follow?

### THE PROCESS:

Sit quietly. Turn your phone off! You may have an issue in mind. If not, just breathe quietly and see what comes up. This is a quiet non-judgemental state, where you can observe what is happening in your body. Just notice how thoughts come and go, and how breathing changes.

If you have a specific issue or problem in mind, WRITE IT DOWN and keep it in front of you.

Then tap the eight points from top of head to under arm, and notice the thoughts, ideas, and memories that come up, as you keep the issue in my mind. Notice changes in breathing, skin temperature, and sites of body tension. Just allowing things to deepen or pass by, as they choose.

When something comes to mind, you may ask yourself *"What does this remind me of?"* The question may elicit an even deeper significant incident or core issue from the past. Sometimes the tapping and attending to yourself may feel more like a quiet meditation.

You may also like to try something that works for me. I have discovered that if I tap with one hand and write with the other, I record more information. I think of these messages as gifts from my unconscious mind. I suspect that when I used my dominant hand for both writing and tapping, since there was a significant break in the tapping I shifted my attention away from the open state. So by using my hands in this way, Continuous Tapping becomes more of a meditative process.

While working with EFT, if unexpected memories, thoughts or feelings come up, try to notice them without any judgment and WRITE THEM DOWN. If you wait until the end of your session to record this mind-body information, you may discover (as I did) that some of these new insights and surfacing core issues are difficult or impossible to recall. Such is the power of unconscious process. We suppressed them in the beginning because they were too painful or difficult to accept. But we are grown up now and can look at past painful experiences in a new way. So catch them and note them down as soon as they surface, and in just enough detail to remind you when you are ready for another round of EFT.

We all need to bear in mind that when new ideas or memories pop up while we are doing EFT, they have more than one purpose. They may be an unconscious effort to protect us from the distress of addressing old painful experiences, but they also offer us the opportunity to go deeper into ourselves and resolve something.

If you are working with an EFT practitioner, she may help you to keep track of the emerging issues, hence keeping notes may not be so important. However, if you are working on your own, short notes will take the pressure off trying to remember everything. You can keep tapping for the current issue, knowing that you will return to those vitally important, emerging core issues when you are ready.

Happy and successful Tapping!

## AUTHOR'S BIOGRAPHY AND CONTACT DETAILS

Barbara Smith is the only EFT Master currently practising in New Zealand. She began her counselling career twenty-five years ago, qualifying first in Marriage Guidance, then as an experiential tutor in Group Life Laboratories. Since she discovered EFT in 2001, Barbara has integrated EFT into every aspect of her life. A Certified Hakomi Therapist, she now works as a counsellor and trainer in private practice. She holds accreditations with the NZ Association of Psychotherapists, the NZ Association of Counsellors, and the NZ Accident Compensation Commission. Barbara describes herself as a graduate of the university of life: as daughter, life partner, mother, grandmother, counsellor, trainer, friend and colleague. She is passionate about EFT, which has made her personal and professional life effective beyond her wildest dreams. www.eft-newzealand.com and barbsmith@xtra.co.nz

REFERENCES:

1. Peter A Levine, 'Trauma Through a Child's Eyes', 2007
2. Robert C Scaer MD, 'The Body Bears the Burden' (Hayworth Medical Press, 2001)

# Addiction and EFT

## Loretta Sparks, EFT Master, EFTCert-Honors

After working for over three decades with alcoholics, addicts and their families, I have a great respect for the power and nature of addiction and the courage it takes to confront this disease. I'm also aware that the nature and scope of addiction is often misunderstood—misunderstanding that is reflected in the way the term addiction is used to describe a multitude of behaviors. The term addiction is variously used to describe something you 'really' like; the abusive use of a substance; a physical addiction to a substance and a chronic, addictive disease.

It is vitally important that the EFT practitioner understands that when dealing with addiction she may be looking at a relatively simple situation, for example, salivating and feeling compelled to eat chocolate at the sight or thought of it, or at the other end of the spectrum, a very complex and often life threatening medical problem associated with chronic addictive disease . . . or anything in between.

### How do I get started in working with addiction?

If the person seeking help is an alcohol or drug addict or has a significant eating disorder: e.g. bulimia or anorexia, then it is essential that an assessment be performed by a physician with expertise in those areas (for example, in USA, look for physicians who are Board certified by the American Society of Addiction Medicine, ASAM[1].) Once the physician has cleared the individual medically, then our work begins, and a clinical assessment must be done to determine the appropriate level of care. The higher the risk of lapse or relapse, the higher the level of care needed. One question to address is: *'Is this individual stable enough to maintain abstinence and be treated by you in office, or do they need a higher level of care?'* Higher levels of care are increasingly structured from Intensive Outpatient Programs, where the individual is seen several hours a day for two or three weeks, or Residential Treatment, where the individual lives for 30 days up to a year. Because of the complex medical nature of chronic addiction, EFT should be considered only after the individual has been cleared medically or in conjunction with medical care. EFT can support a client at any level of care, even inpatient detoxification; however, EFT must never be used in place of medical care.

## Why does addiction occur?

The 'whys' of addiction are not simple. They are as diverse and complex as the people who suffer from them. The situations that seed addiction in one person may not in another. There are unknown personality factors that impact on an individual's view of their life experience. But clearly few of us get through our early years unscathed. One way or another, almost all of us got hurt, some way, at some time, and injury was sustained. In response to those childhood injuries, limiting core beliefs were constructed; and for many of us, these limiting core beliefs become part of the fabric of our awareness and the lens that we look at life though.

A person with addictive disease has layers of issues and constellations of traumas held together by negative belief systems.

> Fueled by fear and anxiety of the past as well as the future, the individual's addiction seems to take on a life of its own and appears to all concerned to be the PROBLEM. However, in reality, the addiction is the addict's SOLUTION.

The real problem is the addict's negative worldview. Initially, this worldview (made up of limiting core beliefs) served to protect the addict as a child in an unsafe world; a kind of fortress that provided refuge from the threat of pain and fear. Eventually, the child outgrows the fortress and becomes imprisoned in it as an adult. The individual is then condemned to a world of emotional, if not physical isolation, and the dysfunctional strategies needed to maintain it. He is continually led to a view of self that is negative and unacceptable, a view of life that is negative and unacceptable, and a view of his personal power that is negative and unacceptable. This then is the operational guidance system that drives the addiction: a negative view of self and life, and no way to change them.

## How can people recover from addiction?

*"In order to heal from a disease, you must change so completely it no longer recognizes you"* is an old shamanic saying. C.G. Jung, the Swiss psychiatrist, who figured prominently in the early configuration of the philosophy of Alcoholics Anonymous (AA), stated that only a *"radical rearrangement of consciousness"* could have any lasting effect on the individual suffering from chronic addiction (Sparks, 1993).

A radical rearrangement of consciousness that changes the individual's negative attitude is the focus of EFT in the recovery processes.

The greatest challenge of early recovery, after abstinence, is the necessity of ending the seeming safety of isolation and beginning the process of learning to meaningfully attach. Community support groups, such as the 12 Step Program of AA[2] offer such an opportunity. These groups challenge the basic emotional and often physical isolation of the addict and offer a place of fellowship that supports abstinence. *"I can't, we can"* is an apt recovery slogan that underscores how vital the community is to recovery. British psychiatrist John Bowlby, who wrote three books exploring attachment, separation and loss, writes:

'Intimate attachments to other human beings are the hub around which a person's life revolves, not only when he is an infant or a toddler or a schoolchild but throughout his adolescence and his years of maturity as well, and on into old age. From these intimate attachments a person draws his strength and enjoyment of life, and, through what he contributes, he gives strength and enjoyment to others.'[3]

Leaving isolation and addictive substances and/or activities behind, the journey into a radical rearrangement of consciousness begins.

## What are the main stages of recovery from an addiction?

There are three distinct stages in the recovery process.

STAGE 1. The first stage is when the individual comes to the full realization that he is out of control. He knows he should stop, he wants to stop, he plans to stop, but he can't stop.

STAGE 2. The second stage is when he has developed enough recovery that he experiences an active, internalized resolve that he won't restart.

STAGE 3. The third stage emerges when recovery has progressed to the point where sufficient reduction of anxiety has taken place that the individual is not only clear that he won't restart, but he is also clear that he can manage life on life's terms so he does not have to engage in an addiction.

The needs of the client change with each stage of recovery. Regardless of the stage the client is in, EFT can provide the essential key to assistance.

## How can EFT be used to aid recovery from addiction?

The EFT treatment protocols presented here deviate from the basic sequence of EFT in that they have been augmented to address common barriers or blocks to the treatment of individuals struggling with addiction.

Cravings and compulsive urges are not only a threat to recovery at any stage, but initially they are the only clue that the client's stress/anxiety has gone beyond their ability to cope. It is essential that the client be taught very early in treatment the EFT protocols to deal with these urges, so that when an addictive urge strikes they will be prepared to deal with it. How long the treatment lasts varies from person to person. Some individuals with food addictions have reported being free of a craving for months; others report only hours of relief. For alcohol and drugs, including tobacco, usually up to several hours of respite is provided. Regardless of how long a treatment lasts, it provides a merciful reprieve from the demands of the addiction.

## What is the EFT 'Brief Form' for addictions?

1. Identify the craving or compulsive urge to work on. STAY FOCUSED ON THE SPECIFIC CRAVING OR URGE BEING TREATED.

2. Rate the strength of the craving or compulsion on a scale of 0—10, 10 being strongest.

3. Clear specific psychological reversal as follows: While tapping the karate chop point, repeat the following affirmation 3 times:

   ⚜ *Even though I have this craving (or urge) for* _____ *(e.g. 'a cigarette'), I deeply and completely accept myself."*

4. Create a 2—4 word reminder phrase for the problem, e.g. *"craving for a cigarette"*.

   The sequence: Tap 7—10 times on each energy point while saying the reminder phrase:

   | | |
   |---|---|
   | UNDER EYE: | *'craving for a cigarette'* |
   | UNDER COLLARBONE: | *'craving for a cigarette'* |
   | UNDER ARM: | *'craving for a cigarette'* (Note: You may need to delete this treatment spot in the chemically dependent—it sometimes drives up distress) |
   | THUMB: | *'craving for a cigarette'* |
   | INDEX FINGER: | *'craving for a cigarette'* |
   | MIDDLE FINGER: | *'craving for a cigarette'* |
   | LITTLE FINGER: | *'craving for a cigarette'* |
   | KARATE CHOP POINT: | *'craving for a cigarette'* |

   Tap firmly, but do not cause pain.

5. Rate your distress again. If there is reduction of 2 or more points do the 9 Gamut AKA Brain Balancer): Tap continuously on the back of your hand, while doing the following • Look straight ahead • eyes closed/open • eyes sharp down right/left • roll eyes in a circle right/left • hum a tune for 5 seconds/count to 5/hum again.

6. Repeat steps 4 and 5, adjusting the reminder phrase to *"the remaining _____" (e.g. 'the remaining craving for a cigarette')*. Continue until the distress is gone.

7. If, in subsequent rounds of tapping, the distress level stops dropping, this indicates a mini psychological reversal: To clear, continuously tap the karate spot while saying,

   ⍦ *Even though, I still have some of this problem with _____ I accept myself deeply and completely.*

8. Repeat steps 4, 5, 6 and 7 until the distress is gone.

9. If there is no alleviation of the craving/compulsion, use the full EFT Plus protocol.

## What should I do when EFT doesn't seem to work?

Energy disturbances, psychological reversals, sensitivity to allergens and energy toxins are commonly found in treating addiction. Where they are present, EFT will not work at all or work at an excruciatingly slow pace. The energy system disturbance encountered most often is referred to as a neurological disturbance or 'switching'. Switching can be issue-specific or a product of extreme stress caused by emotional or physical problems, including allergen and energy toxins. Since anxiety and stress are at the heart of addiction, it is not surprising that many clients experience chronic levels of switching and need to address these symptoms regularly.

Another type of block to treatment is psychological reversal. A psychologically reversed state exists when you literally act in opposition to your goal, even though you have the knowledge and ability to accomplish it. For example, many veteran dieters have a professed desire to loose weight and have an impressive reservoir of information on how to achieve a healthy weight loss, but seemingly flounder in the weight loss attempts. There is much to learn about psychological reversals and what literally occurs when they are engaged; however, the self-sabotaging element clearly appears to come from limiting core beliefs about our self, our lives and our ability to make positive changes in our lives {see *From Self Sabotage to Success*}. Reversed states exist on a continuum of severity from massive to minimum (mini). Psychological reversals may be specific to the problem being addressed or they may be based on attitudes about releasing the specific problem (criteria-related reversal)[4] (Gallo, 1998, 2000). Treating psychological reversals allows you to disengage them, but sometimes only temporarily. However once they are disengaged, you can then treat the problem as part of a negative core belief support system that limits your client's positive life choices.

Allergens and energy toxins can also cause treatment blocks. Basically, what is meant by 'allergens and energy toxins' is any substance, fume, fluid, solid or energetic, ingested, inhaled or experienced, that weakens an individual's energy system. A few suggestions are made at the end of the following treatment protocol to address these system weakeners.

## What is a specific protocol for allergens and energy toxins?

1. Identify the problem to work on and STAY FOCUSED ON THE SPECIFIC PROBLEM BEING TREATED.

2. Rate the distress the problem causes you on a scale of 0—10, 10 being worst.

3. Clear for energy system disturbances: This may be done standing, sitting or lying down: • cross the left ankle over right • cross the right wrist over left • inhale through nose with tongue on the roof of mouth near front teeth • exhale through mouth with tongue resting on the bottom of mouth near front teeth • breathe comfortably for a few minutes.

4. Clear specific psychological reversal: While tapping the karate spot on the side of your hand, repeat the following affirmation 3 times:

   ✤ *Even though I have this problem with* _____ *(name specific problem), I deeply and completely accept myself.*

5. Create a 2—4 word reminder phrase for problem, e.g. *"anger at my father."*

   The sequence: Tap 7—10 times on each energy point while saying the reminder phrase:

   | EYEBROW: | *Anger at my father* |
   |---|---|
   | SIDE OF EYE: | *Anger at my father* |
   | UNDER EYE: | *Anger at my father* |

| | |
|---|---|
| UNDER NOSE: | *Anger at my father* |
| CREASE OF CHIN: | *Anger at my father* |
| UNDER COLLARBONE: | *Anger at my father* |
| UNDER ARM: | *Anger at my father* (Note: You may need to delete this treatment spot in the chemically dependent—it sometimes drives up distress) |
| THUMB: | *Anger at my father* |
| INDEX FINGER: | *Anger at my father* |
| MIDDLE FINGER: | *Anger at my father* |
| LITTLE FINGER: | *Anger at my father* |
| KARATE CHOP POINT: | *Anger at my father* |

Tap firmly, but do not cause pain.

6. Rate your distress again. If there is reduction of 2 or more points do the 9 Gamut (AKA Brain Balancer): Tap continuously on the back of your hand, while doing the following • Look straight ahead • eyes closed/open • eyes sharp down right/left • roll eyes in a circle right/left • hum a tune for 5 seconds/count to 5/hum again.

7. Repeat steps 5 and 6, adjusting the reminder phase to: *"the remaining _____ "* e.g. *"the remaining anger at my father."* Continue until the distress is gone.

8. If, in subsequent rounds of tapping, the distress level stops dropping, this indicates a mini psychological reversal: To clear, continuously tap the karate spot while saying:

   ✢ *Even though, I still have some of this problem with_____I accept myself deeply and completely.*

   Repeat steps 5, 6, 7 and 8 until the distress is gone.

9. When the distress is gone, ask the client to review in detail the situation or memory that they had been focusing on as if it were a 2 minute movie. Have them monitor their distress as they tell the story. If the distress gets to 2 or 3, do the tapping sequence again until it is at 0, then continue to the end of the story, tapping each rise in distress as it is experienced until the client is at a 0.

# What should I do if the distress level 'still' hasn't dropped?

*STEP A: CLEAR MASSIVE PSYCHOLOGICAL REVERSAL:*

Place your attention on the specific problem being treated and rub the Sore Spot on the left side of your chest, saying out loud:

> ✤ *Even with all my problems and limitations, I deeply and completely accept myself.* ('Shortcomings and defects of character' may be used in place of 'problems and limitation' for members of 12 Step fellowships.)

*STEP B: CLEAR REMAINING PSYCHOLOGICAL REVERSALS:*

Place attention on the problem to be cleared:

Tap directly under the nose and say 3 times emphasizing the capitalized words:

> ✤ *Even if I NEVER GET OVER this problem, I accept myself deeply and completely.*

Tap the karate spot on the side of the hand continuously while saying each of the following sentences 2 times, emphasizing the capitalised words:

> ✤ *I accept myself deeply and completely, even if:*

- *. . . I am not ready to eliminate this problem with _____ .*
- *. . . I don't deserve to get over this problem with _____ .*
- *. . . I feel it's not safe to get over this problem with_____ .*
- *. . . I am scared to try to deal with this problem with_____ .*
- *. . . I will feel deprived if I get over this problem with_____ .*
- *. . . I will not do what is necessary to get over this problem with_____ .*
- *. . . I will lose my identity if I get over this problem with_____ .*

Then repeat steps 5, 6, 7 and 8 above. If no drop in level of distress—go to STEP C.

(Note: additional reversals, specific to the client's experience, may be added to this list. You may want to use the following Limiting Belief Scale in dealing directly with the psychological reversals that effect addiction.)

## LIMITING BELIEF SCALE

For each of the following statements, give a number from 0 to 10, with 0 meaning you strongly disagree with the statement and 10 you strongly agree.

1. _____ I'm embarrassed that I have this addiction to_____.
2. _____ I will never get over this addiction to_____.
3. _____ I'm not sure I want to get over this addiction to_____..
4. _____ If I solve this addiction to_____, I will feel deprived.
5. _____ I don't have the strength to stop this addiction to_____.
6. _____ If I really talk about this addiction to _____, something bad will happen.
7. _____ This addiction to_____ can only be solved by someone else.
8. _____ If I ever solve this addiction, I will lose a part of who I really am.
9. _____ I don't want to think about this addiction any more.
10. _____ I should solve this addiction, but I don't always do what I should.
11. _____ I like people who have this addiction better than people who don't.
12. _____ It could be dangerous for me to get over this addiction to_____.
13. _____ When I try to think about this addiction, I can't keep my mind on it.
14. _____ I say I want to solve this addiction, but I never do.
15. _____ It could be bad for someone else for me to get over this addiction.
16. _____ If I get over this addiction, I can never go back to having it again.
17. _____ I don't deserve to get over this problem.
18. _____ This problem is bigger than I am.
19. _____ If I got over this problem, it would go against my values.
20. _____ Someone in my life hates this problem.
21. _____ There are some good things about having this problem.
22. _____ I've had this addiction so long, I could never completely get over it.

*STEP C: CLEAR NEUROLOGICAL DISORGANIZATION WITH COLLARBONE BREATHING:*

Often if an individual has or has had allergies, asthma, ADD or dyslexia, they will need Collarbone Breathing for EFT to work efficiently.

- Place two fingers tips of the right hand on the right collarbone point and tap the gamut point (back of hand) continuously, while doing the following breathing sequence:
- Breathe normally, for a minimum of 5 taps.
- Take a deep breath and hold it for 5 taps.
- Let half that breath out and hold it for five taps.
- Take half a breath in and hold it for 5 taps.
- Exhale.
- Bend the same two fingertips of the right hand in half, touch the knuckles on the collarbone and tap the gamut point on the back of the right hand while doing the breathing sequence again.
- Place the same fingertips on the left collarbone point and tap the gamut point while doing the breathing sequence again
- Bend the fingers in half, touch the knuckles on the left collarbone point, tap, and breathe as above.
- Repeat above using fingertips and knuckles of left hand.
- Repeat steps 6, 7, and 8 above. If there is no drop in level of distress—go to D.

*STEP D: IDENTIFY AND CLEAR ENERGY TOXINS AND ALLERGENS.*

If there has been no reduction in distress at this point, we must consider allergens and/or energy toxins as the possible block to treatment. Ask your client to stop using scented products, such as laundry detergent, fabric softener, household cleaning products, colognes, hair spray, room deodorizer, etc. If his pillow is more that 6 years old, a 10th of its weight may be made up allergens (dead dust mites, dust mites, dust mite dung and mold) which he then directly inhales while sleeping 6 to 8 hours a night. Have the client either wash, replace or cover the pillows with covers designed to block the allergens.

## Why are allergens and energy toxins so challenging in addiction?

People with addictive disease have an unusually high rate of sensitivity to allergens and energy toxins, which may interfere, not only with their energy treatment, but also be an additional source of anxiety and threaten their abstinence. The word 'allergens' here refers to those substances that cause allergies. An allergy is an abnormal response to a food, drug or something in our environment that generally does not cause symptoms in non-allergic people. We don't know why some people develop an abnormal response, for example to pollens or shellfish, while others do not. It is estimated that as many as 20 percent of the population have some symptoms of allergy at some time in their lives.[5] Allergies can start at any age. Energy toxins are similar to allergens with the addition of the negative impact of the toxin's electromagnetic field on the individual's energy system. The major difference between the two is the degree of disturbance that is caused. Allergies manifest physically, emotionally and energetically and energy toxins manifest emotionally, energetically and at times only energetically.

The treatment problems that are caused are threefold:

1. First, because they can block energy treatment from working, there can be the assumption of treatment failure.
2. Second, a successful treatment can be undone when the client is exposed to the allergen or toxin.
3. Third, they can be an additional cause of stress and anxiety.

## How can a client identify stress?

Since repression of feelings is one of the major elements in the addictive profile, it follows that the client's ability to identify stress is poorly developed, if at all. More often than not, clients in Stage I of Recovery are not able to identify themselves as stressed, but they are able to identify their behavior associated with certain situations and are surprised that that behavior is stress-related. The following scale is used as an introduction to stress identification. Clients benefit from keeping a daily 'Stress Calendar' where they rate their stress 3 times a day. It is helpful to start all individual and group sessions with a check-in in which the client assesses his stress using the rating scale:

## Stress Level Ratings:

10  OUT OF CONTROL

Examples: violence (physical or verbal), addictive behavior (either primary or secondary), alcohol, drugs, food, sex, gambling, spending, obsessive relationships, work etc.

9  OVERREACTING

Examples: jumping to conclusions, not willing to listen, disagreeing, threatening, sarcasm, glaring, geographic overwhelming loneliness, frustration, raging, resentment, and self-pity, saying 'always' and 'never' when hurt or angry.

8  DEFENSIVE

Examples: denial, anger, bargaining, silence, withdrawal, blame, criticizing, judging, justifying, excuses, gossip, explaining, intellectualizing, rationalizing, minimising, theories, moralising, generalisation, switching, evasion, pleading, apologising etc.

7  SPACING OUT

Examples: not being present to situation at hand, can't hear what's being said to you, because of your own 'self- talk,' zoning out, getting lost in daydreams, etc. Do not notice stress is building in you. Do notice others not taking care of business

6  MANAGING OK

Examples: barely getting everything done, needing help, but do not ask for it, telling yourself to 'try harder,' 'plan your time better,' start to let go of self-care activities, having a hard time saying 'no.' Not noticing stress building.

5  MANAGING OK

Examples: life's demands and your energy (physically, mentally and spiritually) are mostly balanced.

4  MANAGING OK +

Examples: your physical, mental and spiritual energy is nicely balanced with life's demands.

3  MANAGING EASILY

Examples: your physical, mental and spiritual energy exceeds life's demands.

2  MANAGING EASILY +

Examples: abundant physical, mental and spiritual energy.

1  VACATIONING

Examples: total and complete sense of relaxation.

## How can a client effectively manage stress?

Effective stress management at Stage I Recovery includes:

1. Using the Stress Level Rating scale in Stage I Recovery allows the client not only to measure their stress, but also to identify its effects on their behavior. (Many clients are surprised that the behavior they commonly experience is an indicator that they are stressed, for example, 'spacing out'.)

2. The client measuring his stress level 3 times daily.

3. Doing one of the EFT protocols after each time stress is rated. The energy treatment should focus on either the client's stress in general or on any specific problem they are finding stressful at that moment.

4. Teach your client the recovery acronym, H.A.L.T. The acronym stands for Hungry, Angry, Lonely, Tired, any of which when not addressed can create enough stress to lead to a loss of abstinence.

5. Proactive planning to avoid or deal with H.A.L.T. is essential. If a client is not able to plan or practice basic self-care, physically, emotionally or socially, treat it as a problem and address it with EFT Plus.

6. If possible, defer trauma work until Stage II, as it can destabilize the individual's newly acquired abstinence.

## What about therapy and support for family members?

Family members of the addicted are themselves often in need of assistance dealing with the multiple stressors in their lives. Family members are introduced to the Stress Level Rating scale and taught the EFT protocols. They are also encouraged to keep a stress calendar and use EFT a minimum of 3 times a day for generalized stress reduction. Supportive psychotherapy, which includes EFT, is helpful to deal with the stressors past, as well as the present. Family members should be assessed for trauma work.

## How can I help a client to overcome the effects of trauma that contribute to addiction?

In Stage 2, the client's need for trauma work is evaluated. Take a careful history of the client, noting all physical, emotional and social traumas. Traumatologists believe that chronic childhood traumatization not only impacts the formation of the personality structure, but may deform it, leaving a child with personality challenges that ill prepare them to deal with life or attach to others in any meaningful way. Judith Herman, MD, writes of the chronically traumatized child:

'The child trapped in an abusive environment is faced with formidable tasks of an adaptation. She must find a way to preserve a sense of trust in people who are untrustworthy, safety in a situation that is unsafe, control in a situation that is terrifyingly unpredictable, power in a situation of helplessness. Unable to care for or protect herself, she must compensate for the failures of adult care and protection with the only means at her disposal, an immature system of psychological defenses.' (Herman, 1992, pg. 96) [6]

It is not unusual for many of these clients to be poor historians or to have repressed a lot of their negative past experience—childhood as well as adult experiences. Some of these clients can benefit from 'prompting' that assists them in focusing on specific areas. For example, when a client reports that they have absolutely no memories of their childhood, a seemly innocuous questions such as: *"When you were a child, where did your family usually eat dinner?"* may yield a treasure trove of information. Clients respond to questions like these with ease and provide an opportunity for the clinician to ask more questions about the relationships within the family of origin.

Information about childhood illnesses, including allergies, asthma, injuries, surgeries, hospitalization, etc. can be extremely significant in identifying early trauma. Specifically, ask about experiences related to attachment (e.g. *"When you were a child, who could you go to if you were scared?"*), and about abandonment, separations and losses. Ask if anyone had ever been physically inappropriate with them as children. (Direct questions about sexual abuse may trigger strong feeling of shame and be a barrier to disclosure.) The information the history yields directly or inferentially provides the therapist with a laundry list of events, often repetitive events, that not only gave birth to the limiting core belief structure, but also to a worldview that continually reinforces that structure—a worldview that is practically invulnerable to mediating intervention and, therefore, to change. The addict's worldview keeps them stuck in the past and crippled in the present.

Effective intervention with energy treatments at this Stage allows the clinician to address and resolve these traumas and their collateral damage in a manner that supports the process of recovery. By deconstructing the negative worldview through the resolution of defining traumas, the clinician is in service of the very heart of recovery, the radical reorganization of consciousness.

## Some concluding comments

Those of us who directly assist the addict know only too well the tenacity of chronic addiction. Any attempt the addict makes at lasting change seems to be systemically resisted; physically, mentally and spiritually. From an energetic perspective one might argue that allergens, energy toxins, psychological reversals and neurological disorganization are the diseased system's attempt to maintain stasis. The more entrenched the addiction, the more formidable the barriers to recovery and the greater the effort to scale those barriers. However, with the use of EFT, clinicians have an opportunity to directly and effectively address those barriers and empower their clients, providing a powerful support of the recovery process.

I have specialized in the treatment of addiction for over 30 years. During that time I have treated thousands of men and women with addictions. I have been privileged to bear witness to their journey of recovery and courage. For the individual suffering from addictive disease to 'let go' of the world as they understand it and trust the process of recovery, requires a level of courage that is asked of few of us.

# AUTHOR'S BIOGRAPHY AND CONTACT DETAILS

Loretta Sparks, LMFT is a licensed psychotherapist, a Diplomate of Comprehensive Energy Psychology, EFTCert-Honors and an EFT Master. She has been treating the chemically dependent and their families for over three decades. You can reach Loretta at *www.energypsychotherapy.com*.

## BIBLIOGRAPHY

Alcoholics Anonymous. (1984). 'PASS IT ON': The story of Bill Wilson and how the A.A. message reached the world. New York: Alcoholics Anonymous World Services, Inc.

Bowlby, J. (1980). Loss: Sadness and Depression. New York: Basic Books, Inc.

Blum, K., in collaboration with Payne, J. E. (1991). ALCOHOL AND THE ADDICTIVE BRAIN:New Hope for Alcoholics from Biogenetic Research. New York: The Free Press.

Callahan, R., with Perry, P. (1991). Why do I eat when I'm not hungry? New York: Doubleday.

Coca, Arthur, (1996). The Pulse Test. New York: St. Martin's Paperbacks.

Craig, G. (2000). Emotional Freedom Techniques: The Manual. The Sea Ranch, CA: Author.

Durlacher, J. (1994). Freedom From Fear Forever. Mesa, AZ: Van Ness Publishing.

Fleming, T. (1999). You Can Heal Now: The Tapas Acupressure Technique (TAT). Redondo Beach, CA: TAT International.

Gallo, F. (1998). Energy Psychology: Explorations at the Interface of Energy, Cognition, Behavior and Health. Boca Raton: CRC Press.

Gallo, F. (2000). Energy Diagnostic and Treatment Methods. New York: W. W. Norton.

Hawkins, D. R. (1995). Power Versus Force: An Anatomy of Consciousness. Sedona, AZ: Verita Publishing.

Kessler, R. C., Crum, R. M., Warner, L. A., et al. (1997). "Lifetime Co-occurrence of DSM ~ R Alcohol Abuse in the National Comorbidity Survey." In Arch. Cen. Psychiatry. 54, pp 313-321.

Kushner, M. G., Sher, K. J. and Erickson, D. J.. "Prospective Analysis of the Relation Between DSM-III Anxiety Disorders and Alcohol Use Disorders." In Am. J. Psychiatry. 156, pp 723-732.

National Institute of Health. (1999) "Principles of Drug Addiction Treatment: A Researched Based Guide." NIH Publication No. 99-4180.

Rapp, D. J. (1980). Allergies and Your Family. Buffalo: Practical Allergy Research Foundation.

Rapp, D. J. (1996).IS THIS YOUR CHILD'S WORLD? How You Can Fix the Schools and Homes That Are Making Your Children Sick. New York: Bantam Books.

Schuckit, M. A. and Hesselbrock, V. (1994). "Alcohol Dependence and Anxiety Disorders: What is the Relationship?" In Am. J. Psychiatry. 151, pp 1723-1734.

Selye, H. (1974). Stress Without Distress: How to use stress as a positive force to achieve a rewarding life style. New York: Signet.

Sparks, T. (l993). The Wide Open Door: The Twelve Steps, Spiritual Tradition & the New Psychology. Center City, MI: Hazelden.

Zimberg, S., Wallace, J. and Blume, S. B. (1978). Practical Approaches to Alcoholism Psychotherapy. New York: Plenum.

## References:

1. *Link to contact details for* American Society of Addiction Medicine, ASAM
2. 12 Step Program of AA
3. Bowlby, 1980, p. 442
4. Gallo, 1998, 2000
5. Rapp, 1980.
6. Herman, 1992, pg. 96

# How to Get Yourself Out of the Way

## AN ADVANCED PERSONAL PEACE PROCEDURE

### HELEN WALKER, AAMET TRAINER AND PRACTITIONER (LEVEL 3)

## What does 'getting myself out of the way' really mean?

Students of EFT are well aware that true healing occurs 'through you, not by you'. When we can get ourselves out of the way, when we can eliminate our self-talk, our beliefs and so on, we can let our intuition get to work and we can experience genuine healing at the deepest level.

On many occasions, while teaching EFT, the topic of 'through you, not by you' has come up, and I discovered that many course delegates who wanted to work at this level had an initial problem that hindered their progress. They knew how important it was to get themselves out of the way, but had no idea how to go about achieving it. The same basic question would come around again and again—HOW do I 'get myself out of the way'?

I realised that what each of these delegates wanted was a guide to help them, a step-by-step technique or methodology that would allow them to move forward.

What you are about to read in this article is the process and EFT technique that I teach for 'getting yourself out of the way'.

485

The stages of the process are:

1. SELF-AWARENESS

   Analyse and meditate upon your personal philosophy so that it becomes a tool for developing self-awareness

2. SELF-ACCEPTANCE

   As awareness of self, or ego, increases, use EFT to heighten self-acceptance

3. THE ADVANCED PERSONAL PEACE PROCEDURE

   An EFT technique to use daily until the ability to 'get yourself out of the way' is automatic

## How long will it take to learn to 'get myself out of the way'?

All personal development work requires commitment and discipline. Consequently, it is important for everyone to understand that 'getting yourself out of the way' isn't a skill that is acquired instantly. Rather, it is something that requires thought and effort, and takes some time to develop.

Many of us would like our spiritual growth to be like our fast food. We want to drive in to the weekend workshop, order the 'Enlightenment Ready Meal' and drive off into the sunset. Alas, it doesn't work like that!

There is nothing instant about the words 'development' and 'growth'. Both imply a process that takes time. Are you willing to commit the time and effort required to 'get yourself out of the way'?

Personal growth is challenging and can be disconcerting. You are moving out of your comfort zone. If you feel truly ready for the challenge ahead, remember you always have EFT to help you when you feel stuck. As you read this article, you may become aware of some of your own 'stuff'. If this happens, be sure to tap until you have clarity about your responses. Work with another EFT practitioner if necessary.

A word of caution is appropriate at this point. If you are new to EFT, or to this kind of work, please ensure that you have used Gary Craig's foundational Personal Peace Procedure consistently for some time and have cleared major issues to the best of your ability, before you attempt this advanced technique.

So, let's begin!

## How important is self-awareness in this process?

Human beings are clearly differentiated from the animals by our capacity for self-awareness. We have the ability to mentally step outside of ourselves and become external observers of our own behaviour. We are even able to think about and analyse our own thought processes!

We are actually capable of developing our self-knowledge to such an extent that we can begin to recognise when we are getting in the way of our own personal progress.

We are also capable of raising our self-awareness to a level where we can recognise when we are stopping ourselves from being of genuine help to others.

Stephen Covey says: *"Until we take how we see ourselves and how we see others into account, we will be unable to understand how others see and feel about themselves and their world. Unaware we will project our intentions on their behaviour and call ourselves objective. This significantly limits our personal potential and our ability to relate to others as well".*[1]

Anyone who wishes to pursue their own personal growth, or to work in providing emotional assistance to others, is, in my opinion, obligated to increase their self-awareness and to develop the skill of recognising when 'self', or ego, is getting in the way.

When we are self-aware, we are more open to intuitive insights. As a result, we will be able to achieve more when using EFT for self-help, and we are more effective when using EFT for others.

## How easy is it to increase self-awareness?

Increasing our self-awareness can be an uncomfortable experience. We are choosing to examine who we are in close detail and we don't always like what we see.

When we choose to increase self-awareness, we are taking a first step on a life journey. The work is never done, and, as the path is pretty steep at the start, the prospect can seem overwhelming.

Although it may take some time to climb, once you get over that initial steep incline, you realise that none of the other hills is insurmountable, and the view is amazing!

The path to increased self-awareness is often difficult and can be unsettling at times but, paradoxically, when we choose to walk it, we move closer to inner peace.

## Isn't this journey all about my ego?

In a way, yes, but what do we mean by ego? We often equate the ego with big-headedness, arrogance, pride or self-satisfaction. Frequently however, when we look at ourselves, and see someone who is shy, self-effacing, lacking in confidence, or low in self-esteem, we naturally assume that ego is not a problem for us!

Remember that our ego is our sense of 'self'. When we are acutely aware of 'self', we are aware of a disconnection between ourselves and something else. Ego comes into play when we feel a sense of separation—separation from our fellow man, separation from the material goods or emotions that we want to have or experience, separation from full physical health, separation from our responsibility for this planet, separation from our sense of a Higher Power.

As long as we feel separate, discrete, different, better than, worse than, isolated from—then it is our ego that is in the driving seat.

## What is the difference between ego and spirit?

On a day-to-day basis, most of us operate from ego-consciousness, but the voice of the ego is not the only one seeking our attention. Deep within each of us, there is a core of inner energy that reminds us of our true nature and who we really are. This inner energy is our spirit. The voice of your inner energy will always offer a perspective that is to your greatest advantage. It will tell you what you need, which is not always necessarily what you feel you want.

When we work from ego-consciousness, we take the short-term view. Ego takes the easy way out. Ego knows that life is difficult and does everything to resist this, seeking pain-relief and instant gratification. It projects outwardly.

When we come from spirit-consciousness, we take the long-term view. Spirit recognises that life is difficult, accepts this, and seeks to discipline itself to handle life. It focuses inwardly.

Raising our self-awareness increases our ability to operate more easily from spirit-consciousness.

It's important to remember that our ego isn't the enemy. The ego is doing its best for us. It's trying to protect us and to minimise pain. The ego is trying to get our 'wants' addressed as quickly as possible. Our job is to recognise when the ego is yelling loudly and, when we hear it, to be grateful for having been alerted to an opportunity for further personal growth.

## How can I use this procedure for my personal growth?

Personal growth is a life-long pursuit, but when we begin, we need small, manageable goals. Otherwise, the task ahead can seem too much for us. It is said that it takes 21 days to form a habit so I suggest you commit to using the Advanced Personal Peace Procedure for 30 days in the first instance. By that time, you will find that it has become part of your daily routine. With persistence, it will become part of who you are!

As stated at the beginning, Stage 1 of this technique is about analysing and meditating upon your personal philosophy so that it becomes a tool for developing self-awareness. What is your personal discipline or belief system? Do you have a clear set of rules for life? Perhaps you follow a religion or have adopted a philosophy that provides guidelines for a happy existence. Maybe you have evolved your own code of ethics over the years.

Some people read a book like 'The 7 Habits of Highly Effective People'[2] or 'The Success Principles'[3] and decide to live according to the suggested system. Others practise yoga, tai chi or martial arts and adopt the philosophical structure that they are based on. Many people simply use 'do no harm' as their life guide. We all have a set of beliefs about what is right and what is wrong, even if it has never been explicitly stated. If you've never thought about it before, take some time out at this stage to decide what your personal ethos may be.

## Can you illustrate this with a specific example?

Analysing and meditating upon our personal philosophy offers the perfect opportunity to develop the skill necessary for the first part of the process, self-awareness.

For example, if your life philosophy is 'do no harm', then take the time to think about what that means. Who is not to be harmed? Animals? Other people? Yourself? And what is meant by harm? If I have an unhealthy lifestyle, am I doing physical harm? If I constantly berate myself for not being good enough, am I doing emotional harm? If I try to 'rescue' someone and don't allow that person to walk their own path, make their own mistakes and learn from them, am I doing harm by blocking the spiritual growth of another human being?

Tough questions, I know, but if we are to grow in self-awareness, the ability to ask and answer such questions is essential. If we do not do so, then statements like 'do no harm' become meaningless and valueless.

My personal philosophy is based on five principles from a Japanese spiritual discipline that has its origins in Buddhist/Taoist practice. (These principles will be familiar to anyone who practises Reiki.) They represent ONE possible path to follow—the one that works for me. There are many paths.

In the next section, I will show you how to analyse these principles to see how they can help us to raise our awareness of 'self' or ego. Remember that you can use the same analysis process on your own personal discipline in exactly the same way.

## Stage 1—Self-awareness

*ANALYSE YOUR PERSONAL PHILOSOPHY SO THAT IT BECOMES A TOOL FOR DEVELOPING SELF-AWARENESS*

In the first section, I asked you to determine your personal discipline. Stage 1 is about analysing that discipline so that it becomes a tool for spotting the ego in action. We can't 'fix' the problem if we don't know it's there, so we have to clearly see our ego at work before we can get it out of the way.

As I mentioned earlier, my personal discipline is based on five principles from Japanese Buddhist/Taoist practice.

Loosely translated, the principles are as follows:

JUST FOR TODAY:
- Release all anger
- Release all worry
- Honour every living thing
- Live with integrity
- Be grateful for all your many blessings

Notice that the language of the principles is very simple. When we examine the principles in detail, however, we begin to get a glimpse of just how powerful they are. To explore each one in depth unveils the route to self-mastery and would require much more than these few paragraphs.

We will merely analyse each of the principles in turn to see how they can help us become more aware of our ego.

## How can 'releasing all anger' increase my self-awareness?

Anger is a normal human emotion. All emotions (positive or negative) exist for a reason. They have a job to do. The purpose of our negative emotions is to let us know that something is wrong.

When we are angry, we are not happy about something or someone (possibly ourselves). We are out of alignment or out of balance. We are off track.

Anger is simply an indicator that something's wrong. If we see anger as something other than this, it can become problematic. If we don't recognise the message in anger ('something's wrong!'), we may lash out in rage and temper, hurting those around us. Frequently though, we do the opposite.

Not only do we fail to recognise the message, but we see the messenger as 'bad'! We feel guilty for having the messenger show up in our lives, and we try to suppress it. We use vast amounts of precious energy keeping anger down. Anger is one of our many emotional alarm bells. Pushing anger down inside ourselves and hoping it will disappear, is like sticking our fingers in our ears and hoping that the bells will stop ringing just because we ignore them.

Of course, the opposite is true. When you ignore the alarm, it just gets louder and louder and louder. Think of anything that makes you angry. (Remember to include annoyance, frustration, irritation, jealousy, faultfinding and any other angry feelings.) Now think about your part in that anger. Is there any part of that anger that involves you insisting on having things YOUR way?

Are you angry because someone isn't doing what YOU WANT them to do, isn't behaving the way YOU WANT them to behave, isn't responding the way YOU WANT them to respond, isn't living the way YOU WANT them to live?

This analysis is our opportunity to develop self-awareness. Practice listening to your self-talk and hear the part being played by your ego:

- *I'm angry because of what she said—translates as: She didn't speak to me the way I WANT her to.*
- *How dare he treat me like that!—translates as: He didn't treat me the way I WANT to be treated.*

- *I really resent the way this government ignores the social needs of inner city communities—translates as: This government isn't doing what I WANT it to do.*
- *I'm angry with God for allowing these things to happen—translates as: God isn't doing what I WANT Him to do.*
- *I'm angry at myself for making such a stupid mistake—translates as: Even I am not doing what I WANT!*

So when you're feeling angry about something, here's the ultimate ego question: *"Is there any part of this anger that involves you stamping your foot like a petulant child and saying 'this isn't the way I WANT it to be'?"* If so, that's your ego talking!

Take an analytical look at your anger. Which parts exist because you're not getting things your own way? If you were to set those parts aside for a moment, what's left? How much of your anger is actually your ego? Now that you can see your ego's contribution to the situation, would things be different if you could get yourself out of the way?

## How can 'releasing all worry' increase my self-awareness?

When we are worried about something, we are coming from a place of fear. If we weren't frightened, there wouldn't be anything to worry about!

Let's imagine a scenario. Your daughter is going on holiday alone. She leaves on the 1st of August and will return on the 15th of August. As soon as she leaves, you settle yourself down to a fortnight of worry, as you vividly imagine all the terrible things that may befall her.

There are two possible outcomes:

One, she returns on the 15th, and nothing bad has happened. You have spent two weeks biting your nails, getting high blood pressure, suffering from insomnia, and nothing bad has happened.

What benefit was gained by your worrying? (None) What value was gained by your worrying? (None) How did your worrying help to improve the situation? (It didn't)

Alternatively, she returns on the 15th (or earlier) and something bad HAS happened.

What benefit was gained by you worrying? (None) What value was gained by you worrying? (None) How did your worrying help to improve the situation? (It didn't)

Whether bad things happen or don't happen is NEVER influenced by how much we worry. Whatever you undertake in life, by all means, make plans. Envisage alternative outcomes and have contingency plans if you want to. But once you've done that, make the choice (and it IS a choice) not to worry, because worry has never had the power to alter things that are beyond our control. Take ownership of those things you CAN control, and recognise your ego at work when you are trying to influence those things you can't.

- If you're worried about global warming, stop worrying (as it benefits no-one) and ensure that you're doing your best to minimise your contribution.
- If you're worried about failing an exam, stop worrying (as it benefits no-one) and ensure that you're making your best effort to revise.
- If you're worried about your health, stop worrying (as it benefits no-one) and ensure that you're doing as much as you can to live a healthy lifestyle.

Think of anything that makes you worried. Now think about your part in that worry. Here comes our opportunity to develop self-awareness! Practice listening to your self-talk and hear the part being played by your ego:

- I'm worried that my son might miss his train—translates as: I'm frightened because I CAN'T CONTROL this situation.
- I'm worried that there may be an accident—translates as: I'm frightened because I CAN'T CONTROL this situation.
- I'm worried about weapons of mass destruction—translates as: I'm frightened because I CAN'T CONTROL this situation.

So when you're feeling worried about something, here's the ultimate ego question. *"Is there any part of this worry that involves me stamping my foot like a petulant child and saying: 'I'M not in charge here, and I DON'T LIKE IT!'?"* If so, that's your ego talking!

Take an analytical look at your worry. Which parts exist because you're not in control? If you were to set those parts aside for a moment, what's left? How much of your worry is actually your ego? Now that you can see your ego's contribution to the situation, would things be different if you could get yourself out of the way?

## How can 'honouring every living thing' increase my self-awareness?

These four words carry incredible power behind them, and are worthy of much study. We're just going to look at them to see how they can help us to recognise our ego at work.

When we truly honour another person, we recognise someone who is doing the best they can, given their resources, past experiences, the writing on their walls, and their perceptions. We recognise someone who has a basic set of needs—food, warmth, security, love, sense of community, etc—and who is doing what they can to get those needs met in the best way they know how. As soon as we see ourselves as better than them, worse than them, separate from them in some way, our ego is at work! Once again, we have the perfect opportunity to develop self-awareness! Practice listening to your self-talk and hear the part being played by your ego.

- Imagine wearing that hat with that coat!—translates as: I'm better than you. I wouldn't make that mistake. I SEE MYSELF AS SEPARATE from someone like you.

- Drug pushers are the scum of the earth—translates as: I'm better than a drug pusher. I wouldn't lower myself to those levels. I SEE MYSELF AS SEPARATE from someone like that.

- I'm not good enough for someone like him—translates as: I'm a lesser human being than he is. His gifts and talents are superior to mine. I SEE MYSELF AS SEPARATE from him.

- It's alright for you! You haven't had to deal with the things I've had to deal with—translates as: I'm unique in my suffering. No-one's had it as bad as me. I SEE MYSELF AS SEPARATE from anyone else who has problems.

If we honour EVERY living thing, then we have to honour ourselves too. This principle clearly states that we have to afford ourselves the same respect that we are duty bound to offer to others.

Unfortunately, I know MANY therapists who are busy helping other people and do not take any time to help themselves. Ironically, they feel that devoting time to themselves on the spiritual, emotional, mental and physical level equates to selfishness. They wrongly interpret caring for themselves as being egotistical!

We are certainly working from ego-consciousness when we try to help someone else without walking our own talk. If I don't honour myself enough to try to eat a healthy diet, or continually work to clear my own emotional blocks, my ultimate stance becomes *"Don't do as I do, do as I say!"* Can you hear my ego talking?

This is not to suggest that you have to be completely ego-free in order to help people. You just have to be working on it! Bear in mind that if you hold back from helping others because you feel you aren't in a state of readiness, then that feeling is driven by fear, and is just as ego-based as the opposite feeling of *"I want to fix the world"*.

[Continually striving to help others without being willing to fully honour ourselves can have significant implications for the body's energy field. For more on this concept, I refer you to Dr William Tiller's presentation on the 'EFT-Beyond the Basics' DVD set.[4]]

## How can 'living with integrity' increase my self-awareness?

When we live with integrity, we are fully congruent. Our thoughts and our feelings are in harmony. What we think and feel is reflected in our actions and behaviour.

When we live with integrity, we fully own all aspects of our being. We openly embrace the 'shadow self' so that we can learn from it.

When we are in denial about aspects of our 'shadow', we are avoiding something that we don't like about ourselves. Our ego is saying *"No, that's nothing to do with me. I'm better than that."* We don't want to acknowledge that, for example, we may have been overly aggressive, we may have caused great distress by our incessant worry, or that we may have been judgmental about others.

When you see glimpses of your shadow and those glimpses make you feel uncomfortable, recognize your ego at work. It's trying to 'protect' you from the potential pain of acknowledging who you really are at this moment in time.

But avoidance never works. It's a bit like the alarm bells of anger. The more we allow our ego to push away those parts we don't like, the louder they will become as they clamour for our attention.

The sooner we reject our ego response, (while being grateful for its attempts to help!), the sooner we can progress down the road to personal peace.

## What about 'be grateful for all your many blessings'?

When we work from ego-consciousness, we seem to concentrate on what is wrong in our lives and we tend to see lots of things to complain about. Our focus is me, me, me! Ironically, however, as we work to become more self-aware, we actually become more aware of the world around us. If we look at that world with our eyes truly open, we can begin to see that we have many blessings for which to be grateful.

Every evening, review your day, find five blessings and then be thankful for them. When life is tough and things are going badly, it can sometimes seem very difficult to see ANY blessings, so keep it simple!

*EDITOR'S NOTE:*
My clients have found major benefit from writing these five blessings down every night in a Gratitude Journal.

Can you be grateful that it was sunny/ rainy today? That you had enough food to feed yourself and your family? That your favourite TV show was on this evening? That there is a lovely tree/flower in your garden? That you are able to read the words on this page?

You'll be amazed at how your focus changes when you have an attitude of gratitude!

## Stage 2—Self-acceptance

*AS AWARENESS OF SELF OR EGO INCREASES, USE EFT TO HEIGHTEN SELF-ACCEPTANCE*

On face value, the principles that we analysed in Stage 1 seem to be simple guides for how to live. Take a look at your own rules for life. They are probably stated in very simple terms—'Do no harm', or 'Begin with the end in mind', or 'Thou shalt not steal'. Despite the apparent simplicity of the words, once we take the time and trouble to analyse what they really mean, many people have second thoughts and decide that they're far too difficult to adopt for life!

## I find this very difficult in practice. Why is that?

Most spiritual philosophies are simple. They are rarely easy!

The reason that principles appear to be so difficult to take on board for life is because we think that in order to adopt them, we have to stop being who we are now, and suddenly become an enlightened being overnight.

If, however, we give ourselves permission to be who we are in this moment (*I deeply and completely accept myself*), then we free ourselves to take whatever time we need to raise our awareness of the ego in action, and then take steps to reduce its influence.

Notice that each of the principles in Stage 1 is preceded by 'Just for today'. Buddhist thinking tells us that there is no past, no present and no future as we normally define them. There is only 'now'. Space and time are merely human constructs and therefore don't exist.

This is a difficult concept for most of us to get to grips with, because we perceive the reality of space and time through our five senses. (The important point here is that we equate our 'reality' with what we 'perceive'.)

In order to make it easier to adopt these spiritual principles on a day-to-day basis, the concept of 'now' has been expanded into 'just for today'. Whenever we adopt any new way of being, allowing ourselves to do it 'just for today' makes the process easier and more manageable. We are also more inclined to forgive ourselves if we slip up! You will see that an important aspect in Stage 3 of the process is that we work one day at a time and at a pace that is comfortable.

When we start to look at our own lives in terms of ego-consciousness, it is very easy to fall into the trap of guilt for how we have been in the past, or even self-blame for our continued failure to change. A crucial part of the self-awareness process is that we view our behaviours and motivations without judgement or censure. We act merely as observers.

## How can I make self-acceptance easier with EFT?

We are blessed to have EFT to ease the way! The EFT setup phrase is an extremely elegant tool for self-acceptance. Many people are highly resistant to the words *"I deeply and completely accept myself"* because they find it impossible to accept themselves entirely, or to accept their past, or their potential future.

But what if the setup phrase were simply about accepting yourself in the 'now'? Not tomorrow, or even in the next 10 minutes, but right now, this instant. Look at the

*EDITOR'S NOTE:*
Self-acceptance is addressed in several of the articles in this book, each describing a slightly different approach.

perfect point of balance that is held when we focus the setup phrase in the 'now'.

> ✦ *Even though I have this problem, I deeply and completely accept myself.*

On the one hand, I acknowledge that I have a problem. On the other hand, I give up my resistance to having this problem within this moment. I have resisted the problem in the past, and I may even resist the problem in the future, but right now, in this moment, I accept that this is who I am and this is the problem that I have.

In that moment of self-acceptance, we lose our attachment to both the past and the future, and we are open to the stillness of 'now'. We are not critical of who we have been, and we are not fearful of who we will become. We simply accept that this is where we are at this moment.

There is much to be gained simply by contemplating the beauty of a setup phrase that holds us in the 'now'. As you become more self-aware, use EFT to increase your ability to self-accept. Modify your EFT statements to make the present moment more explicit if necessary.

For example:

> ✦ *Even though I'm jealous of her, that's just where I'm at right now.*

> ✦ *Even though I'm jealous of her, that's just how I feel, and that's just how it is.*

If you are still judging yourself, build that into the setup. Acknowledge that you have the problem, and that you are struggling with it, and then add the acceptance statement:

> ✦ *Even though I'm jealous of her, and I don't like feeling that way, I accept that it's just how I feel at the moment.*

> ✦ *Even though I'm jealous of her, and I'm frightened that I may never stop being jealous, I accept that in this moment I am a jealous person.*

Keep modifying and changing the setup until you can find a statement that allows you to stay in the 'now'.

Being in the 'now' allows us to release our resistance to who we are at any given moment. When we become self-aware, and we begin to see how much our ego gets in the way, it is essential that we are able to accept who we are without censure.

In Stage 3, we will be using setup phrases that acknowledge and accept our ego.

> ✦ *Even though I'm jealous of her, I recognise that my ego may have played a part in this. I can accept this without judging myself. It's just human nature.*

## Stage 3–The advanced personal peace procedure

AN EFT TECHNIQUE TO USE DAILY UNTIL THE ABILITY TO *'GET YOURSELF OUT OF THE WAY'* IS AUTOMATIC

Once we have learned how to spot our ego at work (Stage 1) and we are able to view our ego-based actions without judgement (Stage 2), we are ready to begin using the Advanced Personal Peace Procedure.

Commit to using this procedure for 30 days. At the end of this period, you will have trained your mind in such a way that the thought processes involved become part of who you are.

## What are the steps of Advanced Personal Peace Procedure?

1. Review your day noting down those events where you experienced negative emotion
2. Select a specific event to work with
3. Use EFT to remove all negative charge from the event noting down each of the responses that you have
4. Look at each response with a view to analysing the ego content.
5. Use EFT to acknowledge, without judgement, the part your ego has played.
6. Repeat steps 2-5 for each event that day
7. Repeat the whole procedure every day for 30 days.

## Can you give me an example of the procedure in use?

1. *REVIEW YOUR DAY NOTING DOWN THOSE EVENTS WHERE YOU EXPERIENCED NEGATIVE EMOTION:*

   Looking back over your day, you note the following:
   - Snapped at your daughter
   - Felt really intimidated by the boss at work
   - Got annoyed because next door's cat had been in the flower bed again

2. *SELECT A SPECIFIC EVENT TO WORK WITH:*

   Let's begin with the first one. You snapped at your daughter, Jane, because she asked you to pay her car tax for her when you were out. You did some EFT at the time because you realised your response was inappropriate, but you still keep replaying the event in your mind for some reason.

3. *USE EFT TO REMOVE ALL NEGATIVE CHARGE FROM THE EVENT NOTING DOWN EACH OF THE RESPONSES THAT YOU HAVE:*

   It is essential that you use EFT to remove ALL emotional charge from an event before you begin to analyse it. You will NOT be able to undertake an impartial analysis if you are still emotionally linked to the problem. Only when you have cleared all of your negative responses to the issue will you be able to take the objective, third party viewpoint, essential for getting yourself out of the way. You've already used EFT on *"Even though I snapped at Jane . . ."* and *"Even though I think she's too dependent on me . . ."*

   You note down that you were short-tempered and that you felt concerned about Jane's ability to manage her own life. As you do so, you realise that you are still replaying the event because of a belief that she would be much more in control of her situation, just like you were at her age, if she had only taken your advice and gone to university instead of getting a local job. You are not aware of any negative charge on this belief.

4. LOOK AT EACH RESPONSE WITH A VIEW TO ANALYSING THE EGO CONTENT

   In this one event, you experienced anger towards Jane, worry about her ability to cope, and a belief that she should have followed your advice.

- Did any part of that anger come about because someone or something wasn't doing/saying/being what you wanted?

- Did any part of that worry come about because someone or something is beyond your control?

- Did any part of that belief come about because you are judging someone as being different from you?

I wanted Jane to take responsibility for herself. I got angry because she wasn't doing what I wanted. Jane's actions are irresponsible. I got worried because I cannot control the outcome if she continues in this way. Jane doesn't live her life as I lived mine.

I am not honouring her right to make her own mistakes and learn her own lessons in life. I am also judging her as being less capable than me, therefore I see myself as superior to her.

5. USE EFT TO ACKNOWLEDGE, WITHOUT JUDGEMENT, THE PART YOUR EGO HAS PLAYED

Tap on the event (or aspects of the event) with the following statements and note how you feel:

☩ *Even though **THIS EVENT MADE ME FEEL ANGRY**, I recognise that my ego may have played a part in this. I can accept this without judging myself. It's just human nature.*

REMINDER:        *I felt angry because I wasn't getting what I wanted*

☩ *Even though **THIS EVENT MADE ME FEEL WORRIED**, I recognise that my ego may have played a part in this. I can accept this without judging myself. It's just human nature.*

REMINDER:        *I felt worried because I wasn't in control*

☩ *Even though **I DIDN'T HONOUR JANE** as an equal, I recognise that my ego may have played a part in this. I can accept this without judging myself. It's just human nature.*

REMINDER:        *I didn't honour Jane as an equal*

Now assess if you are feeling any guilt about the part your ego played in the event. Remember that step 5 is about recognising our ego without judgement. If you feel bad about it in any way, repeat rounds of tapping as required. Feel free to modify the setup phrase as necessary or as appropriate.

If you find you are resistant to acknowledging your ego's part in the event, then you still have some more work do in clearing your negative emotions before you try to apply this technique. Apply EFT to the original event, and similar or related events, until you feel clear enough to try step 5 again.

Depending on how much personal growth work you have done, you can also adjust the language of the setup phrase, so that you continue to feel comfortable and non-judgemental.

You may tap initially on: ***Even though this event made me feel angry***. In this statement, we blame the event for our response.

This can be adjusted to: ***Even though this event made me respond with anger***. In this instance, although we still blame the event, we acknowledge that we choose our own response.

You may be ready to take full ownership of the part played by your ego and say: ***Even though I responded with anger to this event***.

Sometimes a subtle change of wording can make a huge difference to our ability to hear what is being said. The essence of step 5 is that we accept who we are without censure.

## 6. REPEAT STEPS 2-5 FOR EACH EVENT THAT DAY

Begin the procedure again for the next event in your day if you feel able to do so. If working on one event is all that you feel able to manage, do not try to do any more. Also, do not judge yourself for not being able to do any more!

Remember that we have committed to free ourselves to take WHATEVER TIME WE NEED to raise our awareness of the ego in action.

## 7. REPEAT THE WHOLE PROCEDURE EVERY DAY FOR 30 DAYS

If you repeat this as a daily exercise for 30 days, you will find that your awareness of your ego in action will have increased considerably, and you will find it easier to spot your ego when it goes to work.

Eventually, you will start to become aware of your ego BEFORE it goes to work. This is where you want to be! When you are self-aware enough to catch your ego before it becomes involved, you can enter any situation knowing that you are able to get your 'self' out of the way!

# SUMMARY

'Getting out of the way' is about recognizing the ego at work and then doing something about it! To my mind, this is not a skill to be learned. Rather it is an attitude, or a mindset. For me, it is a way of life borne out of my chosen spiritual discipline.

In essence, you cannot get yourself out of the way unless you first recognize and accept yourself. This state of being could be achieved simply by the persistent application of EFT alone, because EFT ultimately raises self-awareness and encourages self-acceptance. This is why Gary Craig's foundational Personal Peace Procedure has such enormous potential for those who choose to adopt it.

However, when we go beyond the foundations, commit to using the Advanced Personal Peace Procedure and work consistently at 'getting out of the way', we can speed up the process! We automatically begin to 'be in the flow'. As we learn to reject the voice of the ego, we begin to hear the voice of our true spirit. We become more able to access the flow of wisdom and love that surrounds and fills us.

My own spiritual discipline requires that I spend regular time in a meditative state. These moments of quiet and solitude allow the space necessary to be able to hear the voice of the spirit. Because this is a life discipline, it becomes easier and easier to access those moments of stillness in order to hear that voice.

In the therapy setting, I have access to a 'flow' of endless information about my client if I allow myself to be still, and to be present. Some people call accessing this information 'using their intuition', some call it 'psychic ability', and some call it 'being in the flow'.

Whatever terminology is used, the more we can get ourselves out of the way, the more effective we can be as a channel for the limitless love and well being that is our birthright. When I act as a therapist, I am merely a conduit for the power of the Universe to flow. As soon as I think that power is mine, the ego has taken over, and I am no longer in that flow.

Getting myself out of the way is not something I only do, or think about, prior to working with clients. It is a way of life.

## AUTHOR'S BIOGRAPHY AND CONTACT DETAILS

Helen Walker is a former corporate trainer and schoolteacher. In 1998, she began her training as a therapist and in 2003, she founded 'Inner Energy' which provides training courses in EFT and workshops in personal and spiritual growth. She has taught EFT in the UK, Europe and the USA, including teaching at two international EFT Masterclasses.

Web:     www.innerenergy.co.uk
E-mail:  info@innerenergy.co.uk

## REFERENCES:

1. Stephen Covey. The 7 Habits of Highly Effective People. (Simon & Schuster UK Ltd., 1989)
2. Ibid.
3. Jack Canfield. The Success Principles. (Harper Collins Publishers Ltd., 2005)
4. Gary Craig. EFT-Beyond the Basics. DVD set

# The Trauma Buster Technique

REHANA WEBSTER, EFT MASTER, EFTCERT-HONORS

The Movie Technique {see *Glossary*} is a powerful process for internal change. This article describes a customized version of this standard technique, which I call the Trauma Buster Technique (also known as the Advanced Movie Technique). Using it, I have had excellent results with some of the most difficult trauma cases, and my clients have found it to be a very effective tool for working at home on their own issues.

> **EDITOR'S NOTE:**
> A critical component of this technique, and several others described in this book is the ability to re-write history; to create a memory that is different from the original 'true' one.

## What is the Trauma Buster Technique?

This modification of the standard Movie Technique involves consciously adjusting the sub-modalities of the movie in order to change its impact. We experience the outside and inside world through our 5 senses, and sub-modalities can be described as the 'structure' of each sense.

> While we can't change the actual experience of something that has happened in the past, we may be able to change how the experience is structured and therefore how the memory is experienced or remembered.

For example:

- Visual sub-modalities include color, shape, movement, brightness, depth etc.

- Auditory sub-modalities include volume, pitch, tempo etc.

- Kinesthetic sub-modalities include pressure, temperature, texture, location etc.

- The impact of this is profound. For example, if you have a memory that is remembered as a picture, you are very likely to be able to change the experience of that memory by changing (for example) the brightness, distance or focus of that picture.

As Gary Craig teaches the Movie Technique, you take an unpleasant event for which you want to neutralize the negative feelings and turn it into a movie, giving it a title, a particular length and figure out who is starring in it. Start tapping on the karate chop point and proceed with the short-cut protocol of tapping while viewing your internal movie. Stimulating the points by tapping on them balances the flow of energy thereby removing blocks and unwanted negative emotions.

In the Trauma Buster Technique, imagine that the movie is on a TV screen at the further end of the room which allows you to view the movie in 'third person' and distances you from the event. Tap on the points as you watch the movie and notice how it feels and where you may be experiencing higher amount of distress.

## How can I vary the movie using this technique?

You can try any or all of the following variations:

1. BLACK AND WHITE: Turn the movie into black and white. Recall the last time you saw a B&W movie and what the quality was like. An example of this is The Wizard of Oz which was both in black and white and in color.

Notice in black and white how the definition between the foreground and background was not distinct. Run the movie as many times as you want as you tap on the points and rate it every time to test the results.

2. BACKWARDS: Tap on the points and run the B&W movie backwards like rewinding a video or DVD. What did it look like with everything going backwards? Remember to include people walking backwards, cars driving backwards and eating food in reverse, etc. Rewind the movie and rate it till you are satisfied with the results.

3. CARTOON: Make the mental movie into a cartoon. Do you have a favorite cartoon show/character or did you have one when you were young? Turn your movie into a Technicolor cartoon and have the players represented by Bugs Bunny, Popeye, Mickey Mouse, Wiley Coyote, etc.

4. MUSIC: Add music to the movie. This can be done at any stage. Choose something like polka or rock 'n' roll. Adjust the volume of the music or hear it in one ear and then the next. Get up and move with the music. Watch your movie with the adjustments while you are tapping on the points.

5. SOUND: Another variation to use if someone is talking in your movie is to make the sound louder, softer, slower, or faster. Or change the voice to Donald Duck or Mickey Mouse, or sing it like Johnny Cash, Luciano Pavoratti or Madonna!

6. AS IF: Last but not least, consider adding an 'as-if' dimension to the movie. Create a new ending. In fact, change any part of the movie to get the result you would have preferred. Remember the unconscious mind does not differentiate between then and now.

Test and retest your work. Rate the mental movie after each version. Notice which step works best for you and use that variation more frequently.

## Case Study: PTSD

Michael, a 27 year old truck driver, was sent to see me because he had not been able to get any help for the after-accident symptoms he was experiencing. Michael had been involved in a fatal road crash a year ago, where the driver of the other vehicle had committed suicide by driving head-on into Michael's truck.

Michael remembered vividly the aftermath of the accident. He described the carnage in detail and rated his negative feelings at 10 + on a 0-10 scale.

Michael was plagued by flashbacks, up to 50 per day which had not diminished over time. He also had intrusive thoughts which he couldn't control. By the time he came to see me, he had given up hope of every getting his life on track again.

Michael was very willing to try anything to help him, so we did one session of tapping. He was highly amused and quite skeptical. I asked him to make a movie of the incident and then go over it as we tapped. I asked him to recall the visuals plus the sounds, smells and feelings while he saw the movie of the incident in his minds eye. We went all through the variations of the Trauma Buster Technique.

I took Michael through the steps of the Trauma Buster as follows.

1. BLACK AND WHITE: After relating the incident to me, I asked him to make a black and white movie of it and play it on an imaginary screen. After he had done this we rated how he felt about the accident, and the rating had diminished from a 10 ++ to around 5.

2. BACKWARDS: I asked Michael to 'rewind' the black and white movie so that the incident was now running backwards in his mind's eye. When he had finished, the rating was down to a 2.

3. CARTOON: We skipped this step as it was not appropriate.

4. MUSIC: I asked Michael if he had been to the circus as a kid and to recall the music he might have heard there. Then I asked him to imagine hearing the circus music while he saw the black and white movie in his mind's eye, and rewind it at the same time. The rating was now below 1.

5. SOUND: We skipped this step.

6. AS IF: Finally I asked Michael to change the black and white movie and imagine a different outcome. I encouraged him to make up whatever he thought would have been better than the actual event. He chose to imagine that the accident was avoided because he saw it coming and swerved out of the way. Instead the other vehicle ran off the road and the driver just got out of the car without any injuries and walked away.

My observations were that his body language shifted during the process, however when I asked Michael to rate the incident, he was not completely sure that it was a zero, even though he said something had clearly changed about how he felt regarding the accident. I asked him to keep a diary/journal and record how many flashbacks he had on a daily basis.

One week later Michael came in for his second session. We went through his journal and he informed me with a huge smile that he had had no flash-backs or intrusive thoughts about the accident/carnage since the first session. He was simply amazed that, after all the sessions using traditional psychological interventions and medication, this painless, simple and quick treatment had worked wonders. I asked him what had changed and his reply was: *"It all seems far away somehow. I can see the accident clearly in my minds eye if I want to, but it doesn't intrude upon my consciousness and it just seems far away . . . is the only way I can explain it".*

## AUTHOR'S BIOGRAPHY AND CONTACT DETAILS

Rehana Webster, BSc., EFT Master and NLP Master Practitioner, was among the first group of practitioners in the world to be certified as an EFT Master by EFT founder Gary Craig. She has taken EFT to new heights with her skills in the area of neutralizing Trauma, PTSD, Anxieties, Panic Attacks, and other behaviors categorized as irrational.

Rehana lives in Perth, Australia and conducts workshop and trainings inter-nationally in all levels of EFT and The Art of Delivery (using NLP techniques in the application of EFT). To read dozens of interesting case studies, and find out more about Rehana, please visit her website at www.behaviourchanges.com. She can be contacted at connect@behaviourchanges.com.

# EFT and Magic Buttons Bear

LINDA WOOD, AAMET TRAINER/
PRACTITIONER (LEVEL 3)

## How did the Magic Buttons Bear come about?

The birth of the first Magic Buttons (or Magic for short) was in 2005. A few months after making several bears based on a strong intuitive feeling, I was teaching a Level 2 EFT training when the thought came to me to use the bears. Not having a clue what would happen and taking the chance of falling flat on my face, I gave each student a bear and asked them to do an inventory of their own body and find some discomfort. I wanted them to actually 'feel' if something was going to happen with tapping on this bear. Then I had them give it a rating (SUDS) after which we all began tapping on the bear using one person's words while the others borrowed benefits.

Suddenly, one man in the group began squirming around uncomfortably in his seat so I asked him what was going on. He said: *"I don't know but something is happening in my lower back."* I checked in with the other students to see how they were doing with their issues and then quickly shifted to using this man's words to explore what was going on in his back. The whole time we were all still tapping on the bears but by now everyone was watching this man in total amazement, totally distracted from their own issues. Suddenly he said: *"Oh my gosh, money stuff is coming up and it's to do with things my Dad believed."* We tapped and cleared and eventually this man said: *"I don't know what's happening here, these are incredible!"*

## What are some of the ways to use Magic Buttons?

There is no tougher client to work on than ourselves. Because we are so used to stuffing our emotions and denying them, many of us find it difficult to get to our own core issues. Using Magic is the perfect way to stand away from your own problems and see yourself in a new way. Have Magic 'be' you while you are your own therapist and you'll often see the issues popping up like popcorn because you are not as able to keep them stuffed down.

I've had several adults who say they never took stuffed toys to bed with them as children but now take Magic to bed, sometimes for comfort, other times when they are too lazy to tap on themselves they then tap on Magic. Others have said they love having the bear to tap on because they used to always talk to their stuffed bears as children so they can easily relate to this.

## Can you give me some suggestions for teenagers and children?

Magic is the perfect doorway into your child's world. The secret to using Magic with kids is to always have the problem 'be' Magic's problem. For example, when you know your child is upset about something, instead of asking them what they are upset about or if they'd like to talk about it or tap for it, (most will say no) just get Magic out and begin tapping in front of them: *"Magic has a problem at school and he's still a great bear."*

It will only take a few seconds or minutes before the child is beginning to engage and offering you other things that 'Magic' is upset about. (See my 'grandmother's story' at the end of this.) And if you keep pretending they are 'Magic's' problems, the child will be much more willing to give you more information.

Magic is a tool, not a toy. What do children do with toys after a very short time? They toss them into the corner and want new ones, different ones. So if you keep Magic sacred and special and tell the child that he needs to be put away and recharged when not in use, the child learns to respect him as a useful tool. I can't tell you how fantastic it is when children begin to learn to recognize that they 'need' to get Magic out to work through a negative emotion, or even that they do have a choice whether to keep or change the emotion! And all of us who have bags and bags of stored emotions from childhood KNOW how important this is for children. Remember too that issues clear very quickly in children.

Teenagers are often much more willing to tap on a silly bear than to do this silly tapping on themselves. I've had reports of parents saying their teenagers will say: *"Mum, will you get Magic out and tap on him for me?"*

What I have discovered through surrogate tapping and through tapping along with children, is that you form a much deeper bond with whomever you are tapping for or with (see Ophelia's story at the end). So often when we talk to our children we are only talking on the surface. When we open the doors to EFT with kids, we are going into the much deeper levels of ourselves. You'll have a more meaningful relationship with your child. What do you hear so many kids say about their parents? They say: *"My parents don't listen to me. They don't understand me. They don't hear me."* When you learn to use Magic and EFT WITH your children you will be amazed at the results. Have you ever heard the phrase: *'The family that prays together stays together?'* What do you think will happen with the family that taps together?

## Can Magic help me to be a better parent?

One of the toughest jobs in the world is being a parent. There are no manuals when a child arrives, no instructional books. Parents just have to wing it and worry if we are doing it right while we try to keep our own emotional issues under control too.

It will help to let kids know that Mums and Dads are humans too, that we need help from Magic and most of all, that we love them even when we lose our tempers.

When Mum or Dad get angry, either at the kids or at each other, how do children take that? Often they think they have not been good enough or that Mum and Dad don't love them anymore. When you find yourself erupting, learn to catch yourself and say to the child: *"Oh, oh, I think we need to get out Magic. Would you like to help Mummy tap with Magic?"* You can make huge difference in your child's life, the family's life and your own life by learning to handle these little upsets as they come along rather than letting them build and build until they're like a pressure cooker going off.

Many parents have asked how they get their child to talk to them about what they do at school. They say that when they ask the kids will just say: *"Nothing."* Get Magic out when you find an appropriate time (it could be bedtime) and begin tapping and say: *"Magic went to school today. What do you think he learned? Do you think he had fun there? Do you think anyone played with him?"* The child should begin responding with his own stuff while pretending that it is really Magic.

Kids love Magic and fun and little secrets too. Tell your child: *"Only YOU can hear what Magic says and only he can hear what you say, so if you have something that you want to tap on, you can whisper it to Magic, then tap on him and he'll take care of it for you and no one but you and him can know what it is unless you want anyone else to know."*

When you are working with SUDS with kids, they will respond much better if rather than asking them for a number, simply have them hold out Magic Button's arms for how much Magic feels this emotion or issue. Then tap until Magic can put his arms completely together.

## What are some things not to do?

One huge rule that I teach parents is to never hand a Bear to a child and say: *"Here, go fix yourself."* They can't get to their problems any quicker than we can get to ours. Plus, kids think everything is their fault anyway. Always tap WITH your kids. And always let the child lead. Start Magic off and then go with the child's flow. Help them feel 'important.' Kids love to help.

Another key rule is that no matter what the child tells you, you must never react in shock or surprise. And worse than that, never lecture or scold them if they tell you something you don't want to hear. If you do, you will almost certainly lose them. Keep pretending the problem belongs to Magic Buttons the Bear and remember that when you do this, your role is the therapist during this, not the parent. You'll do FAR more good for that child by helping them tap through this and possibly reframe it rather than stopping to scold or correct your child.

## Can you say something about the importance of attention?

One thing that kids need even more than love is attention. Many people have done experiments with cooked rice in which jars of rice were placed in labs and students were told that every time they walked by one jar of rice to say: "I hate you" to it. They were instructed to walk by the second jar of rice and say: "I love you." And the third jar they were to totally ignore.

At the end of thirty days, the "I love you jar" is typically nice and mellow and yellow, the "I hate you" jar is black and rotten, but the jar that was ignored is the most rotten of all.

This shows us how important our words are for one thing, but also how important our attention is. Kids don't need all of our attention. If they know they are going to get even 10 minutes of our total attention at the end of the day, they'll be fine with that. And they'll never forget it. It will always be meaningful to them throughout their entire lifetime.

Use Magic at the special time of day, just before your child goes to bed. Ask your child if she wants to tap on Magic's buttons or on their own magic buttons? Many times she'll want to do a bit of each. Say something like: *"Let's just tap around the buttons and talk about the day. What do you think Magic didn't like today?"* Clear the negatives first. Help her dump any negative rubbish from the day onto Magic Buttons. You might also ask her: *"Do you think Magic is worried about anything that might be coming up tomorrow?"* (Tap for whatever comes up. It might be a test at school or if friends will play with her etc.) One HUGE benefit of using Magic in this way is that you can ask the child questions and get to the problems without the child feeling interrogated because you're not asking the child about herself, you are asking about Magic Buttons! CHILDREN HATE FEELING INTERROGATED.

Then ask your child what she did like about the day as you continue to tap on Magic Buttons. This helps her form patterns of gratefulness and thankfulness. When we are working with adult clients, we recognize that they can easily tell you what they don't like and don't want, but they often really struggle to find answers when we ask them what they DO want. That is because we are so used to focusing on the things we don't like about our lives. Our brains naturally flow toward those deep grooves and it's difficult to change that pattern of thinking. You can train kids to begin to form new patterns of looking for what is GOOD rather than what is not, so that it becomes easy and natural for them.

Have your child continue to tap as she blesses all those she loves and sends love to all those people she has trouble loving. And most of all, have your child bless and love herself. Train her as young as you possibly can to love and appreciate herself now. Then have your child tap as she injects what she wants for the next day so that she is setting up good energy for a great day tomorrow. Your child should now be ready to settle down for a great night's sleep and you'll feel great too, and she should start off with all that positive energy tomorrow!

## How can I use this for or with complaining friends?

We all have friends who will call up and complain about how tough their life is or how angry they are at their boss, job or spouse. If we sit and listen to this we often will be taking on that negative energy. We're not helping ourselves and we're not helping our friends. Next time you find that happening, grab Magic and begin tapping while your friend talks. Before long you will begin to hear the friend injecting a few positive words and you can begin injecting some positive reframes as you respond and you'll change the whole energy of the situation for both yourself and your friend.

## Can I use this for my wife or husband?

Have you just had an argument with your spouse? Has your writing on your walls been arguing with his writing yet again? Get Magic out and tap as if he were your spouse. Tell him exactly how you feel. Let him have it, then remind yourself what you loved about him in the first place. When we first fall in love, we only see the good in our partners and it even grows. As we get more and more used to each other we begin to see the faults, and as we focus on them and put energy on them, they begin to grow. Before long we have forgotten what we loved about our partners. Use Magic to clear any negativity and to remind yourself what you loved about your spouse in the first place. When he comes back home or into the room the energy will be completely different. It will seem as if he has changed, but it's what you are attracting that is different.

## Can I use Magic Buttons for illness?

Many times we are angry about what the doctor has told us about an illness, or we are angry at the disease itself. Have Magic BE your doctor and tap on him and tell him exactly how you feel. Have Magic BE your illness or disease and talk to that disease until you can begin to make friends with it. Our problems *become* problems because we are resisting them. There's an internal civil war going on with them. Tap to call a truce.

If you think about cancer for instance, everyone is trying to 'fight' cancer yet it grows even bigger and bigger. Work to accept it and then let it go and see what happens. Call that truce with it.

## How can I use Magic for addictions?

Do the same with your addiction. First have Magic BE you and tap to accept yourself WITH this addiction and to accept yourself 'even if' you never get over it. Then have Magic BE your wine or cigarette or shopping addiction. If Magic is your cigarette, you might tap and say things like: *"You are killing me and yet I cannot give you up. I hate that you have so much control over me. I started out enjoying you and now you are ruining my life and my health and I want to love and accept myself anyway. Even if I never can live without you, I want to love myself anyway."*

## Can I use Magic for buried emotions or issues?

Sometimes a client may have buried issues about a parent while at the same time feeling that it's not appropriate to say bad things about them because of beliefs about 'honouring your parents.' Hand the client Magic Buttons and tell him: *"This is your Mother. Tap and get all those emotions out."* He will be amazed at the emotions about Mum that he has stuffed because of his and society's beliefs.

---

I've yet to have anyone not be able to get it out on the bear. This is why the bears are stuffed much more firmly than a toy bear.

---

Have Magic BE your emotion. One client said to me: *"I should be angry about that. Why am I not angry about that?"* Upon exploring further as to why he couldn't get angry, he eventually identified that it wasn't safe for him to be angry because he might get out of control. I then asked him if it would be safe to tap on the bear and get the anger out. He said: *"Yeah, I could do that."* And he did!

Have Magic be the boss who made you redundant.
I once had a client who just couldn't get over her intense anger *at* the three people who met with her to tell her that she was being made redundant. This anger was keeping her from moving on to any other job.
After a few rounds of tapping for this issue, I suddenly got the idea to have her pick out three bears to represent those who'd done

this to her. We lined them all up just like they'd been sitting in that meeting and she tapped on herself as she let them all have it. She told them all the things she'd wished she could have said.

A few weeks later she emailed me to tell me that she was completely over all that and moving on with her life. It had been over a year and she'd just not previously been able to let go until her work with Magic Buttons.

Sometimes we just need a way to get these unsaid things out. And sometimes we just need to know that something is there to comfort us in our times of greatest need. Magic can fulfil all those and so much more.

## What about surrogate tapping with Magic Buttons?

And, of course, Magic is perfect for when you want to help another with healing at a distance (surrogate healing). Magic is the vehicle to focus your attention and intention, which are the two great healers. The keys to surrogate tapping for another is to first tap for your OWN feelings. The feelings you are feeling about another's situation are inside you, so tap to get those out of the way. Then remember that we all have Free Will and even God cannot interfere with Free Will. This is why we must always ask for help when we need it. When tapping for another, be careful not to try to impose your will onto them. You can avoid this by injecting words such as:

> ✦ **Even though you have this serious problem, I wish to remind you that you have everything you need within yourself to find a solution to this. I send you extra love and light so that you can see your way to your own answers.**

## How can this work, and work so effectively?

It has to do with mirror neurons.

In 2008 while working publicly with a client, I asked to be wired to neurofeedback equipment and monitored while tapping only on Bears. I thought: *"Gosh, I could fall flat on my face here in front of hundreds of people with the monitoring being shown on huge screens."* To the amazement of all of us, the results showed that, not only were the brain waves doing what they normally do when people are wired up and tapping on themselves or clients, but at some points the brain waves were shooting out 5x stronger than if we'd had our eyes closed and were meditating!

The neuro-feedback expert explained that this could be due in part to mirror neurons, discovered first in animals. When one animal is sitting eating a banana for instance, and another animal is simply WATCHING, the same neurons will be lighting up in the animal that is watching, as are lighting up in the animal that is eating. Experiments with acupuncture have demonstrated a similar phenomenon in humans. When needles are inserted at specific acupuncture points in one person, the neurons associated with those same points light up in an OBSERVER, just as if the needles were being inserted into THEIR acupuncture points. Thus it would appear that when we tap on bears, we get the same results as if we were tapping on ourselves or on a client.

## If I don't have a bear, what can I do?

Okay, so let's say you don't have a bear to work with and you're not getting to all the pieces by tapping on yourself. What do you do? I'll share a couple innovative ideas with you.

Idea number one is to have a child 'draw' their own bear on a piece of paper, colour in the buttons and tap on that.

Idea two is to have them draw their favourite cartoon or Nintendo or action hero and do the same. Kids love to draw and this can be quite creative as well as fun for them.

Idea number three is that when your client finds an issue that relates to him at a younger age, have your client draw himself at that age, colouring in the tapping points, then have your client tap on the picture as he talks to the person in the picture. Ask that person what they needed at 'that time.' Then ask him what he needs at 'this time' so that we can both heal and move on.

Remember that it's up to you to take what you read here and use it to explore, and find your own innovative ways to stretch the successes of EFT even further.

## Case Study 1: Betrayal—as described by the client

*"Linda, when you came to give a demonstration of surrogate tapping with 'Magic Buttons' at Gwyneth's recent Level 3 training, it was the first I'd heard of tapping on teddy bears. As no one else volunteered to be a client for your demo and as the*

*experience was new to me, I decided to volunteer. I explained briefly that even though I'd already done plenty of tapping over an issue of being cheated out of thousands of pounds and lied to by a supposed friend, the pain kept returning. I didn't want to feel the way I did about this woman, yet I couldn't seem to tap it away and let it go.*

*I am not going to go into the details of all the tapping rounds; the main reason being that I can't remember. Like so many of our clients I came out of this session with a feeling of amazement and detachment from the situation.*

*But I do recall tapping for things such as:*

- ✣ **Even though you screwed me out of £25k . . .**

- ✣ **Even though I hate you for what you did to me . . .**

- ✣ **Even though I was stupid . . .**

- ✣ **Even though you were supposed to be my friend and friends don't steal £25K from each other . . .**

- ✣ **Even though you betrayed me when you did what you did . . .**

*I remember tapping this poor bear to death as if it were the ex friend and calling her awful names and tapping on how I couldn't believe she had treated me like that. I also recall the revelation I made that it was with this friend that I had first attended an EFT class. I remembered not wanting to tap on her at the time. As a trained nurse and therapist this 'not wanting to touch' had been at odds with my character. How could this so-called spiritual person be so fake and how had I been so taken in? I tapped and I cried.*

*Then came the turning point, forgiveness! How could I forgive this awful person? Still tapping on the bear and crying, I told you that I couldn't forgive her, so you continued guiding me with words like: "I can't forgive you, I'll never forgive you, I don't have to forgive you, maybe there's some part, someday, that I can somehow forgive but not now. What if I could somehow forgive some part so that it doesn't have to poison me?"*

*Suddenly I remember looking at you and saying: "I could forgive her soul."*

*So we continued tapping on our Magic Buttons bears while saying:*

- ✣ **Even though you did this awful thing to me I can forgive your soul, your soul is good, I don't hate your soul . . .**

*I had suddenly realised that her behaviour and personality were not her soul. My belief that we are all one could stand as I could forgive her soul. Wow, this felt like such a relief! I wasn't an awful person because I could now let go of this hate, this pain. I could let it go, forgive her soul, and also forgive myself for not knowing, for being taken in by her. What a release! All the while tapping on the bear!*

*Now, weeks later I can look back over the last few years being fully aware of all that happened, but without the pain inside me and most importantly without the anger and hate towards the woman that set me up, or towards myself for not knowing better. If someone had told me how powerful surrogate tapping on a teddy bear had been I'm sure I never would have believed them."*

## Case Study 2: Unexpected side benefits

One day a lady phoned me and wanted to know if I could work with her granddaughter, Lucy, to help with some extreme phobias. I told her I could but that I'd like to have the little girl, the Mother AND the Grandmother all come along. She said she'd mention this to her children and see what they said.

A couple days later she phoned to say that her son and his wife had rolled their eyes when she mentioned EFT so now what? I told her that if she wanted to come spend a half day with me, I'd teach her how to work for herself, and as a surrogate for the granddaughter.

Grandma drove several hours to get to me and brought Grandpa along. Grandpa was being a good sport and supporting his wife in this but it was clear to see that he was quite sceptical too. He did, however, choose a bear to work with but pushed his chair back into the corner and let his wife come up to where I was sitting.

I'd previously asked Grandmother to make a list of Lucy's issues so that I could show her how to work with each one.

Let me make it clear that we were not trying to measure SUDS or collapse anything but rather I was just taking each issue and showing her how to tap for them. Keep in mind also that Grandmother knew very little about EFT. She had never taken a course or watched any DVDs but had only read up on it on Gary's website. She picked up on it very quickly however.

And soon, as I was showing her how to tap for different issues, Grandma's own issues began coming up, emotions inflating like a balloon, then releasing as if the air was being let out, all the time while we each tapped on Magic. It was at this point that Grandpa began moving his chair closer, looking on with great interest and tapping along on his bear with more enthusiasm. Soon he was injecting different points about Lucy.

I told them that a good place to start is always either in the womb or at birth and asked if there had been any problems with her birth. They both began to remember the traumas of her birth, the doctors having to use instruments to pull her out, the blood collecting at her head and them not being allowed to touch her for a couple days. I explained to them that they would need to tap on each one of these aspects and we ran through a round for each so they would get the idea. They also took notes on what we talked about.

Upon leaving they both felt like they had a tool that would definitely help them and they could see by the changes in Grandma that it could indeed work. Grandma, armed with her new Magic Buttons Bear, chosen specifically by herself for her granddaughter, left feeling quite relieved to have finally found something to help her deal with her little granddaughter's extreme fears and phobias (note that normally had I been helping her tap as a surrogate, I'd have had her 'tune in' to her granddaughter and we'd have worked with SUDS and numbers to clear issues, but this session was more about teaching Grandmother how to do this both on her own and with Lucy).

It's important here to realize that no one knew Grandma and Grandpa had come to see me. Yet, as coincidences would have it, Grandmother had no sooner gotten home, anxious to practice a bit with her Magic Buttons before introducing it to Lucy, than suddenly they received a desperate phone call from her son. He told them that Lucy was screaming uncontrollably and not wanting to go to bed and they were so desperate for help because this had been going on for three weeks yet they'd not told anyone about it. He asked: *"Do you think you and Dad can help in any way?"*

Grandma thought: *"Oh no, I only just learned this and now I have to go put it into practice. Can I do it?"* Not feeling she had much choice she put Magic into a secret bag and went over to see what she could do. She suggested that everyone else stay downstairs and settle the baby who by this time was also screaming, while she go upstairs and talk to Lucy.

As she entered the bedroom, Lucy was standing there shaking and crying and begging her not to make her go to bed. Grandmother ignored her, sat on the bed, took out Magic and began tapping on him as I had just taught her:

✢ *Magic Buttons is scared to go to bed and he's still a cute bear.*

Lucy began to settle a bit and watch and listen and soon she began interjecting things like:

✤ *Magic is scared of noises. He's scared of aeroplanes. He's so scared of blood* (and she gave a tremble all over her body as she said that one.)

Grandmother just kept tapping and used the words that Lucy came out with. Some of the issues Grandmother knew about and some were little surprises. By this time Lucy had joined in and would tap a bit on Magic then reach up and tap on her own magic buttons. Before long, about 40 minutes, she was totally relaxed and sound asleep.

As Grandmother went back downstairs to report what Lucy was doing, Mum and Dad were shocked: *"How did you do that?"* they asked.

Grandmother had to come clean and pull out Magic and explain to them that she'd been to see me. Of course, by now they no longer rolled their eyes but were asking how to get in touch with me to learn more.

On the third day after seeing me, Grandmother emailed to report:

*"Joy oh joy—Lucy went to bed with a smile on her face tonight. Calmness returns to their house! Mum said that when she took Lucy to school this morning—she walked past the dogs tied to the school gates without any fuss. A FIRST!! She is also talking about other things not bothering her any more."*

She then went on to say: *"BUT PERHAPS THE BIGGEST SURPRISE INVOLVED ME! Here we worked on Magic Buttons for Lucy, yet on Monday I had a day shopping, just for mundane stuff and some Christmas presents but for some reason I felt totally exhilarated, almost on a high! Normally I would have been very anxious and wanting to get back home away from the crowds. I was so happy I wanted to sing and skip (I had to contain myself!) It lasted all afternoon."*

A couple weeks later she again reported to me: *"I want to tell you that Lucy is a different girl—going to bed happily, even though she still gets up and goes into mum and dad's bed about 3 in the morning (I'm working on that). She has a much calmer, happier outlook on life at the minute and so has the rest of the family and they are talking more with her about her worries."*

(Note: That I'd not done ANY more work with Grandmother nor had she yet taken any classes or watched any DVDs. She had simply continued to tap on Magic Buttons like I'd shown her in that one half day session and here is what she is still reporting to me . . . months later.)

Several months later when Grandma was going to go on a long plane trip:

*"Now I think I told you that I had this big journey coming up and was so worried about the flying part of it, not the safety aspects but the 'trapped in' feelings.*

*If I was to make a plane journey, before I had to go to a hypnotherapist for a session or two but this time I knew, after your training and with Magic Buttons I could do it myself—and I did. In fact, although I prepared myself with relaxation and music downloaded on my iPod, I didn't really need it—the tapping did the trick and I got a real rush of excitement and adventure instead as the plane took off. After that, the other flights to complete the journey were easy!!*

*All of the above resulted from that one half day session where you simply showed us how to tap on Magic for our granddaughter's problems. I've now signed up for EFT courses in my area and have ordered Gary's DVDs so that I can learn as much as possible about this amazing therapy."*

## Case Study 3: Ophelia's surrogate tapping story

Although many of us have seen amazing things after tapping for some-one else, none of us can really say for sure if it was definitely the tapping that caused the changes. Recently, however, I had my own 'proof' that surrogate tapping is not only working but working on some very deep connecting levels. I call this my 'Ophelia Story.'

A few months ago, while visiting my son in the U.S, I noticed his little dog, Ophelia, was holding one leg up and hopping along, and if you didn't pick her up just so, she would yelp. She also couldn't manage to hop up onto the sofa without having a stack of cushions propped against it. When I asked my son what had happened, he explained that he didn't know and was terribly con-cerned about her. He'd recently taken her to the vet for x-rays but they showed nothing physically wrong.

With my son being a scientist, I didn't dare mention that I'd do some tapping or healing for Ophelia so whenever I was holding her, I'd secretly do some mental tapping and a bit of Reiki, but she wouldn't sit on my lap for very long so I didn't get much done while there. By the time I left, I was seeing no change, yet upon seeing how upset my son was by his 'baby' having this prob-lem, I vowed to myself that I'd do a more thorough job of tapping for her when I got back to England.

Once I'd unpacked and overcome jet lag, I got out my 'Magic Buttons Bear' and began surrogate tapping for Ophelia. I began by tapping for all the things that might have caused disruption in her life lately—Mummy going away to another graduate school and Daddy selling the house and moving into a strange house with a stranger/roommate, Mummy coming home every few weeks, then with longer and longer times in between visits. Then Daddy moved again and Mummy didn't come home anymore: ***"What if Daddy leaves too?"*** (One of the first things that I do when tapping surrogately for animals is to take a look at what is going on at home and in the relationship of the owners.)

I tapped a few times for two or three days, then sort of forgot about it.

About a month or so later I returned to the U.S and my son and Ophelia came to my house. Lo and behold, Ophelia had suddenly become 'my' dog. She didn't want to be away from me and when my grandkids would try to get up on my lap, she'd snap at them as if to say: *"Go away. This is MY grandma."* All of us were quite shocked because Ophelia had never been my dog. I'd always had to bribe her with treats and when the treats were gone, so was she. I also noticed her leg was much better.

A few months later I went back again to the US and was the last one to arrive at a big birthday party. As I walked into the noisy party, and began talking to people, my son suddenly started hollering from across the room. He very excitedly and surprisingly said: *"Mom, listen to Ophelia. She recognized your voice out of all these voices and she's going mad in her kennel wanting out. She's been hiding in that kennel because of all the people, but now she wants you!"* Again, I was shocked and so was he. Not only was her leg almost completely healed, but she was 'attached' to me and didn't want me out of her sight for the two days that I was there.

## Some concluding words

My unscientific conclusion to all this is that not only does surrogate tapping work, but it also somehow forms an attachment between the sender and the recipient. Although I've witnessed so many amazing things with this amazing EFT Tool, I still am continuously in awe along with everyone else as we continue to explore Magic's use with EFT.

## AUTHOR'S BIOGRAPHY AND CONTACT DETAILS

Linda Wood is the Inventor and Creator of the first EFT tapping bear and is the world's first EFT Bear Therapy Expert. Along with her invention of this amazing tapping tool, she has also reinvented our traditional idea of hour-long therapy by stretching it into her All Day Intensives.

Linda, also known as a popular International Speaker and Workshop Presenter, works alongside the masters as well as on her own and is known for reaching right into the hearts of her audience.

She's gifted with a natural intuitive rapport and brings into her sessions many Spiritual Healing techniques as well. She has a unique style which seems to take EFT into its deepest levels.

Website: www.magicaltappingbear.com
Email: dialacoach@hotmail.com

# Glossary

**AAMET**—The Association for the Advancement of Meridian Energy Techniques—see www.aamet.org for more information.

**AAMET Practitioner**—a practitioner who has been certified in the use of one or more meridian energy techniques by a certified AAMET Trainer, in accordance with the regulations and guidelines defined by AAMET.

**AAMET Trainer**—a trainer who has been certified in the training of practitioners in one or more meridian energy techniques by a certified AAMET Trainer of Trainers, in accordance with the regulations and guidelines defined by AAMET.

**Apex Problem**—discounting the magnitude of the emotional relief from tapping therapy (i.e. 'I guess I wasn't really that upset'), or explaining the relief by attributing it to something else that is easier for the client to believe (i.e. 'the medication that I've been taking for months with no effect suddenly started working').

**Aspects**—the different elements of an energy disruption, each of which may need to be cleared separately. For example with a snake phobia there may be 'fear of the snake', 'fear of the wriggling snake', 'the moving tongue of the snake', 'the feel of the scales on my hand', etc. Clearing one aspect may not (and often does not) remove the entire issue. This is why testing and persistence are so important.

**Being Specific**—tapping therapy works best when targeting specific events. For example, saying 'My mother yelled at me when I was growing up' is far too vague. Instead, use a specific incident such as 'At my 12th birthday when my mother yelled at me in the kitchen'.

**Borrowing Benefits**—a benefit of tapping group work. Participants identify their own issues and SUDS levels for those issues. They then tap along with a central volunteer going through a round of tapping on her specific issues, and they repeat the phrases of the volunteer. Overwhelmingly the participants experience a reduction of their issues, even if the issues are completely different from the central volunteer.

**Chasing the Pain**—sometimes when tapping on physical pain the pain will shift from one area of the body to another, or change in type or intensity. Persistent tapping on the pain wherever it occurs can often uncover emotional underpinnings for the pain, and lead to its disappearance.

**Choices Method**—a variation of tapping therapy and EFT; widely used. It involves changing the second half of the setup statement from 'I deeply and completely love and accept myself' to a statement that begins with 'I choose …'. {see 'The Choices Method'}. A specific protocol, the Choices Trio, is frequently used when delivering this method.

**Constricted Breathing Exercise**—a technique designed to both give an easy demonstration of the effectiveness of tapping therapy, and to uncover emotional issues. It is often used in workshop settings.

1) The participants are instructed to take several deep breaths to expand their lungs, and set a comparison point.

2) The participants then take a deep breath, rating it on a scale of 0–10 in comparison to their deepest possible breath.

3) A round of tapping is done, using the setup 'Even though I have this constricted breathing, I deeply and completely accept myself.'

4) A new rating is taken. Typically the breath is much deeper now.

5) In order to uncover emotional issues, questions may be asked such as 'What does your constricted breathing remind you of?'

**EFT Master**—a designation of excellence in Official EFT (see below) conferred by Gary Craig. The designation is no longer conferred by him, and the highest corresponding designation for Official EFT is now EFTCert-Honors.

**Generalization effect**—when there are many similar or related incidents with a negative charge, tapping on some of them and neutralizing the charge from those will often have the effect of removing the charge on all the similar events.

**Imagining the tapping**—rather than physically tapping on the acupoints, the client imagines tapping on them. This is a useful technique when physically tapping is inconvenient or impossible (for example, in public, or when the client is immobilized as in a CAT-SCAN machine). It is also useful when using tapping to bring on sleep, and can be quite effective.

**Meridian Tapping Techniques** (MTT)—see Tapping below.

**Movie Technique**—An Official EFT technique that is similar to the 'Tell the Story' Technique but more protective of the client's privacy.

1) The client is instructed to make a movie of a disturbing event and give it a name. The movie should have only one emotional 'crescendo' and be relatively short (minutes long). Otherwise, the event should be broken into multiple movies.

2) Before the client views the movie, preliminary tapping is done on 'This _____ movie' to remove initial distress. SUDS level should be at or near zero to proceed.

3) The client visualizes the entire movie, and then shares what intensity is remaining. It is not necessary for the practitioner to know the contents of the movie.

4) When the client reports that there is no longer any intensity for the movie, she is asked to run it one more time, attempting to intensify it. If the SUDS level is still at zero, this process is complete.

**Official EFT**—Emotional Freedom Techniques, a method of tapping developed by Gary Craig. Full details of Official EFT can be found at www.emofree.com.

**Official EFT Certification**—a certification in Official EFT conferred by Gary Craig. Three levels have been designated: EFTCert-I, EFTCert-II and EFTCert-Honors, although at time of this publication only EFTCert-I is available by examination. Full details of this certification can be found at www.emofree.com

**Personal Peace Procedure**—an Official EFT technique for clearing core issues, bringing additional calm to life, and many other benefits.

1) The client makes a list of all past events in life which have negative emotion attached to them. If an event occurs to the client, but doesn't seem to have negative emotion attached to it, it should still go on the list.

2) The client taps on one to three items on the list each day to neutralize the negative emotions.

**Pre-framing**—A statement by a practitioner that opens a client to a new possibility before a tapping round is performed. Pre-frames may include setting low or reasonable expectations for tapping success, or reducing resistance to the oddness of the tapping process. (For example, 'We're in a demanding environment here in front of a crowd, so we don't know how much success we'll see, but let's try.' Or 'This is going to be one of the weirdest-looking things that you may have ever done, but let's give it a try.')

**Psychological Reversal**—a condition that prevents tapping therapy from being effective. Causes of psychological reversal include a reversal in the normal energetic flow of the body, as well as other causes. (See 'Identifying and Neutralizing Reversals')

**Reframing**—Suggesting an alternative interpretation for an incident or belief. This is an important concept in tapping therapy, also used in other personal growth modalities. The requisites for reframing include 1) rapport with the client, and 2) a willingness to suggest, but not lead the client to a new cognitive place. Reframes are most powerful and effective if they come from the client.

*Reframing examples:*

*If a client forms a belief based on an event, such as 'This means I'm a bad person' a practitioner could ask 'Is there any other interpretation?'*

*Note that the practitioner did NOT say 'Is there a way that you could interpret the event so that you're a good person?' This is an example of leading the client, and may likely backfire.*

*A reframe may also be incorporated into the setup statement using a Choices statement, such as 'Even though I believe that this means I'm weak, I choose to be open to new possibilities'. After the round, the client could be asked 'Are there any new possibilities that occur to you?' Again, the content is left up to the client.*

*A good guideline is to introduce reframes after the SUDS level has dropped to 5 or less. With a higher SUDS level, a reframe may not 'land', that is, it may be rejected by the client no matter how open-ended it is.*

**SUDS–Subjective Unit of Distress**. A scale used to measure the intensity of emotion that then can register the relative progress of emotional freedom achieved with tapping therapy. Typically the scale is 0 to 10, with 0 being 'no distress' and 10 being 'top intensity'.

**Setup statement**–a statement that is spoken at the beginning of a tapping round. It may be used to remove psychological reversal, or to create a re-frame, or a positive choice.

**Tail-ender**–statement that comes in response to the statement of an affirmation, and refutes it. Sometimes referred to as 'the little voice'. For example, saying an affirmation of 'I easily make $50,000 a year' might trigger a thought of 'no you don't!' The phrase 'no you don't' is a tail-ender.

**Tapping/Tapping Techniques or Meridian Tapping Techniques**–generic names used to describe processes, techniques and/or procedures that involve tapping with the fingertips or hand on specific parts of the body (see Tapping Points) for purposes of personal change and transformation. Variations include imagined tapping, and tapping on animals or inanimate objects.

**Tapping points**–points on the body that correspond to the energy meridian endpoints. Although there are standard tapping points, different practitioners vary in the number and location of the points that they prefer.

**Tapping Therapy**–therapy conducted by a professional practitioner, into which tapping or tapping techniques have been introduced as a principal or important modality.

**Tearless Trauma Technique**–an Official EFT technique designed to relieve trauma with the minimal amount of pain or suffering.

1) The client is asked to pick a traumatic event, and NOT to imagine it, but to simply guess at his intensity if he were to imagine it.

2) An EFT round is done on 'this (traumatic event) emotion'.

3) The client is asked to guess again about what his intensity might be now.

4) Subsequent rounds are done until the guessed-at intensity is zero.

5) The Movie Technique, or Tell the Story Technique, can be used at this point.

**Tell the Story Technique**–An Official EFT technique that involves the following:

1) Any initial discomfort about telling the story is eliminated using EFT.

2) The client begins telling the story at a 'safe' point.

3) Any time ANY intensity is felt, the client stops and taps on that intensity until it is zero.

4) After the entire story is told, it can be re-told, looking for additional details and aspects until it is completely neutralized.

5) The end result is that it is 'just something that happened' with no emotional charge. The client may even have trouble remembering the incident.

**Testing**—When an issue appears to be cleared, it is important to test to see if the SUDS level remains at zero. Preliminary testing can involve visualizing the issue or event, then attempting to visualize while exaggerating the details. Testing using an actual situation (for example, testing for relief of claustrophobia by putting the client in a small enclosed space) is the optimum testing method, but should be approached with care. When the issue is a past event (such as trauma over a car accident) testing involves visualization, trying to get upset, and possibly trying to re-trigger (does the client have any discomfort getting into a car? Does the amount of traffic or do the driving conditions trigger anxiety?)

**Touch and Breathe**—a variation on EFT and tapping therapy. Instead of tapping the meridian points, touch each point gently and take a slow deep breath.

**Writing on Your Walls**—refers to the conscious and subconscious messages that comprise a person's belief system.

Note: Many of these items and the Official EFT techniques are explained in much greater detail on the Official EFT website, www.emofree.com.